Inishfallen

FARE THEE WELL

BY

Sean O'Casey

The wheel of th' wagon's broken,
It ain't goin' to turn no more;
The wheel of th' wagon's broken,
An' there's weeds round th' ranch-house door.

NEW YORK
THE MACMILLAN COMPANY
1949

TO

WALTER McDONALD, D.D.

*Professor of theology in St. Patrick's Roman
Catholic College, Maynooth, for forty
years; a great man gone, and almost
forgotten; but not quite forgotten*

PRINTED IN THE UNITED STATES OF AMERICA
BY THE HADDON CRAFTSMEN, INC., SCRANTON, PA.

CONTENTS

High Road and Low Road   1
Mrs. Casside Takes a Holiday   16
Hail and Farewell   45
The Raid   57
Pax   79
Drifting   93
Into Civil War   115
Comrades   134
The Clergy Take a Hand   145
Blessed Bridget o' Coole   163
Where Wild Swans Nest   182
A Terrible Beauty Is Borneo   200
The Temple Entered   223
Dublin's Gods and Half-Gods   252
Dublin's Glittering Guy   268
The Girl He Left Behind Him   299
Silence   320
Inishfallen, Fare Thee Well   370

BOOKS BY SEAN O'CASEY

PLAYS

Two Plays
The Plough and the Stars
The Silver Tassie
Within the Gates
The Star Turns Red
Purple Dust
Five Irish Plays
Oak Leaves and Lavender
Red Roses for Me
Cock-a-doodle Dandy
In the press

BIOGRAPHY

I Knock at the Door
Pictures in the Hallway
Drums Under the Windows

GENERAL

The Flying Wasp
Comments on the present-day theatre
Windfalls
Verses, stories, and one-act plays

HIGH ROAD AND LOW ROAD

THINGS had changed, but not utterly; and no terrible beauty was to be born. Short Mass was still the favourite service, and Brian Boru's harp still bloomed on the bottles of beer. But the boys were home again from prison-camp and prison cell. First the venial sinners from Frongoch; then the mortal sinners from Wakefield, Reading, Dartmoor, and other jails. They've had their lesson, thought the sophisticated British Authorities, and from this out they will be pure and prim. The convicts warned by the spitting and hissing of their departure to their prisons, hoped they'd steal quietly through the city to fireside and bed; but the people had changed utterly, and thronged their streets to cheer them. The wail of the Irish ochone had changed into the roar of the Irish hurrah. Again, the felon's cap had become the noblest crown an Irish head could wear. Nothing could be too good for the boys. When one spoke, all had to remain silent. They led at all meetings, dominated committees, won at cards, got everything anyone had to give, and were everywhere forced to lay down the law on all philosophy, patriotism, foresight, prophecy, and good manners. Was he out in Easter Week? became the touchstone of Irish life. And it was those who hadn't been out themselves who roared silence at anyone venturing to send a remark into a conversation led by a

I

lad home from a prison or a concentration camp; for the
lads, themselves, were exceedingly modest about it all, and
were often embarrassed by their hangers-on, who forgot
that most of Dublin, willy-nilly, was out in Easter Week;
that there weren't many Dublin houses without bullet-
holes in them; and that casualties were heavier among
those who weren't out than among those who were. So for
a long time, Easter Week became the Year of One in Irish
history and Irish life.

Now the manœuvring began: the young leaders, still
alive, circled round each other, wary and watchful, eager
to snap up a well-considered trifle of position that would
give them the power to govern. Spirals of political movement began to appear, with Michael Collins dancing a jig
in one; Arthur Griffith doing a new Irish-Hungarian
dance in another; and Eamonn De Valera, a fresh young
fellow, a bit of a dancer himself, side-stepped from one
group to the other, hands on hips, advising them to join
hands, and foot it featly here and there, pointing a pliant
toe himself to show others the way—now glide! De Valera
was very supple.

At the big Sinn Fein Ard Fheis, stout with unity, the
choice for President lay between a young man, a middle-
aged one, and an old veteran; between De Valera, a soldier,
and a man; Arthur Griffith, the politician; and Plunkett,
Count of the Holy Roman Empire—wherever that was.
There was the freshman, in a prominent place, waiting to
blot out the figure of the old stager, Griffith, from the view
of the people; just, too, when he was about to have a life-
size picture taken. The modest young man was about to

2

turn into the daring young man on the flying tripeace. Griffith was threatened with the job of sitting behind De Valera for the rest of his life, and he looked glum. Plunkett had only his prayers to help him; and Griffith had no chance, for the fires of Easter Week were still a halo round De Valera's head; he had been the last to surrender, and had shown such ability in minor military manœuvres, that had he had a fuller direction of the whole contest, the British would have been given a far tougher job to do. Griffith heard all bassi, tenori, soprani, and baratoni in the country singing, top-voiced, *We'll Crown De Valera King of Ireland.* So Griffith stood out to say, I withdraw in favour of Mr. De Valera, a soldier and a man. The white-bearded Vatican Count Plunkett stood forth to say, I withdraw in favour of Mr. De Valera, a man and a soldier, and the thing was done; so with a mighty cheerio, Ireland elected an heroic homily to be her leader.

It was a curious choice to Sean, for to him, De Valera seemed to be no Gael either in substance or in face, though he was probably one in theory. Though it is recorded, he played hurley when he was a kid, Sean couldn't see an excited De Valera rushing round a hurling field; and, certainly, he had never known him in the team attached to the Central Branch of the Gaelic League; he couldn't see De Valera abandoning himself to sweat and laughter in the dancing of a jig, nor could he see him swanking about in sober green kilt and gaudy saffron shawl; or slanting an approving eye on any pretty girl that passed him; or standing, elbow on counter in a Dublin pub, about to lower a drink, with a Where it goes, lads. No, such as he would be always in a dignified posture at Dail or Council, or helping to spray prayers at a church gathering. He knew, like Griffith, next to nothing about the common people. He was of the house with the bow-window, lace curtains, and the brass knocker—planetoids to the planet of the Big House. He was outside of everything except himself. Sean had listened often to him pouring out phrases by the ten thousand, not one of which had even on it the glisten of a tinsel dew-drop. There seemed to be no sound of Irish wind, water, folkchant, or birdsong in the dry, dull voice; not that of lark, linnet, blackbird, or thrush; not even the homely caw of an Irish crow: the entire man was invested with a mantle, made whole with half from the cloak of Dan O'Connell and half from that of Thomas Davis, pinned wide in front by an inscription of the Sacred Heart. Griffith's voice, at least, was cold; De Valera's was neither cold nor hot—it was simply lukewarm, and very dreary. But it inspired his followers, now almost the whole of Catholic Ireland, who looked upon him as a Bonnie Prince Charlie in sober suiting, and bruited his fame about the land with many banners. De Valera had chained together all ambitious and disagreeing Irishmen in the bond of peace and unenduring fellowship, so that England got nervous at this unforeseen sight, and began to order men in Connacht to go into Ulster, and men in Leinster to go into Munster, putting those in jail who waited to pack up a pair of pyjamas, because delays were dangerous.

Sean, to help on the good work, wrote a stirring ballad called *The Call of the Tribe,* and hurried to Liberty Hall to get Seumas Hughes, who was then secretary, or some-

4

thing there, to the Transport Union, to put music on it. Seumas thrilled over the verses, saying he'd do all a man could to compose an air worthy of the song's sentiments. So in a week's time, off Sean hurried again to get the song adorned with the promised music, but it was handed back to him without a mark; Hughes telling him that he had had orders from above not to have anything to do with that fellow Casside. Dejected and oppressed, Sean tore the song into little pieces, and threw them from him into the silent square so that they might be lost with the valour, the enterprise, and the bold endeavour that had graced and lighted up the place when the indomitable Larkin spoke his flaming words from the window above, now sealed up and dumb with the gloom of a fell and angry caution. Orders! From whom? Not, surely, from Bill O'Brien, for he was a democrat of democrats, blandly tolerant of all men, and eager, as few other men were, to love his neighbour as himself?

Still, an odd man, this Bill O'Brien who now guided the workers of Ireland with the more cautious marching command of Right, right, right, right, right, instead of the old fiery one of Left, left, left, left, left, when the hearts of men stirred to the shout of the militant workers. Liberty Hall had been shoved back into order after the battering it had got from the guns of the Helga, but there was a woebegone look on its face, for its great men had gone, and Ichabod was its name now. It was but a hatchway now for the payment of dues by its members. Odd the building looked, disarmed of its temper and temerity, and it seemed to be ashamed of still standing there with one of its champions dead, and the other in a faraway prison. The Union's Executive had gone far from the madding crowd of workers, and had taken over a Georgian house in Rutland Square whose dignified doorway, tiled hall, plate glass, pinewood counters, and stately desks gave it a presence that made it ashamed of its parent, Liberty Hall, with its raucous voice, turbulent manner, and defiance of all power inimical to the workers' cause. Here, behind a formidable desk, sat William O'Brien, known among the workers as Old Bill, thinking deeply, and manœuvring cleverly, to gather all Ireland's workers into what was called The One Big Union.

Bill had no look of a Labour leader about him, but rather that of a most respectable clerk at home in a sure job; though Sean had met him at a Socialist gathering where little Walter Carpenter, the Wicklow Englishman, had auctioned tiny red flags—the first, he said, seen in the streets of Dublin—a man named Lee buying one for a fiver, and Bill taking one of a few left for ten shillings; the joyful event ending by a Mrs. Cogley singing *The Marseillaise,* and all singing, in unison, *The Red Flag.* O'Brien had a cold, keen mind, masked by a set, pale face, beaded by two small eyes darting out a point of light in any quick and sudden glance taken at another; a short brown beard covered the chin, its line carried along by two dark brows sprouting harshly across a bony-looking forehead. His body was usually bent forward at the waist from the habit of constantly stooping forward to balance away an imperfection in a foot. Sean had often listened to his cold voice speaking; and, at times, when angry, the face waxed deadly white, and the cold voice took on a bitter tone, without a spark of warmth in it, so that its intensity made a sensitive listener shiver.

He seemed to be a self-centered man, finding in himself all that was needed to live a cool and concentrated life; hardly ever seeming to take notice of things left or right of him. Riding his bicycle, he invariably looked straight ahead, as if he were passing through deserted streets; and at a meeting, the rather sour, but certainly sharp, face never wavered a hair's breadth from a straight-out stare to the centre in front of him. A frozen sense of self-importance animated the man; and the clever, sharp, shrewd mind at white heat behind the cold, pale mask, was ever boring a silent way through all opposition to the regulation and control of the Irish Labour movement. So this curious, silent shape, always neatly dressed, wearing in the lapel of his coat an invisible last shred of the tattered red flag, once held high by Larkin and Connolly, could be seen only at meetings, or on a bicycle on his way to one; or in his newly-furnished office, if one had a passport for admission; but never, as far as Sean knew, at a picture gallery, at a play, at a music hall; or in a pub with a pint before him, or a half a malt waiting at his elbow; never even to be seen rambling a country lane with a lassie on his arm; too high-minded, too busy, too full of all sweet, good things in himself to be troubled with these things of the earth, earthy. With De Valera, he would share the eternal glory of sacrificing himself for the common good; a bud that was to open into the tripartite government of all Irish life, the one to be supreme in politics, the other in labour, with a churchman to

7

see that all went well with the faith, so that a new trinity, one and indivisible, should live in peace, unity, joy, and quadragesimal jubilation under the siestal shadow of the mighty mitre of Armagh.

As Sean couldn't be busy one way or another, he forged a third method, and joined the few who formed the little Socialist Party of Ireland, a Lett named Sidney Arnold (who since the Red Revolution in Russia, said his name was Semyon Aronson), Hector Hughes, a young barrister, and others. So Sean went about campaigning for Meals for Necessitous Schoolchildren; delivering handbills in the streets to the few who wanted them, hastily organising meetings, and doing most of the work while the others did most of the talk. To keep himself from the sin of idleness, he got together a concert, including a one-act play, in which he himself took one of the principal characters, and persuaded Arthur Armstrong to give them the Olympia free for the great occasion. On the night of the event, Armstrong met Sean, who had come early to prepare, and told him, angrily, that the thing hadn't been advertised, and no-one would be there, the bleak result of which would hurt the good name of his theatre; and he exploded into wrath when Sean told him his one trouble was that the Olympia wouldn't be able to hold all who came. Some time later, the stage carpenter came in, and the anxious Armstrong asked him if there was any sign of an audience collecting outside. Audience? echoed the carpenter; Jasus, th' street's jammed, an' they're holdin' up th' traffic! Then there came upon Armstrong fear that his theatre would be wrecked, and he rushed round, madly, looking for stewards. With tremendous difficulty, the doors were opened, and the stewards were swept off their feet by the incoming tide of people; so swift and sweeping that many with tickets for the boxes were carried up to the gallery, and some of those with tickets for the gallery were borne, almost shoulder-high, into the boxes. When the theatre was full, the doors bolted and barred, Sean, dressed for his part in plus-fours and gorgeous pullover, stood on a window-sill high up in the building, and appealed to a great crowd below in the street to go home quietly, and forgive the theatre for not being a bigger one. And, when all was done, Sister Helena, of the St. Laurence O'Toole Sisters of Charity, received a goodly sum to furnish out penny dinners for the poor.

Prime dinners, wholesome dinners here—only a penny each! and Sean smiled ironically to himself, as he cautiously passed out over the polished floor of the convent, when he thought that no-one needed a penny dinner more than his mother and himself; but pride kept the two of them miles away from one. Oh, pride, oh, foolish pride! Oh, sweet and generous God, Who bringest the harvest in due season and fillest the heart of man with good things, here are two of Thy children who need a dinner of some sort, but who haven't a ha'penny to buy a penny one. Let us say a silent prayer of thanks for what we've got, and what we are to receive in the sour bye and bye: Oh, God the Father, God the Son, and God the Holy Ghost, we whisper hearty thanks well up to Thee for the fruits of the earth which Thou hast not bestowed upon us, though Thy intention was good; though Thou hast failed to fill our hearts with food and gladness. We praise Thee, at least, for the fine display of all Thy good gifts in the wide shop windows; for the bread that strengthens the heart of a few men; and for the wine that maketh glad the hearts of others: moselle, hock, those of the Rhine, Sauterne, Burgundy, and the heady joy coming from Champagne. Though our hearts and those of our neighbours be thin with meagre joys, and fading towards dryness, we magnify Thee for the feverish dreams we have had sometimes, during fasts and the higher festivals, of all good things; of cheeses, camembert, stilton, cheddar, and roquefort; of the dark-gold sherries of Spain and the rich, red vintage of Portugal. We rejoice in our foiled dreams of the luscious plums, pears, and peaches of Europe, the delicious citrus fruits of Africa, the dates and figs of Barbary, making our poor mouths water, and our hearts widen out in free-will acknowledgement of Thy goodness and fair play; not forgetting the coffee of Mocha, pineapples of the Indies, and the gold-crusted bread born of the grain from Canada and Illinois, which, with well-brewed tea, gathered from the aromatic plant of Assam, enables us to live on, and enjoy, in dream, the goodly things Thou hast bestowed upon the children of men. We bless Thy name, too, for the kind hearts, that are more than coronets, who have got together the valuable penny dinners for the poor, invoking St. Anthony, himself, that he may induce Thee to provide the miracle that will put a cigar in every grimy hand when each gorgeous feast has ended.

Two fierce fights were going on for liberty: one on the little green dot in the world's waters, called Ireland; and the other over a wide brown, grey, blue, and scarlet expanse of land, later to overflow into the many-coloured, gigantic bloom of the Soviet Union. The first for a liberty of the soul that was to leave the body and mind still in prison; the other for the liberty of the body that was to send the soul and mind as well out into the seething waters of a troubled world on a new and noble adventure. Dublin was astir, for many were busy in its secret places hammering out in thought the iron nature of an ironic people into a shape of an Irish Republic. Young men, in slum and shady avenue, were concerning themselves with the idea of giving up any comfort they had, and risking their lives, that they might be numbered among them who would be remembered, if not forever, for awhile anyhow. Some had died already, and Thomas Ashe was dead now. Killed through the rigours of forcible feeding. In Mountjoy Jail, one of Eire's golden boys was changing into dust.

Sean had written two laments for Thomas Ashe, for he had been an old friend of his when both had been pipers; and now, with a Fergus O'Connor, who had published the two laments, he was on his way to the prison to get news as to when the body of the dead man would be allowed out for burial. This most handsome man, Ashe, six foot tall, straight as a standard, with a leonine head, bannered by a mass of hair that was almost golden, this most handsome man was dead. Turning into the long avenue leading to the prison, with a few birds still twittering on the languid trees, the entrance gate looked like a toy door in a toy fort in the distance, with a few tiny black figures before it, waiting permission to go in to a toy dead brother, a toy dead son. But the gate grew rapidly larger as they came closer, and beside it, then, the thing towered high over them all, fitting and frowning the figures now into the look of sad humanity, waiting to go forward and endure the last act of reluctant charity of burying their beloved dead.

In silence, there they stood, Sean in his old clothes his broken cap pulled sullenly down over his eyes; O'Connor in well-cut Irish tweeds and costly cap; and the relatives in solemn black, stood before the heavy, dull-brown gateway, with its subsidiary wicket to one side for admission of privileged persons on business bent; silently praying, the lips of the black figures moved slightly in an unheard murmur, of *Eternal rest grant to him, O Lord, and let perpetual light shine upon his brave soul*; acting as a chorus to O'Connor chanting in a low whisper Sean's lament for the dead man, the pity in it forcing the tears to trickle down his cheeks before the high and heavy oaken gateway, braced with many a thick and unbreakable iron clamp.

And here, now, was another sad moment, the tale of the death of another young man for another cause, though both fought and died for freedom. The young man who died holding a Rhine bridge at Arnhem has been awarded the Victoria Cross. Defending a bridge and a blazing house for three days, he fell at last and went away forever. Sean tried to picture this young man, Lieutenant John Grayburn, wounded twice, leading his little group of gallant paratroops to safety before he died, with the questioning, kindly-truculent face of the Scot, tall and determined in his battledress; but no figure like unto the picture he tried to think of came before his eyes. Instead, he saw a little fellow, well made and promising, in a nicely-ordered sailor suit, the gold insignia of a petty officer promoting to prominence the little sleeve; his baby eyes aglow, a face flushed with resolution to hold his own, a tiny human storm of sturdy stands and gallant rushes to keep what he called his goal safe. A bud appearing to flaunt forward to a flower so soon; a red flower to fade quicker than it formed; so soon to fall, to die, and disappear forever. Nothing now to Sean, but the misty sight of a young man, dim, and a little boy, clear, wending slow along the low road to the bonnie banks of Loch Lomond, or sailing over the sea to Skye. Ah, Johnny Grayburn, Johnny Grayburn, Sean will often see these two—the little fellow countering him in childish football; this one clearly; and a dim, tall fellow, wounded shoulder and back, fighting, till he falls forward to be lost in the tangle of the earth's sad fruitfulness. And what have you left of yourself behind, for coming life to see, to honour, and admire? A blink o' scarlet ribbon holding up a copper cross, with a golden centre. Not enough, not enough, Johnny Grayburn; not enough to pay for your sturdy body, your handsome face, the promise of the future man. I was very fond of you, Johnny Grayburn, for you were all that every youngster ought to be; the makings of a fine, intelligent, colourful human being. Fresh as an angel over a new inn door. So strong, so sure of life, so sure of fame, maybe; so sure of his own boyish pride, so sure that God was with him. The day of his youth was the day of his glory; and that day passed off into everlasting darkness. His life a short and gallant story with a swift ending. Both of them: Ashe and Grayburn. They had an intimation of immortality, and then they died. They had not time to grow old. *They shall not grow*

old as we who are left grow old—Oh, whining heresy of
sentimental age, condoning the crime that young life has to
die, turning life to a whimper. That youth's sweet, scented
manuscript should close is never sad, for age is no weariness after a well-fought fight; and the years welcome the
young mind journeying on to the elder thought, a life
where hope is merged into a fuller conquest. The grey is
never far beneath the golden locks, and when it shows
itself, it but tells that life has ripened.

So there these two lie, but a few moments or so apart
from each other; the one who died for Ireland's humanity,
the other who died for the world's; the one in the grey-
green of an Irish Volunteer, the other in the muddy-
yellow of England's battledress; both now lost, swallowed
up in the greed of eternity. There they lie together—but
a moment apart in time, inert, motionless forever. Maybe
their end is soft and simple to those who have been furnished with the means of handing over the early and the
little later years of youth to mannerly nurses, to be nurtured in the midst of polished nursery, resplendent toys,
neat skirts, and spotless caps with saucy streamers stretching out like flimsy wings behind them. But the bereft
mother, who has suffered all of her boy's turbulent rising
into a steadier life, will always find a sorrow in another's
son, a ghost in an empty chair; she will have a cold heart
when she hears a youthful laugh, or the free step of one
outside on the pavement; her lips will be as cold as ice when
she feels again the warm kiss from the soft lips of the past
of one who is forgotten by all, though she remembers. Let
mitred souls who think they can outlive Time, stealing
men's sense with sign of stole and chasuble say what they

14

will away from these dead forms; insomuch as Christ is risen, and become the first-fruits of them who sleep; that these dead shall go through the endless endlessness of eternity, knowing all, and known of all within their grade of sanctity; shall sojourn actively where is neither sun nor moon to shine in it; for the light thereof is the glory of God; where all the ageing ages shall be but as the time wasted in the blinking of an eye; and the life of the longest lived universe shall be to them less than the life of a bubble afloat in the swift air.

No, thought Sean; this is but a serious fancy, hiding human foolishness and frailty; no more possible for the sad dead to achieve than for a fair lady to stretch a white arm, seize the moon, and hang it round her neck. It would be a dream to say amen to the hope of Christians. All that man can do is to make what man's life may be; to make what man's life must be; to ensure that life coming on to the stage when the curtain rises shall play his part out till the curtain falls. That is as much as we know; that is as far as we can go. Then—

> *Then star nor sun shall waken,*
> *Nor any change of light;*
> *Nor sound of water shaken,*
> *Nor any sound or sight;*
> *Nor wintry leaves nor vernal,*
> *Nor days nor things diurnal;*
> *Only the sleep eternal*
> *In an eternal night.*

The rest, if there be a God, must be left in His cool, accommodating hands.

MRS. CASSIDE TAKES A HOLIDAY

SEAN had at last writtten something for money. It was a tiny booklet called *The Story of the Irish Citizen Army*, and Dublin publishers, Maunsel & Son, had promised to print it, provided it passed the British Censor. He was to get Fifteen Pounds on its day of publication, and all the energy left to him became a curse as day after day, week after week, passed without showing any sign of the censored manuscript. Beyond an occasional day of scrappy work they were living on Mrs. Casside's old-age pension, which, when four shillings rent was paid, left six to provide them with all the bad things of life. When the manuscript did come back, it was a creased and tangled mass, with Sean's small, cramped longhand heavily underscored on every page with red, green, and blue pencil lines. With his eyes the way they were, it took him a week to get the sheets into orderly rotation. They were curious-looking documents now: the first Censor had encircled with red anything he thought to be dangerous to the British Government, peace, and God's truth; the second Censor, mind superior, went over what had been marked in red, and confirmed whatever he thought damaging by adding a green circle to the red one; and the third, mind *superiorum*, decided, finally, what was indeed dangerous, by encircling the red and green attempts with a lofty blue one of his own. After what seemed to be ages of labour, Sean filled the gaps in, the Censors, with a few more alterations, passed it, and Sean found himself waiting for fifteen pounds.

Fifteen pounds! Enough, with the pension, to keep them for seven months; for five, if they bought lavishly to give themselves the clothes they needed so badly. The sun became by day a golden sovereign, the stars by night turned into glittering silver shillings. Though the walk was a long one, every second day, or so, Sean tramped up to Baggot Street to stare at the humble façade of the publishers who were to give to the world his book. One day he went in to ask for the cheque, or a portion of it, but was told it wasn't due yet. Next week, he returned, to be told the Manager was away. The golden sovereign in the sky began to dim, and the shimmer of the stars at night began to tarnish. At last, he was told if he came in a week's time, the cheque would be waiting for him.

A few days before he was to call, he heard his mother coughing, and asking what was wrong, received the usual reply that it was but a bit of a cold. He persuaded her into bed, and gave her a hot cup of tea; all that he had to give; all that remained in the house to give its head. If he only had enough of the promised fee to buy a little brandy. He heard her coughing through the night, and grew frightened, for he dreaded her death. He had lived so long beside her, from the day she had brushed his brown childish hair from his forehead to the one that found grey hairs tingeing his temple. She had been his comforter, his rod and his staff, his ever-present help in time of trouble. She had been so understanding, too; never crossing him. Ever silent when she saw him thinking out things in a reverie; breaking into the quiet crooning of some favorite song when she saw the reverie was over. Night after night, when he had been stretched on the old sofa, dreading the onset of paralysis, to screw up his courage he had sung, full-voiced, almost every song he knew, and hymns when the songs gave out; and she had joined in discreetly, adding her sincere and quavering tone to the more militant sound of his voice. Tired of singing, he had read to her from Scott and Dickens, stopping often to listen to her young, fresh, and gleaming laughter, so strange from one who had gone through so hard, bitter, and thankless a life for nearly eighty years; fifty of them little less than terrible; years that had withheld joy, raiment, food, and even hope; for she never had a hope that she could ever be better than she was. But she was always a proud woman, hating charity as an enemy, and never welcoming it, so that all these bitter years had never mastered her, never diminished the sturdiness of her fine nature. Tom's death had silenced her for awhile; Ella's pitiable end had been a battering blow, but she recovered enough to sing a swan-song: a confident, patient, lovely folk-version of the Nunc Dimittis. She went jauntily to her death; whether to another life or no, death scored no victory over her; she never felt its sting. God or Nature, had, at least, given her that reward.

On the day **he was to** go for the fifteen pounds he bent over the sofa, a little fearful of leaving her alone.

—I'm off now, he said, trying to speak cheerily **as**

he put his hand on her hot forehead, and I won't be long.

—You never watered the poor flowers last night, she complained, for I had to get up in the night to do it myself. I don't know what they'd do without me.

—You're not to get up, he said earnestly; and as she stayed silent, d'ye hear me? You're not to stir from where y'are.

—I'm really a lot betther, Jack, she smiled up at him, and wouldn't hurt if I got up for a little. There's a few things to be washed, and hung out to dhry.

—I'll wash them when I come back, he said irritably, and put them out to dhry. I've already left them soaking.

—You're not to get up. Promise me, mother, he added appealingly, that you'll stay comfortably where you are; for he knew the quick urge in all women like his mother to be forever useful in illness or in health. He was afraid, too, of the epidemic of influenza raging everywhere, killing hundreds of the young and vigorous weekly, so that street after street had dark convoys of funerals passing through them daily. If she got that in her low state she was done. Mother, he repeated, you're not to get up.

—If you go on pamperin' me this way, she said, her deep eyes a bonny twinkle, you'll spoil me forever from doin' anything again.

Pampering her! There she was, feverish, cough-ridden, lying on a hard, flea-infested sofa, a few scraps of blanket covering her—and she thought she was being pampered! She who hadn't had for years a sound boot on her foot, a solid meal in her belly, or a warm stitch on her back. The Christian iron of resignation had entered her soul!

—An' don't worry she called out as he reached the door, if you don't manage to get th' money today—we'll manage somehow.

He went out thinking of her. She had had a quiver full of children—some said thirteen; and but five of them had reached an adult age. Two went in their infancy from croup, and a third—a lively little girl, by all accounts, called Susan, after her mother, from the same complaint at the age of six. She had never mentioned the little lass; but Michael and Ella had spoken of her to him. Of the two Johnnies, she had spoken, because he, the third, had managed to live. Ella had told him her mother had spoken about Susan several times. When Susan died, she seemed to have crept into her mother's heart, for, Ella said, tears had always decked her eyes whenever the little one's name had been mentioned.

All who had survived were clever, each in his own way: Archie, clever-handed, could do almost anything with wood and a few tools, and could model astonishing things from papier mâché; Tom, with method and order in his slower cleverness, would have made a grand soldier; Michael had been a superb hand with pencil and crayon, and would, if chances had been good, have made a fine artist; while Ella, graceful and retentive, with her white hands at home on the keys of a piano, reading music easily at first sight, full of Scott's poetry, familiar with Shakespeare and Milton, might have become a gleam from the beauty of Beethoven and Bach. But they were all four failures: no-one was there to point a way further on from where they found themselves when they entered into personal and responsible life. Social surrounding and the Idylls of Religion persuaded, or shoved, them back to where they had started from; the colours of life gradually faded, and they groped boastfully and defiantly about in the gloom again. Social privilege and Christian conduct took their talents away from them, and buried them in a wasteland.

It lay in his pocket at last with his good right hand surrounding it—the cheque for fifteen pounds. Pay to Sean O'Casside, on Order, the sum of fifteen pounds sterling; so he started homewards, face flushed, heart panting, lips murmuring thanks to God. He'd buy a hot-water bottle to keep his mother's feet cosy; oranges to cool her hot tongue; some meat to make beef-tea to renew her strength, and some sugar, tea, and a few eggs—for a start. Oh, yes, and he'd call in on his way, and get Dr. Delany to see her; a five-shilling fee, and she was worth it. But first, he'd have to get this cheque turned into money.

Here was the Bank named on the cheque. Here was the Bank. A heavy door against which he had to push his full weight to open it. A place rich in polished mahogany and the shining of brass grilles. A solemn, subdued air, like what you'd feel in a church. A glass-panelled door, well behind the mahogany barricades, with the title of *Manager* written across it in letters of purest gold. Wise-looking heads, some old, some young, bent down, battling over big books. Sean felt awed, and a feverish feeling swept over him so that his hand trembled when he held out the cheque. Cash for that, please, he had asked with a dry tongue that made his voice husky. He got it back again. Couldn't cash it, oh, no. It was crossed or something. Find one with an account, and, maybe, he'd do it. Sorry; no, couldn't oblige him. He hastened out, and hurried into another. Sorry; they couldn't possibly do it for him either. Where did he get it? What did he get it for? Where did he live? No; they couldn't cash it for him: rules were rules. He hurried out frightened, and ran back to Maunsel's. Mr. the Manager was out. Oh, no; they never paid in money. Rules were rules; but anyone would cash it for him.

He hurried homewards again, excited and afraid. Now his way was blocked by a crowd staring towards Trinity College; blocked his way, and held him there, fuming, and cursing silently. A hell-blast blight them all! His mother might well be in her last moments, might be calling for him, and he stuck there among these gapers! A stream of coloured pennons fluttered over the College entrance. He could hear his mother calling faintly, Jack, Jack; where's Jack? He tried to push into the crowd to get by, but he was stopped by a policeman. Can't I pass? I have important business to do. No; have to wait now till he goes in. Wait till who goes in? The Lord Lieutenant. Why, what's on? Cricket match, or something. Jasus! hold up a finger, and you'll get a Dublin crowd. How often had his mother said that to him! Here they were hard at it. Supposing she wanted anything, and he wasn't there to get it! Here comes the gent now; Life Guards round the carriage drawn by snow-white animals flecked with golden-brown patches, and a squadron of arrogant hussars to follow. Trit trot, trit trot goes Dublin's dearest toy into trit trot Trinity College. Six hundred pounds a week for going about all plumes and pleasures. Wonder what would happen if I went in and asked him to cash the cheque for me? In duty done in a state of life, God sorted men out in a comical way; here am I with fifteen pounds in my pocket that are no good to me; there he goes trit trotting into a temple of learning with more money than he can inconveniently spend. If his mother was ill, there'd be nurses sitting on every chair in the house, doctors coming in by every door and trying to climb in by every window, with chemists in every store compounding medicines. There'd be silk sheets under and over her on a bed as cosy as a well-built bird's nest in the heart of a sunny tree; while silky white magnolias and crimson rhododendrons nodded anxiety outside a window discreetly curtained with brocade. And if she died, no less a protestant than an archbishop, no less a catholic than a cardinal, would be robing themselves in a chasuble and stole, afire with embroidery, to go trit trot to where the coffin lay, and there waft her upward with a first-class testimonial to the reception saints and angels waiting to set her down among heaven's best people.

—Wait a minute, he thought as he went on when the crowd had scattered—a skirt and a warm petticoat for the mother—say a pound; trousers, boots, and a cap for himself—say another one; five weeks' rent owed—a third; and near two more for tea, sugar, coal, bread, and milk. They go quick, one after another—five of them vanished already at one swoop!

He went into McCartan's hardware and crockery shop;

23

asked to see some hot-water jars; chose one, and presented the cheque. The girl assistant took it into an inner part of the shop and came back with the boss who stared at Sean as he returned the cheque.

—We don't do business this way here, he said. We'd soon be out on the street if we done that. Put that hot-wather jar back in its place, Sarah; and he watched her till she did it, then came to the door to stare after Sean as he hurried down the street. A curse seemed to doom the coloured bit of paper in his pocket. Where was he to get the beef, the jar, the fruit, and other things he needed for the sick woman? He made towards home, the sweat running down him with the dint of hurrying from place to place, the cheque getting crumpled from the nervous fingering of his hand: a moment ago, a treasure; now a drop of poisoned anxiety in the core of his mind.

Taking a last gamble, he burst into Murphy's, to whom he was indebted for goods, easing up to stroll jauntily into the store that was but two ordinary houses knocked into one, but which was stacked with everything from milk and coal and oil to bacon, tobacco, sweets, and fruit. He stretched the cheque over the counter to Murphy, who stared at it wonderingly, wiping hands, smeared with the grease of bacon, before taking it gingerly between his fingers with a murmured Wha's this?

—Just come to pay what I owe, Sean said, carelessly; that's a cheque, Mr. Murphy—just want you to cash it for me.

—Ah, said Murphy, I daren't do that, now, for how do I know it's genuine?

24

—Oh, it's genuine all right, said Sean gaily; you can tell by the weight of it.

—We have to be on our guard. I'll let th' bank see it, an' if they say it's a good one, I'll get you th' money.

—I want the damned money now! said Sean tersely.

—Well, you can't have it; even was I willin', I haven't got such a quantity o' money in th' house.

—Well, let's have half of it then.

—I couldn't, so I couldn't—it mightn't be passed.

—How it mightn't be passed?

—The payer mightn't have a thing in the bank to meet it; I got caught wanst that way before.

Here was another anxiety for Sean! Something new he had never heard of before. Thieves and tricksters—the world was crawling with them! The whole thing mightn't be worth the half of an honest-to-god ten-shilling note! May the flaming weirdness of hell envelop them all!

—How long will it take to get passed? asked Sean.

—Aw, not more'n a week or so.

—I want some money now, said Sean fiercely; the mother's ill, and there isn't a thing in the house!

—Well, I tell you wha', said Murphy sympathetically, I'll let you have credit to another five shillings—that's as fair as I can do.

—That's no use! said Sean furiously, I want to get a hot-water jar for her feet.

—Oh, that? Wait now; th' missus's got one she'll lend you. He ran off to come back with an old white jar in his hand. There y'are, and he handed it over to Sean. A half a crown for it, if it doesn't come back. If th' cheque's passed, you can have what's comin' when I take what's owed.

—Give me five shillings, damn you, said Sean, or hand back the cheque and you can whistle for what's owed to you.

—I make it a rule never to lend money, grumbled Murphy, as he slowly counted five shillings into Sean's eager, outstretched hand.

He hurriedly bought a pound of beef, a few eggs, some cornflower, and several oranges, fancying all the time he heard her calling him, though very faintly the shrivelled lips moved in the crinkled, pallid face in the midst of the fuchsia, geranium, and the musk. He ran back, softly mounted the stairs, and crept into the room. She appeared to be sleeping quiet. Good! He got a small sack, went to Murphy's, and carried back two stone of coal, bread, sugar, tea, and a small jug of milk. Soon he had a good fire going, and when the kettle boiled, he filled the jar, wrapped it in an old torn shift, and carefully shoved it under the old bedclothes to her feet which to his touch felt icily cold. He sensed her feet stretching towards the jar, and heard her lips giving a purring murmur of pleasure. He put the beef into a saucepan to stew; peeled the oranges; squeezed with the pressure of his hands as much juice as he could from them into a tumbler, adding some sugar and hot water. He brought it to her, and she swallowed it in a few quick gulps, though her forehead, when he felt it, seemed now to be as cold as her feet. He noticed that she never asked him about the cheque, and seemed to have forgotten all about it. Too sleepy, maybe, he thought, pushing away the dread that cheques even of the highest value wouldn't interest her any longer now. A tap at the door. Christ! he'd forgotten the doctor, and here he was now without the money to pay his fee! With steady and gentle hands the doctor examined her while she stared at him with a vacancy Sean didn't like.

—A great old woman, said Sean, trying to be bright after the examination was over. Had a hard life, but can stand anything. She'll be all right in a few days; and as the doctor remained silent, added, think so, sir?

—She's a very old woman, the doctor remarked, very old; and tired, too. The pulse is weak; very weak; and he stood, staring at the still figure stretched on the sofa— waiting for the fee, Sean thought bitterly.

—I can't give you the five shillings just now, he said aloud, flushing crimson, for a cheque I got hasn't been cashed yet.

—Cheque? The doctor was startled. What cheque would you have? and he set his soft hat firmly on his head, looking searingly into Sean's face.

—One I got for writing a book, said Sean; it's to be published soon.

—A book? Indeed? Well, the next time you haven't a fee handy, get the Dispensary doctor, please; that's what he's for—to attend to you people. And without another word, he left the room, leaving the house without telling Sean what was to be done for his mother.

He went to the fire, stirred the beef-tea, and tasted it. It was good, better than any medicine for her, he thought. When it had cooled a little, and hearing her stir, he touched her gently into noticing it. Sitting on the old red-covered box, he fed her from a spoon till half of it was gone. Then with a murmured, Grand; that was grand, Jack, she sank back on the hard horsehair pillow that Sean had covered with an old towel to try to keep the bristles from annoying her neck and shoulders.

—Everything's grand to her, he thought; she has accepted anything given to her without a murmur of complaint. A cup of tea; a glass of beer; a sip of orange juice; and now a few drops of beef-tea—all grand, and welcome gifts from the giver of all.

Going down to the yard to fill a kettle to make himself some tea, he was greeted by a neighbour hanging out some ragged clothes on to a rope line.

—Your mother was in great fettle this morning, she said thickly, for she held a clothes-peg crossways in her mouth; she'll live to be a hundhred.

—Why! Were you up to see her?

—Up? No; but wasn't she down here early on puttin' out her few old things to dhry, after washin' them out, an' she laughin' an' jokin' with any that happened to come into th' yard. You could hear her a mile off!

Now he knew why her heart had gone weak and her pulse slow. She had risen while he was away, had washed the clothes, and had hung them out to dry. There they were, hanging limp on the line, a last testimony to a brave and resolute woman. In his mind's flurry over the cheque, he hadn't noticed them before. She had used up her last spark of energy keeping useful in life. It was done now. He might have known that she couldn't keep a promise to lie still and stay in bed.

28

He went back to the room, and looked steadfastly down at the dear, wrinkled face; and his heart sank to see how worn it was, how pale it seemed to be growing. There were the humorously-curving mouth, now tightly, almost grimly closed; the strongly-made nose, and the firm, resolute chin; the sleek hair, still with many dark hairs threading a pattern through the grey locks, that he had combed and brushed every morning for a week now. Life would be chill for him when that warm heart had ceased to beat.

He shook himself violently. It was neither honest nor manly of him to wish her to live longer. If ever a woman in this world had earned a rest from her labours, this was the one. He didn't wish her to live because of any pleasure death might take away from her. He wished it simply because she seemed to make life easier for him. Nay, not seemed; she did. To wish her to live was a great weakness that he couldn't shake aside. He was the one of her children who had been with her all the time. Thirty-five years or so she had cared for, and defended, him. Her works would follow her. What works? Attending to him! That wouldn't fetch her even a good-conduct medal from a local G.H.Q., of heaven! This woman's spiritual hardihood, her unshakable energy, her fine intelligence had all been burned to unusable ashes in the tedious smokiness of a hapless life. Life had wasted all her fine possessions. None, save he, could recognise her for what she was; and he was powerless to yield her any words of praise, for if he spoke them, there were none to hear. She would die alone—unhonoured and unsung. Unwept, too? Almost, indeed; for who was there to weep for her going? The poor had precious little time or chance to weep. She seemed to expect these things from no-one. She was far above any praise that could be given for anything she had done. Silence was the highest praise that could be given her. And the resolve that he, too, would become as she had been—indifferent to the phases of fortune; indifferent, if possible, to what the world regarded as praise, peace, and prosperity; to bear all things—while fighting them fiercely—pain, poverty, and wretchedness with dignity and silence; and, finally, to meet death with a careless nod of greeting, to suffer his cold clasp with a calm closing of the eyes, and a silent hail and farewell to a world left living.

His beginning of bravery wasn't too good. Grief was tightening his breast, and his breath came too quick at the thought of losing her. Self-pity had ambushed his hardy designs, and before he knew it, tears had welled from his eyes, and had splashed down on to the pale face so full of settled peace. The black eyes of her suddenly opened, and, startled, stared up at his anxious face. His tears had roused her from a graceful quietness, just as she was about to round off life with a little sleep.

—Ah! Jack, she murmured pitifully, her lips quivering, her worn and gnarled old hand stroking his, resting on the edge of the old sofa; ah! Jack, Jack, Jack!

He bent down, and kissed her warmly, and the black eyes, still agleam with pity, closed slowly, and her head sank back on to the hard old pillow, as she murmured, I'll be up and about again soon. With another shake of his body, he calmed his emotion, rearranged the old clothes over her as comfortably as he could, glad to see her sliding into her quiet sleep again.

30

He felt a little more hopeful now. She hadn't coughed for quite a time. He listened; she seemed to be breathing more easily. She might get over it. She had, so far, escaped the plague that had darkened every Dublin street with mourning, hanging crêpe from the knocker of every door, white ribbons for the young, black for the old; the heavenly slogan of R.I.P. on every one of them. He'd disturb her no more: he'd let her come out of it her own way, or quietly go her own way out of the world.

He went over to the fire, and set the kettle on it for a cup of tea. He pulled over the little table, set pen, ink, and paper on it, stiffening himself to go on writing his *Three Shouts on a Hill*—a shout at the Gaelic League, a shout at Sinn Fein, and a shout at Labour. Most of it had already been written, and he was now working at the epilogic chapter called Descending the Hill. When it was done, maybe, he'd send it to Shaw, and ask him to write a preface praising it. He wouldn't part with this new work for less than twenty-five pounds. With cunning, that would keep him going for a year, and give him time to think of something else to do.

He went to the window, and looked out at the sky. It was stridently lovely in green and purple and crimson. Like a fat, fully-robed cardinal giving a blessing to the world. Curious that Oscar Wilde hurried to pull down the blind whenever a sunset reddened his room, calling it old fashioned, belonging to the time when Turner was the last note in art. A lily-like, drooping sky murmured to him in delicate phrases, but this red-faced, impudent lass, arrayed in crimson taffeta was too much for him. It was too familiar, and came too close. And yet the pearly chasteness of the evening star swung in its folds, soothing the rowdy showiness of the vaunting heavens. Sean gave welcome to its manly warmth; bawdy it might be, and rough-toned, too; but it had life, and shared it lavishly with the earth beneath. When the sky was thoughtful in its pale and dreamy colours, let the lute be vocal; when the sun flared red and purple, let the trumpet sound.

How quiet the house had grown. Not a mouse stirring. He had never sensed the house so still before, as if life had gone, and left it breathless. Quieter than a nun, breathless with adoration; as still as death itself. He shivered as if a creepy silent wind had entered the room; cold, as cold could be. As cold as heaven would be if God cast a cold look on a well-loved saint.

He went back to the little table to resume his work, but strive as he might, no thought allowed itself to enter his mind. The curious silence remained as if some virtue, some warmth had gone from the little room forever. He glanced over at his mother, and saw her face calmly lying still in a deep sleep. She was just asleep. This curious feeling was but imagination, gone fretful and cold; yet a great dread crept over every beat of his quickening heart. He got up slowly, and walked over firmly to the sofa. He bent down low over her, listening, listening; and then he knew that she was dead. He felt her forehead—it was turning into the coldness of marble. She had gone from him when the silent wind had crept into the room. She had died without one murmur for attention; unbreakable, tireless, and quite confident. Indomitable woman. She had stretched out only

32

when all usefulness had left her body, possessing nothing but the sweet peace that gave courage to her fine, gay heart. She had taken a holiday from life at last. She had come very close to her Michael now; he had won her away from the world at last. She had died divested of decoration, even of one glittering word of praise. No matter. No earthly diadem would be brilliant enough to wear well on that seamed and fearless brow. All the perfumes of Arabia could add no further beauty to those worn and gnarled hands. Only such a gem as the evening star on that forehead could safely set off that hardy, gentle, patient face. He bent down, and kissed her. Her lips were very cold now. Careless, he let the tears fall on the wrinkled cheeks, but no lids fluttered open to let the bright, dark eyes stare hope and courage into his own now; nor did the cracked lips give as much as a quiver. Ah! Jack, Jack, she is dead indeed!

Through a gay, warm, golden haze, curtained with a magenta sky, Sean moved to the business of his mother's burial. But no summer sun could gild the streets with hope, or make them genial for him. Each street was a paved courtyard to a tomb. Although he hurried about, getting three pounds advance from the Agent on his mother's five pounds life insurance, registering her death, seeking a coffin, he scarcely seemed to move. Under the magenta sky, through the shimmering golden haze, everything seemed to come towards him, passing by ere he could see the shapes plain, or mind comment on what he saw, as they flowed by him under the magenta sky, through the quivering golden haze. Streams of funerals came mov-

33

ing towards him, black plumes for the old, now and again, nodded a timely farewell from the horses' heads; but white plumes for the young never seemed to cease nodding a sad greeting from the golden haze enlivening their last hour among the living; the bold, black hearses moving with glossy impudence, the brown coffins aglitter with brass, their lids bearing up a burden of blossoms trying to smile away the silent grief that lay beneath them.

Throughout the golden haze, he saw neither bird nor bee; yes, a butterfly; just one, a tiny white one, lost, knowing not whether to come or go, seeking, maybe, a sad sip of nectar from flowers decking the top of a coffin. Out of the enveloping haze a girl's hands wrapped up for him in tissue paper, tied it with black tape, a snowy shroud and soft pillow; the finest shift his mother had ever worn, the softest pillow her head had ever touched; while dimly he realised that a pound of his had gone into the sunny hilarity around him. Then the hand of another girl, in some faintly sketched-in shop, gave him half a dozen crimson gladiolas, that they might shine a torch of defiance beside the grey head of the brave, dead woman.

Out of the dancing shimmer came the thin voice of a drowsy clerk in the cemetery office droning out the order for the opening of the grave, purchased in perpetuity by the deceased years and years ago for the family, the one piece of property she ever had possessed, and proving to be a sound investment now; and again he felt that another pound had vanished into the bright-blue and gorgeous haze from his store of three.

Then from the satisfied splendour of the sun, crept the rectory garden with the sensitive face of Mr. Griffin, white and worn from a recent illness, quietly looking at Sean, his shoulders heavily shawled, murmuring comfortable words towards Sean's dull ear, words that were coloured soberly with sympathy, that one of God's dear children had come closer to Him to be calmly received into a quiet order of sainthood, with all heaven watching her stepping shyly into the joy of her Lord; for her heavy afflictions had been but for a moment, and had worked for her an exceeding weight of eternal glory; who, having had nothing, now possesses all things; bringing no thrill to Sean's heart, for he welcomed words like these no longer; and through all the sunnied harmony of the day, a dark path led him everywhere, and crêpe bordered the zenith and nadir of all he saw.

Hard he found it to get a coffin—the last gift he was to give her; for, in the shimmer, piles of coffins shone outside the doors of them who made them, and within were towering barricades of them, already sold, yet many more were needed for those who had died in the epidemic. Busy and sweating hands, raised above the coffins, impatiently motioned him away; and hammers thudded ceaselessly, day and night, down on elm and oak and pine to meet the needs of those eager to bury their dead.

At last when he found a merciful dealer, he was satisfied and tired; his legs so numb that no feeling came to them when he moved. He was glad when he passed out from under the magenta canopy, out of the golden haze, into the house, into the cooler room, where Mrs. Casside, dressed in her spotless wedding-garment, lay still, something of a smile on her face, maybe because she had quietly prevented any further discouraging interference with the beginnings of her long journey from where she had secretly crept silently away from life.

Over the white shroud, over the coffin, he draped the red cloth that had covered the box on which she had so often sat. It would be her red flag, ignorant as she was of all things political, and seemingly indifferent to the truth that the great only appear great because the workers were on their knees; but she was, in her bravery, her irreducible and quiet endurance, her fearless and cheery battle with a hard, and often brutal, life, the soul of Socialism; and the red symbol, draping her coffin, honoured itself in warming the dead-cold breast of an indomitable woman.

He was glad, after waiting five days, when the morning of the funeral came. Strive as he might, he couldn't force himself to realise that all life had left the frail body lying so safe and still in its faintly-polished box. He would have been shocked, but not surprised, if he had heard her voice crooning quietly some old, sweet song; or saw her suddenly lean out of the window to send a greeting down to a passing neighbour. Perhaps, a young, black-haired miss once more, she was with her Michael again; he with his white brow and bronze beard, looking down at her, stroking her hand, and murmuring, You took a long time to come to me, Sue; a long, long time. And she would say, I came quick as I could, Michael; and when I found the way, I hurried.

Sean broke off a sprig of fuchsia, another of musk, and

a crimson disk from the geranium, and carefully arranged them under a fold of the shroud, near her right hand. They would be her gold, her frankincense, and myrrh; her credentials to show to the first guardian saint she'd meet. I cared for these, she'd say, and honoured them, for they were of the gifts that the good God gave me. Then, maybe, with a dim smile, he'd ask her what favours she expected to get in return for these trivial things; she'd answer, permission to sing a few old songs, some useful work to do in the daytime, and a chance to walk with Michael under the evening stars.

He knew well that what he saw in his mind's eye was but a fantastic remembrance of one, now gone; one whom he thought he loved because she had been very useful to him. He knew that this hurly-burly of thought and confused vision would gradually resolve itself into a newly-ordered life; a life broken sharply from the more immediate past; and that his new life would go on striding ever further away from the geranium, the fuchsia, and the musk. She had come the way all had come, and had gone the way all had gone; as he would go. The rest was silence. Death wasn't a lonely thing. Here, before him, with all outside lively and quick, death looked sad and separated; but great multitudes had died as she had, in the same way, at the same moment. Never morning wore to evening, but some heart did break. Leaves of grass, all, which today is, and tomorrow is cast into the oven. *In memoriam ad gloriam sed asthoriam non nomoreum,* amen. Leaves of grass, all; that the dews spangled, the frosts bit, the sun burned. It was passing strange—set beside the supercilious

37

contempt some had for mass production; or the passionate, almost idolatrous honour paid by so many to the individual —that the biggest mass production known to man came from the mind of God! Or, if no god lived, then, from the indifferent energy of nature. God imitated his creations, not in two or thousands, but in millions; they were poured out in crowds, from dread and useful viruses, through the leaves of grass up to the innumerable flaming suns. Mass production, mass order, and mass community life seemed to be the fullest and happiest manifestation of heaven's many laws. It wouldn't do to say that each differed from each in some trivial, imperceptible way, blade of grass from blade of grass; leaf of tree from leaf of tree; human face from human face. Who is he who having examined each blade of grass, every leaf of every tree, would say no one of them was like its like? And though human faces might differ, and did, the darkness of hatred, the light of love, the glint of fear, the lightning flash of courage shone the same from every human eye, and the thoughts surrounding them were, in essence, the same in every human heart.

He went to the window, and looked out. A few cabs had gathered to carry a few neighbours to help in the carrying of Mrs. Casside to the grave. Carry me back to old Virginny; back to where she came from, back to ashes and back to dust. All for the forbidden bite of an apple. A benevolent sentence from a benevolent god. Nonsense. Death is but change, and change has been with us, in us, through us, since the world began. We are frightened at the thought of ceasing to be, because the thought implies that consciousness of annihilation persists. But we shall never know that we are dead.

Here came the hearse, crawling along like a polished black beetle under the vivid blue sky, through the golden haze. He felt for coins in his pocket, and slid them through his fingers, counting; just enough to pay his cab-fare, tip the hearsemen and the grave-diggers. She'd soon be buried now out of the world's way. Heavy steps came up the stairs, and when he said, Come in, to a knock on the door, two hearsemen entered, clad in the blue-black suits of their kind, their heads furnished with high top-hats, their faces firmly set in seriousness. They were followed by some neighbours who came to help to carry the coffin down.

—We'll miss her, Sean, said one of them; and the kids will too—badly. A great oul' woman gone west—th' light o' heaven to her!

—There y'are, said the leading hearseman, handing an envelope to Sean; that's for you—th' bill.

—The bill? Oh, righto, said Sean carelessly, thrusting the envelope into his pocket. You can start to screw her down now.

—There'll be no screwin' down, nor no effin' funeral here till th' money's paid, said the hearseman harshly. Right, Bill? he added, turning to his mate.

—The bill'll be paid, said Sean, as soon as a cheque I have is cashed—your manager knows about it.

—I'm tellin' you no funeral'll leave here till th' money's paid, repeated the hearseman fiercely; we want no thricks with cheques.

—Aw, murmured one of the neighbours, you couldn't leave th' poor woman sthranded like that; th' money'll be paid.

—Sthranded or no, said the hearseman, if th' money owed, four pound nineteen shillings, an' sixpence, isn't in them two hands—stretching them out—in ten minutes' time, we sail off, an' you can do what you like with th' stiff; an' them's th' last words!

Sean jumped down the stairs, rushed along the road, darted into a side street, and burst into Murphy's to splutter out the way things were, pleading for God's sake to let him have enough to pay the bill for coffin and hearse.

—Wait, now, said Murphy slowly; for it never does to rush money matthers. Cheque passed awright, couple o' days ago; so we're all serene. Had I known you were in a hurry, I'd a had things ready. I don't know there's as much as you want in the till—th' day's young yet. He stuck a hand into the till, raking forward some coins, and fingering gently a few pound notes. Wait till I see. One, two, three, four—there's four o' them, anyway for a start; an' five, ten, fifteen shillins in half-crowns—for a funeral you should ha' warned me beforehand—sixteen, seventeen, eighteen—if I hadda known, I'd ha' had everything ready—nineteen; now which'll you have—two thrupenny bits, or six coppers?

—When'll I get the rest due to me? asked Sean, swiftly gathering up the notes and coin as they were handed out to him.

—Aw, sometime at th' end o' the week, when I've taken what's mine, an' when th' till's flush. If I hadda known

you were in a hurry, I'd ha' had things ready; but Sean heard only the beginning of the sentence, for he was racing back, breathless, to where his mother patiently lay, waiting to be laid to rest. He handed the money to the hearseman who signed the receipt, the lid of the coffin was screwed down, and then the hearseman gestured to the neighbours to bear the box below.

—The burial docket? he asked of Sean, and carefully put it into a breast pocket. We'll have t'hurry, Bill, he said to his mate, if we're to get to th' cemetery in time to settle th' old lady properly.

Sean heard them hurrying down the stairs, heard the coffin bumping against the corners, and, with a bitter heart stood watching at the top, tense with shame at the scene about the money that had been played before the neighbours. He'd wait till the coffin had been rolled into the hearse, till the neighbours had climbed into their cabs, then he'd run down, and jump quietly into his own. Hearing a half-threatening, half-coaxing mutter of gee-up gee-up, there, he glanced from a window, and saw the funeral moving off at a quick trot without him, while the driver of his own cab, standing on the footboard, was trying to flick the window with his whip to draw Sean's attention to the departure. He rushed hither and thither looking for his cap, and finally tore down bareheaded, opened the door of the cab, and sprang headlong into it.

—Where'r all the others? came from the head of the driver which had suddenly thrust itself in at the window.

—T' others? What others?

—What others! testily—why them's acomin' with you.

—There's no others coming with me, and Sean saw a look of dazed dismay spreading over the driver's face.

—Wha'—ne'er a one?

—No, ne'er a one. It doesn't matter.

—It matthers a helluva lot to me! he half shouted. A cab at a funeral with only a single one in it was never known before in th' world's histhory! If the cab carried you there on your own, I'd never be able to lift me head again in th' light o' day!

—Please go on, said Sean, plaintively, or I'll not be in time to take a part in the burial. I'll let you have five shillings for your pains.

—Five shillins, an' a funeral a gala occasion? With a load o' four, now, I'd look complete, an' be in ten shillins; with a full cab o' six, I'd look complete, an' feel complete, an' be fifteen shillins to th' good. Is there ne'er a one o' yous, he shouted to a sniggering group near by, ne'er a one o' yous man enough to lep into a cab beside a neighbour, near suicide with loneliness an' sorra, an' cheer him up with a glowin' pipe an' a warm word from t'other seat opposite? Ara, this is a poor place for a poor soul to set out on its last journey to meet its God.

Sean was about to jump from the cab, and overwhelm the driver with a burst of curses, but, thinking better of it, he sank back on the seat, and sighed. History was repeating itself; something like this had happened at his sister's funeral. What did it matter in the end? He had seen the last of her long ago. It was an empty world, an empty world for him.

—I tell you wha', said the driver, sticking his head in

again at the window; I'll take you fifty foot from th' gate, where I won't be seen, an' dhrop you there, if you pay me six shillins, an' say no more about it, for fair's fair.

—Yes, yes; agreed, said Sean, after he had slid the coins in his pocket through his fingers to make sure he had enough to meet the demand.

Sean heard the driver flinging curses at his mare, heard the swish of a whip, and felt the animal surging forward at a clumsy gallop; so maybe he'd be in time to see the coffin lowered, when Mrs. Casside, baptized Susan, would be committed to the ground amid the trumpet obligato of the Christian faith, sending its notes, boastful and satisfy-ing, into every present ear, save that of the dead woman, and his own. Fearful consciences would believe the procla-mation, that, at the last day, at the sound of the trump, the dead would rise, and each individual body would be re-united to its individual soul; when the natural would be changed for the spiritual, the corrupt for the incorruptible; that which was mortal for amazing immortality. A tall order. A mystery. That is Paul's only explanation. But what is the soul? Where is it when the body is present, and where does it go when the body is but dust? A substantial form of the body? But how can that be? If I cease to be myself, how can I persist as myself? If, when I die, I become a disembodied spirit, then I am no longer what I once knew myself to be, and so how can it be said that I am what I once was and now am not? The being which is I gets all my joy, exhilaration, feels all my pain, sees things lovely and things evil, hears all soft and harsh sounds through the senses, through the nerves, all in deli-

43

cate and delightful union with the coarser parts of the body; but when I die, all these die, too, and I that was am then no more: nothing left but a fading memory among a few. No; say what they like, there's nothing above but the blue air, or the soft, grey cloud taking the gay sun's gilding; or the black one hoarding a storm for our heads. No; the banner waving over every grave is silence.

But let them say out their jewelled words over Susan's body, to the last word; unto this last; for they were part of her strange and happy dream, and dear to all her secret thoughts; though Sean knew that, unattended, though the mind was lovely and the body pure, the clay of the grave would bring forth coarse grass that would soon hide it from the sight of man forever.

HAIL AND FAREWELL

SEAN was leaving forever the room where his mother had lived so long, and in which she had, at last, died. His brother, Michael, wasn't a congenial man to live with. Never had been, and but for the foolish, peace-loving anxiety of his mother, Sean would have come into violent collision with him long ago. Michael had gone his own sour way, and had dwindled into a wreck before he had come to the end of it. He had treated his mother as a bully would treat an amiable fag in a second-hand public school. She had always dreaded his appearance in the house; and felt fully alert and all at ease whenever he happened to be far away. His glittering gate had always been the door of a public house, and drunkenness was to him an inward sign of outward majesty and strength. When he had money, he was popular with those who had none; a merry fellow, heart of the roll. Spending the little he had on others, who had less, so that he could enjoy the telling, before a rough and reverent gang, of the brief chronicles of half-imagined escapades, seen in the tawdry visions of a drunken bout. Paint him as he was twenty golden years ago, and paint him as he is now, and one would have a horrifying picture of a worker Dorian Gray. Now there is no trace whatever of his young and sturdy grace, fine, intelligent face, well-made manhood, or delicately-moulded hands; no trace whatever. His lovely masculine manhood hadn't lived to grow old; first it had been marred, then utterly destroyed by the life he led, ere a grey rib appeared in his raven-hued hair. Coarseness, vulgarity, and a vicious meanness glowered from his features now, though at times one caught a sudden flash of dark pride, lighting a gleam of grandeur for a second in the penury of the lined and battered face of the man.

Time and again, Sean had lain awake through the night, cursing deep, while he listened to the drunkard keeping their mother from a tardy sleep, lying patient and coaxingly amiable on her hard and bitter sofa-bed; Michael singing sloppily to himself; cursing his hard lot, falling heavily off his chair when he feared she had dozed off, leaving him alone; for he knew she would arise in her old shift to gently help him on to the chair again; or put her own rough pillow under his head if he was too drunk to move. How often had Sean's blood raged into angry heat, longing to run out and encircle the rough, withering throat with his still sinewy hands, to choke and choke the life out of him; always failing in his desire because Sean knew his mother would cling to him and pull at him, begging them both to remember that they were brothers. The end of it would have been his mother in tears, afflicted with dire trembling, and full of a bitter, taunting fear for the future. So Sean had stayed still, and lay on, listening.

Now it was very different: no mother to wail, to plead, to sigh her heart half away from herself. He had a few pounds just received for an article which would keep him going quietly for more than a month of Sundays. He had

46

thought that the mother's death would work a change in Michael. Surely, he would remember, and remembering, regret all the vicious anxiety he had poured into so many hours of her gentle and resistant life. Remember, and be sorry for it, and repent; become a soberer and a wiser man. Sorra bit of it!

Sean was trying to think out the words of a song in the dead of night when he heard the heavy, lurching steps stumbling up the stairs and the raucous, beery voice forcing itself to shape a song, masquerading a spurious delight in the heart of the braggart, hating himself. From the corner of an eye, he saw the tousled figure staggering into the room, knocking clumsily and intentionally against the table at which Sean was sitting, while an envious, dirty hand, sliding along it, sent the little ink-bottle flying to the floor. Sean said nothing, but sat quietly where he was.

—Writin', be God, again! murmured the blurred voice of his brother; some fellas are able to give themselves airs! Scholar, is it? Scholar, me arse! Well, th' ink's gone, so wha'll we do now? Here's one who's forgotten more'n some'll ever learn. There's a man here. Takes a few dhrinks, but a man, all th' same; a man with two good mitts. Writin'! If I was someone, I'd thry to be a man first! But Sean sat still, quiet, where he was.

The malice-wreathed face, blasted away from all humanity, had suddenly thrust itself close to his own, half sickening him with the steam of a reeking savour spurting from the slobbering, panting mouth.

—Who d'ye think y'are, eh? were sodden words borne to his ear by a gust of rotting breath, and Sean, standing

47

up from the chair, stepped back to avoid the stare of the
bloodshot eyes, but the luridly drunken face, staring viciously, followed his own closely, while the wobbling
mouth slobbered out a black rosary of curses, many of the
soiled words slimy with self-pity for the drunkard himself, who felt he could never get back one jot or tittle of
the fair things gone from him forever. Sean, half retching,
and savage, conjuring up some of the old vigour still lingering in his muscles, shot his shoulder against the chest
of the calibanic splutterer, lifting him clean off his staggering legs, and sent him, with the table, crashing heavily
to the floor, to lie there, a hand twisted under him, snoring heavily in a drunken and concussive stupor.

Sean got an old sack, filled it with as many of his books
as it would hold, and set out his first trip to fresh woods
and pastures new, carrying his knowledge with him, esti-
mating that he would have to make three trips at least before he put the last book into the old bag. When he came
into the open, Sean shivered, for there was as yet no sign
of the dawn, and it was bitter cold. No rosy auroran fingers
would be opening the dawn of this morning; but a chill,
bony hand, with the cold moisture of death gemming the
fingers, would pull apart, surlily, the opening gates of the
day. Half of a wan moon hung hesitating in the sky, as if
she had lost her way in the heavens, and waited for some
influence to come and guide her again on to a right road.
The street as far as an eye could carry was silent and still
as a sick animal crouched in some forgotten corner. The
poor blinds and curtains in every window were closely
united in hiding everything behind them, as far as unsteady

48

and timorous hands could conceal things behind tatters. The little shops were tightly shuttered, so that no sign of loaf, tray of tea, root or leaf of vegetable, newspaper, or sweet, showed itself, seemed to say that here older life no longer ate, drank, or read; and that younger life had gone fasting from the lure of caramel and rock. Indeed, it looked as if life had gone, and left the lonely street behind it.

—Hello, Sean! a voice sounded in a steady way in his ear, and then he noticed two young fellows walking softly beside him. Are you doin' a moonlight flit, or wha'?

—Where are you two off to? asked Sean, ignoring their question; a little innocent ramble, eh?

—Ay, replied the one who had greeted Sean, that's it —with a little sup in a bottle for th' Tans, he added, tapping his side.

—Come on, Ned, said the other, we can't keep th' Tans waitin'; and getting into their silent stride again, a loping, trot, they vanished into the gloom ahead.

—The Curfew! He had clean forgotten that! Till these two who had dissolved into the shadow had whispered their mission. A second two would linger at a corner, and a third two at another so that the Tans would face fire from several directions; cross-fire that would send bullets soaring through the windows of houses where the sleeping people were depending on their guardian angels. Soon, somewhere he would hear the bursting of a grenade, orchestrated by the odd emphatic report of rifle and automatic revolver, in another tussle between Saxon and Gael. A most dangerous thing to be out at Curfew hour without a pass, with the excuse that he was on his way to find a doss down for a few nights; with a sack on his back; nothing would convince the Tans that his business was no concern of theirs. Everybody's business was a concern of theirs. In the absence of an ambush, there might be a chance of a few minutes chat with them; but immediately after one, they wouldn't waste time on talk. Would he go back to wait till the daybreak, and the shadows fled away? He'd have to go back and forward three times at least to bring all his books away; but an interview with the Tans wouldn't be much worse than several more long hours spent with a drunken, sprawling brother. There he stood, thinking, his fingers numb with the cold, gripping the mouth of the sack; stood thinking whether to go on or go back, under a sky that was a wide canopy of squalid, haggard grey, muddied by the sleety humours of the night that had gone, weighed down with bellied swathes of clouds, black and lowering; while over where he guessed the sun to be, shone a cold, steely light, like the slim blade of a rapier that the dew had rusted.

Whisht! The whine of a motor. He listened. Away over to the left, he saw the light of a searchlight flickering over the roofs. The Tans! He hurried from the broader street into a narrow lane, to crouch in the recess of a back doorway, his bag of books resting beside him. He heard the motor swinging along the street he had just left, saw the beam of light sweeping down the lane, covering him with a dreadful glory; but it darkened again in a second, and Sean, near a faint, felt his heart panting fiercely.

The ambush! There it was; he heard the sullen bursting of grenades, the solid, piercing reports of rifle-fire, shouts that must come from the Tans, for he knew the Republicans remained sullenly silent, firing impassively, firing steadily at the head, the chest, or the belly of a Tan; and may God make their eyes keen and their hands steady! added Sean piously. But it was very annoying, thought Sean as he shivered in his corner, listening to the not very distant gunfire. The people were getting a little tired of the fighting. Gun-peals and slogan cries were things happy enough in a song; but they made misery in a busy street, or along the quiet, unassuming walks of a village. If it went on much longer, most of the cosy Irish homes would become but handfuls of ashes to be poured reverently into jars, and put safely away on a shelf for sweet remembrance. The sovereign people were having a tough time of it from enemies on the left and friends on the right. Going out for a stroll, or to purchase a necessary, no-one knew when he'd have to fall flat on his belly, to wait for death to go by, in the midst of smoke and fire and horrifying noises. Armoured cars clattered through the city; lorries, caged in with wire and crowded with Tans pointing guns at everyone's breast, cruised through the streets; and patrols, with every rifle cocked to the last hair, crept along every kerb. Every narrow lane seemed to be the dark dazzling barrel of a rifle. Christian Protestant England and Christian Catholic Ireland were banging away at each other for God, for King, and Country. All forgot, for the time being, the deeds alleged to have been done in Russia, so that they could show, in a ripe example, what Christ's faith, hope, and charity could do in a private and confidential war of their own. Christ's faithful soldiers and

51

servants were busy bestowing the chrism of death upon
each other.

Sean had gone on safely when the firing had died away,
had found a room in which to live, fortunately; for his
few friends were afraid to guard his books during an in-
terval because of the many Irish works that were among
them. They might damn the holder if the Tans made a
raid. So here he was back in the old room again, filling his
sack with books for the last time. There still lay the woe-
spattered figure of Michael, mingled with pieces of the
broken table, still snoring riotously in the stupor of drink.
Sean glanced round the old room for the last time. Farewell, now, forever, to Nelson on his way through a fishing-
village street, bound for Trafalgar's Bay; to Victoria in her
deep-purple bodice, divided by the pale-blue sash, the
golden crown, sprinkled with red and blue jewels set firm
on her arrogant head; the mantelpiece clock, veneered to
parade as mahogany, with its glass panel of painted flowers
below its innocent face, centred by a plain circular piece of
glass that showed the pendulum going to and fro, ceaselessly—a wedding-present to his mother from her husband.
A great old clock. Sean had never known it to need repair-
ing. His mother had loved it, never forgetting to wind it
the last thing at night, reminding others of its need whenever she lay ill, as if the thing had life that grew tired;
the winding of it providing the energy for another day's
work. Anything that moved had life to her—the ticking
clock no less than the growing flowers. Two old wooden
chairs, the squat little cupboard that he had used to hold
his books, a broken fender; a few battered things barely

capable of boiling an egg or frying a rasher; the old box by the fire still covered by the red cloth where she had sat out many hours of a lonely life; and the clay-grimed tins that once held so proudly the geranium, the fuchsia, and the musk. They had withered when their good guardian went away. Farewell to them all. Everything here to Sean was dead and gone; he would never set eye on them again, and he never wanted to; without the honour of his mother moving among them, they had fallen from whatever grace they once had, and were damned forever.

Ah! He had near forgotten the old horse-hair sofa where she had slept so uneasily for so long; where she had flung off many an illness, with him attending on her as best he could. No, not quite as best he could; not near it. How often had he neglected to attend to her, to even think of her when she lay ill! No, not too often, maybe, for she was seldom ill; and most times put an ailment over on her feet; but he had neglected her often enough, content to do what he could the last thing at night when he was about to go to bed. She had borne everything without a murmur, aughing even, at times, when a quiver of pain went through her; like a stoic, calm as a Buddha. And death, himself, recognising her courage, had kissed her hand before he led her away quietly. Sean laid a hand reverently on the old sofa for a moment; had he had one, he'd have dropped a red rose on its tattered cover.

Yet with all his feeling, he had never put as much as one green sprig on her grave; never paid it a visit after having helped to lay her there; and never would. The dead, worthy of remembrance, are worth more than a decorated grave yielding profit to the selfish and the vicious. Out of hell comes the thought and deed of making profit from grief and sorrow. God's acre let out to the dead for so much per square foot. Holy roods of soil! The growing bush, however green, the climbing rose, however lovely, the sculptured stone, however grand, are neither seen nor wanted by the dead. If we wish to remember loved ones gone, then let us place the sculptured stone, the green bush, the climbing rose, apple-bloom, and cherry-blossom in public places where the sun shines, children play, and the living pass to and fro. Only the thoughts of the living can give the mortal immortality.

Sean looked down for the last time at the form of the sprawling castaway. Not a sign, not a shadow, of the earlier elegance; the clever, sinuous movement of the finely-fixed hand holding a pencil, weaving vibrant and charming lines over the bare whiteness of paper. No; not even a withered sign of a long-lost artist. And yet in that dreary and distorted face there must be some of the youthful glory hidden away; something, like a palimpsest, under the blear and dreadful misery of the countenance. No, not a mark of anything other than what all men see today. And yet, not so long ago, Sean had seen that perished face lit up with a courage that he could never summon to himself. Standing aimlessly idle on a slip down by the mouth of the river Liffey, Sean and Michael were smoking and watching the bathers swimming about in the deep and murky waters. Suddenly, one of them began to splash and cry out, unable to control himself in the swift flow, frightening the other swimmers who moved away from him, shouting out for

54

the lifebuoy which a man frantically tried to disentangle from its nest in the wet stone wall. Sean saw Michael's scattered face tense into a fine, firm eagerness, saw him bend swift, stiff-jointed and all as he was, whip off his boots, sling aside his coat, and take a short run to plunge into the brown, swift-rippling waters, saw him shoot over to the struggling, drowning man. He swam like an otter, tumbling and forcing himself through the water with a strange, brave movement of glee. Standing ashiver and dripping on the slip again, Sean heard the policeman asking Michael for his name and address, and Michael's reply that a shilling for a glass of malt would serve him better.

To Sean's own knowledge, he had saved more than ten lives in this way, though no mention of any appeared on the face of the earth or the brow of heaven. In the sea, in a river, or in the calm, deep pool of a quarry, Michael would plunge forward to pull a drowning soul to safety. Never either, would he don the dark motley of blackleg or scab. Ay, there was that much to be said for him. Had he had his due, a streak of red ribbon would be glaring from his faded coat now.

Sean stared down at the gaping mouth, the once well-formed face, now miscast with many evil markings, the frizzly moustache caked into horrid lumps with stale, dried droppings of beer, the seamed forehead, and the twisted cheeks: how could anyone who saw, say that that repellent figure bore on its breast the red badge of courage! Perhaps the sign of the sword was equal to the sign of the cross, for here lay stretched a fellow who risked laying down his life many times, not for friends, but for those whom he did not know, and, having saved them, would never see again. Those shapely hands of his were never made for the cankered pastime of handling pints. Clever and cunning, they did many things in their time, from holding a hawser, carrying new-baked, creosoted railway sleepers, hot and stinging, to guiding the delicate movements of pencil and pen. God's curse on today's way of the world! It was not that this prone man in younger days had digged in the earth to bury his talents there: no; he had been quietly robbed of them by the careless and criminal indifference of teachers, spiritual pastors, and masters, who had thoroughly buried them for him.

Curse of God on the way of the world today!

Sean hoisted the bag of books on to his shoulder, gave a last glance round the broken room, and then turned to leave it forever.

THE RAID

THE cold beauty of frost glittered everywhere outside, unseen, unfelt, for the slum was asleep. An uneasy silence echoed over the house, for awake or asleep, everyone knew that death with his comrade, the inflictor of wounds, roamed the darkened streets. Stretched out in a truckle bed in a tenement room, its murky window facing on to the street, Sean thought of the tapestry of the day. He could see the street stretching along outside, its roughly cobbled roadway beset with empty match-boxes, tattered straws, tattered papers, scattered mounds of horse-dung, and sprinkled deep with slumbering dust waiting for an idle wind to come and raise it to irritating life again. Lean-looking gas-lamps stood at regular intervals on the footpaths, many of them deformed from the play of swinging children, bending over like old men standing to gasp, and wait for a pain in the back to go. The melancholy pathway meandered along by the side of the tall houses, leading everywhere to tarnishing labour, to consumption's cough, to the writhings of fever, to bitter mutterings against life, and frantic calls on St. Anthony, The Little Flower, and Bernadette of Missabielle to be absent helps in time of trouble. Upon these stones, I will build my church.

There were the houses, too—a long, lurching row of discontented incurables, smirched with the age-long marks of ague, fevers, cancer, and consumption, the soured tears

of little children, and the sighs of disappointed newly-
married girls. The doors were scarred with time's spit and
anger's hasty knocking; the pillars by their sides were
shaky, their stuccoed bloom long since peeled away, and
they looked like crutches keeping the trembling doors
standing on their palsied feet. The gummy-eyed windows
blinked dimly out, lacquered by a year's tired dust from the
troubled street below. Dirt and disease were the big sacraments here—outward and visible signs of an inward and
spiritual disgrace. The people bought the cheapest things
in food they could find in order to live, to work, to worship:
the cheapest spuds, the cheapest tea, the cheapest meat, the
cheapest fat; and waited for unsold bread to grow stale
that they might buy that cheaper, too. Here they gathered
up the fragments so that nothing would be lost. The streets
were long haggard corridors of rottenness and ruin. What
wonderful mind of memory could link this shrinking
wretchedness with the flaunting gorgeousness of silk and
satin; with bloom of rose and scent of lavender? A thousand years must have passed since the last lavender lady
was carried out feet first from the last surviving one of
them. Even the sun shudders now when she touches a roof,
for she feels some evil has chilled the glow of her garment.
The flower that here once bloomed is dead forever. No
wallflower here has crept into a favoured cranny; sight and
sign of the primrose were far away; no room here for a
dance of daffodils; no swallow twittering under a shady
eave; and it was sad to see an odd sparrow seeking a yellow
grain from the mocking dust; not even a spiky-headed
thistle, purple mitred, could find a corner here for a sturdy

life. No Wordsworth here wandered about as lonely as a cloud.

> The decent dead provoke no blood-congealing fear,
> Like the dread death that lives to fester here.
> Here children, lost to every sense but life,
> Indulge in play that mimics social strife;
> And learn from strenuous practice that they may
> Act well their part at home some future day:
> The girl trains her lungs to scream and shout,
> The boy his arms to knock a wife about.

And yet this riddled horridness had given root to the passion flower. What had been lost was found; what had been dead came to life again. The spirit beneath the coat brocaded, with slender sword quivering, had come into being again, not in brocade, but in rags; not with sword or dainty phrases, elegant in comedy and satire; but with bitter curses, blows as hard as an arm can give, and a rank, savage spit into a master's face. Fought these frantic fools did, led by Larkin and by Connolly; fought till the day-star arose in their shivering hearts, the new and glorious light, the red evangel, the light of the knowledge of the glory of God, manifested in the active mind and vital bodies of men and women and little children. And now something stronger than bare hands were in the battle. Many a spearpoint flame from a gun frightened a dark corner or a shadowy street, making armed men in khaki or black crouch low in their rushing lorries, firing rapidly back at the street grown shadowy again, or the corner now darker than ever before.

Now the old house was still. Comely Bessie Ballynoy, on her way up, had knocked; but finding Sean in bed, had bid goodnight, and gone. Lazy sleep had crawled in by the dark hallway to soothe restlessness and to hush the clamour from the attic above to the basement below. A lousy sleep, dreary-eyed, in loosely slippered feet, torn and muddy, calling in a shoddy whisper for quietness; creeping in yawning, leaving no-one on watch, though every night now was a perilous night for Dublin. In all the rooms, all the cheap crockery stood quiet on the shelves; the chairs leaned against the shaky walls; rosy-faced fires had all gone pale; the patter of children's feet had long since ceased; only dreams crept slyly in to fill the ugly rooms with sparkling peace for a few dark moments, clothing the sleepers with a cautious splendour; setting them, maybe, to sip rare wines from bulging bottles, or led them to yellow sands bordering a playful sea. A younger lass, per-haps, dreamed of scanty night attire between snowy sheets, with a colour-robed prince by the bedroom door in haste to come in, and bid her a choice goodnight; while the younger men saw themselves, sword in hand, driving the khaki cut-throats out of Eire's five beautiful fields.

Every guardian angel relaxed now, and nodded sleepily by tattered counterpane and ragged sheet, for sin usually curled up like a dog to sleep at their feet, waiting for the tenement life to go on again in the morning. So after Cur-few the silent tenement slept, unconscious even that every whining wail of every passing motor sang a song of death to someone; for in sleep the slimy roof above them had slid aside, and left the stars but a hand's breadth out of reach.

When will the day break in Eirinn; when will her day-star arise? How often had he heard these words sung in a languishing voice after an eight-hand reel or a high-cauled cap at *ceilidh* or *sgoruidheacht*! Well, no day would ever break here, nor would the shadows ever flee away. Sean's eyes were closing, and dimming thoughts swooned faintly from his mind into the humming whine of motor-engines coming quick along the road outside. Up on his elbow he shot as he heard the sound of braking, telling him that the lorries were outside of his house, or of those on either side. Then he shot down again to hide as a blinding beam from a searchlight poured through the window, skimming the cream of the darkness out of the room. It silvered the old walls for a few moments, then withdrew like a receding tide to send its beam on another part of the house. Then there was a volley of battering blows on the obstinate wooden door, mingled with the crash of falling glass that told Sean the panels on each side of it had been shattered by hammer or rifle-butt.

A raid! All the winsome dreams of the house had vanished; sleep had gone; and children dug arms and legs into the tensing bodies of their mothers.

Which were they—the Tommies or the Tans? Tans, thought Sean, for the Tommies would not shout so soullessly, nor smash the glass panels so suddenly; they would hammer on the door with a rifle-butt, and wait for it to be opened. No; these were the Tans.

He heard the quick pit-put, pit-put of stockinged feet, faint as it was, coming down the stairs, turning left at the bottom of them, and hurrying along the hall towards the back-yard. His ears were so cocked that he heard the soft,

silkly pad of the hurrying feet plainly through the storm
of blows falling on the street door; then he thought he
heard the back door open softly and gently close again.

—Who could that be? he thought. Might be anyone of
the men. Those who didn't take part in ambushes often
carried ammunition to those who did; and the dockers and
seamen gave a ready hand to the smuggling in of arms. If
it wasn't for his own poor sight, he'd probably be doing it
himself. All were friendly, save the thin and delicate husband of Mrs. Ballynoy, who cared for no manner of politics.
Someone, anyway, slipping into the back to dodge over the
wall into the dark lanes, with fear but without fuss. The
Dublin slums at war with the British Empire; all the power
of an army, flanked by gangs of ruthless ruffians; all the
ordered honour of a regal cabinet and the mighty-moneyed
banks fighting the ragged tits of the tenements. An un-
equal fight, by God, but the slums would win! There goes
the door!

A great crash shook the old house and shook the heart
of Sean, for well he knew the ordeal that might be in front
of him once the light from a Tan's torch smote the darkness of the room. A mad rush of heavy feet went past his
door, to spread over the stilly house; for no-one had come
from a room to risk sudden death in the dark and draughty
hallway. He remembered the two boys brought bound
from Dublin Castle to a dump-field on the edge of the city
by two Auxie-Tan officers, who set them sitting against an
old stone wall, extinguishing each young head under an old
bucket picked from a rubbish heap. Then going away
forty paces or so, they fired away at the buckets till they

were full of holes, leaving what they had done behind them to put the fear of the Tans into the hearts of the surviving I.R.A. men. He thought, too, of Clancy, Clune, and McKee, caught and brought to the Castle, where the Tans interviewed them with the stimulant of bayonets, prodding them gamely till none of the three could sigh any longer, for each at last was dead. Now he could hear neither sound nor murmur—all had gone quiet after the crashing fall of the door. No sound even of a child's protest, though that wasn't surprising, for all of them would be too frightened to squeal till a gun exploded somewhere: all was quiet—the sad silence of a sleeping slum. Yet Sean knew that the house must be alive with crawling men, slinking up and down the stairs, hovering outside this door or that one, each with a gun tensed to the last hair, with a ready finger touching the trigger. He guessed that a part of them were the Auxies, the classic members of sibilant and sinister raiders. The Tans alone would make more noise, slamming themselves into a room, shouting to shake off the fear that slashed many of their faces. The Auxies were too proud to show a sign of it. The Tommies would be warm, always hesitant at knocking a woman's room about; they would even be jocular in their funny English way, encouraging the women and even the children to grumble at being taken away from their proper sleep.

All Sean could do was to try to lie dead still, digging down deeper without a sound into the hard mattress of his truckle bed; stifling any desire to steal to the door to listen; to try to modify his breathing till it became un-

noticed by himself; for a profound silence might make
the Tans disinclined to probe a way in to find out the
cause of it; though the Auxies cared nothing for silence,
but would lift a corpse from a coffin to search for a gun.
He always left his door unlocked now, for past experience
had shown him that the slightest obstacle to a swift entrance to a room always irritated them.

From the corner of an eye he could see through the
window the searchlight gliding, now up, now down the
street, and once for a few moments it blinded him by flood-
ing the room. Then he heard sullen, but loud, thuds of
heavy iron falling on heavy wood, coming from the back,
and he guessed they were breaking in the entrance to the
large shed that was said to be used as a carpenter's shop,
and in which Mrs. Ballynoy's husband sometimes worked.
Now he heard soft, sly steps going down the hallway to
the back. After whomsoever had crept away while the
door was being broken down. He had climbed the wall,
thought Sean, and somewhere—maybe just behind it—
crouched silently in the darkest corner of the narrow lane,
a revolver tight in his hand, his shoes slung round his
neck, so that, if he had to run, no sound of running feet
would give an enemy a cue of a direction through which
to send a hail of bullets: a bitter night for a pair of bare
feet.

Sean could sense the women, and, maybe, the men,
praying while the hammering lasted, to cease at once
when silence came again, for it wouldn't serve them to let
the Auxies hear them trying to talk to God. These silences
were the worst: during the hammering one knew where

they were; throughout the silences one didn't. Then they might be anywhere; might be opening his very own door snakily, softly, now; some of them might be even in the room, for their black uniforms fitted the darkness they loved, and black juices, smeared over their cheeks and brows, mixed them cosily with the darker shadows of the night. Any moment a brilliant torch might blind his slatted eyes, and a string of shouted questions blast his ear; a pressed-in, cold pistol barrel make a tiny livid rim on his naked chest. He tried to forget thought, making his mind one with the darkness, losing his fear in the vastness of space; but it was no use, for thought never got farther than that the Tans were there, and his mind came back to think of how it would feel to have a bullet burning a swift channel through the middle of his belly.

Azrael, Azrael, gentle, dignified being of spirit, graceful spirit of death, come, and minister unto us, and save us merry gentlemen!

> Come lovely and soothing death,
> Undulate round the world, serenely arriving,
> Arriving
> In the day, in the night, to all, to each,
> Sooner or later, delicate death.

Ah! Whitman, Walt Whitman, you never knew the Tans! Death doesn't arrive serenely here, his hands are desperate, and neither is delicately formed. Here the angel of death is a biting bitch!

The silence was startled by the sound of a motor-engine warming up, getting ready to go. He heard steps now in the hall, and the sound of *bravura* jests from a few voices. They were going. They mightn't be, though: they pretended that at times, driving the lorries away a bit, but leaving the men behind, to come with a rush into the house again among foolish people hurrying in their night-clothes out of their rooms to ask questions of each other. Stay still; don't move; not a stir: some of them still might be just beyond the door.

He lay there for what seemed a long time, the sweat of fear damping his body, and making him shiver. Stay still; don't move—someone was beside the door. He heard the handle giving a faint, brassy murmur. Soon, a black-clothed arm would thrust itself within, and a shot might go off that he would never hear. He silently squirmed deeper into the bed, and left the rest to God.

—Eh! he heard the voice of Mrs. Ballynoy whisper from the darkness, Are you there, or did they take you? Are you gone, or are you asleep, or wha'?

—That woman again! he thought resentfully—what a fright she gave me! Awake, Mrs. Ballynoy, he whispered back.

—Well, she said softly, you can take your ayse now, an' sleep tranquil, or get up, an' talk about th' queer things done in a Christian age.

—Wait till I light a candle, he said, making a great creak as he heaved himself out of the bed's hollow.

—You'll light no candle while I'm here, young man, said her voice, dressed in a titter, for a slip of overall's th' only shelter between me and a piercin' look from a

66

young man's eyes; an' it wouldn't be good to go from one exthreme to another on an identical night.

—Did they discover anything? asked Sean.

—Not a thing, though they took two o' th' men away with them. A sudden end to them all, an' a short fall to th' hottest hob that hell can heat! Don't light that candle yet, she added, for minds that have safely passed a danger near them are often reckless in their dealin' with an innocent female; though you're not that kind of a man, I know.

He heard the door softly closing and her hand fumbling with the lock. He hoped she wasn't going to stay. Ah! here's the key, for it's safer to put a locked door between eyes that pry into other people's affairs day an' night, tintin' everything with the colour of their own minds.

—Hadn't you better go back to your room, Mrs. Bally-noy, he warned. You need all the sleep you can get these days. We all do; and someone might be prowlin' round an' see an' think th' worst.

—Ay, she said; bad minds, th' lot o' them—that's why I've locked th' door. An' call me Nellie, for you know me well enough be now. Light th' candle now you can, but leave it on th' far side of where I'll be, for it's only a flimsy apron-overall I have between me an' all harm; and she tittered gaily as Sean very slowly lighted a candle on a box beside his bed.

She was a fine-looking heifer, right enough: long reddish hair coiled up into a bunch that rested neatly on the nape of a white neck; a well-chiselled, pale face, with large grey innocent eyes that seemed to be shrouded in a mist from the valley of the Missabielle; a fine figure set

these charms off, and when she slyly waved this sweet
figure in front of a man, he no longer saw, or wanted to
see, the mist of Missabielle. A rose of Tralee, without the
flower's serenity, maybe; but certainly a lovely rose of
the tenements. But Sean was in no mood now to enjoy the
charm of her fine figure and face. Once let a soul see she
had been in his room and the whole house would be
declaring that he was carrying on with Mrs. Ballynoy. He
should have had the courage to get up and push her out.
He almost wished now that the Auxies had stayed a little
longer.

In the sober light of the candle he saw that she had just
decorated her delightful body in a pair of brown slippers
and a flowered overall reaching only half-way down her
thighs, and showing a wide part of her white swelling
bosom; a show that was very charming, but damned
uncomfortable to one who was determined to take no
notice of it.

—Oh! There y'are, she said, when the candle-light got
steady, nice an' snug an' all alone. She came over and sat
down on the edge of the bed beside him. I'm askin' meself
why a land, overflowin' with prayer an' devotion, should
be so often plunged into dhread in the dead o' night for
nothin'? An' they tellin' me it's for Ireland's sake. Them
politics'll be the death of us some day. I feel terrible shy
in this get-up she said suddenly. Afther washin' the one
good nightgown I have, I was sleepin' in me skin, an' this
overall was th' first thing I laid hands on when the Tans
came thundherin' at the door. Pansies on it, she said,
giggling, pulling it a little from her thigh, pansies for

thought! and she poked Sean in the breast, playfully, with a hand reddened by the soda she used in the washing of clothes.

—Isn't Mr. Ballynoy at home, said Sean, trying to get her mind away from the overall, while he thought of a way to get rid of her.

—Didn't I tell you this mornin', on the stairs, that he was on a counthry job! He would be when the Tans come; though it's little good he'd be in any emergency, bein' born timid, with a daisy in his mouth. So I'm a poor lone lassie now, and she gave him another poke—this time in the thigh.

Don't you think you ought to get back, he warned; the Tans might come again.

—Ay, indeed, they might; a body can never know what them fellas'll do. An' it only a little way from Christmas, too. Ah! she said suddenly, looking away into a dream distance; it's good to be near one of your own: th' only two protestants in th' house, not countin' me husband. Of the crowd, not countin' him, only two who have th' proper way o' worshippin' an' are able to foresee th' genuine meanin' of th' holy text.

—There's me for you, said Sean, thinking neither you nor your husband bothered about religion, one way or another.

—Then you're sadly mistaken. I can't remember a year we missed feelin' the curious chantin' glow in th' air of a Christmas mornin', an' us on our way to church. In a proper mood, an' that was often, I could see what you'd think's th' star, ashine on the tip of the spire's top; an' me

69

ears can hear th' dull plod of the three camels' feet in th' deep sand, bearin' th' three kings with th' three rich gifts from Persia, or some other place in th' wilds of a faraway world; an' all th' time an anxious man seekin' shelter for his good woman, with the valleys levelled an' th' hills hidden be th' fallin' snow, dyein' her rich hair grey with its fallin' flakes, a sly soft carpet for her sandalled feet, an' sore they were from th' sting in its frosty tendherness; while th' tired Joseph thrudged demented behind, wondherin' if they'd find their lodgins only on the cowld, cowld ground. But God was good, an' found the shelther of a stable for the bewildhered, half-perished man, with his thin gown sodden, his toil-marked hands a hot ache, an' his poor feet blue with the bitther penetration of th' clingin' snow; an' afther Joseph had shooed th' puzzled animals to a safe an' ordherly distance, th' little fella was soon snug in a manger on top o' warm heaps of sainfoin, thyme, rosemary, an' lavender.

You're wrong there, said Sean; for how in such a bitther season could anyone come on spring and summer plants like those?

—I dunno, she murmured, unless God turned th' hay an' th' sthraw into th' sweet-savourin' herbs. But it's far betther not to thry to go into them things. Are you afraid to look at me, or what? she ejaculated, turning away from her dream; for Sean had turned his head away to escape the charm of the white bosom and soft thighs. As long as you don't make too free, I don't mind, though I feel a little shy in this scarce get-up.

A shoulder-band of the overall had slipped down, and

she had saucily drawn an arm out of it altogether so that
near half of her body to the waist was bare, and he saw a
breast, rather lovely in the light of the candle, looking like
a golden cup with a misty ruby in its centre. If he only
had her in a shady corner of the Phoenix Park, or in a
room of his own in a house where she wasn't known, the
world would be well lost for a period of ecstasy. But not
here.

—Your husband's a good fellow, he said trying to keep
his mind off her, and would rejoice to see you as you are
now. He thinks a lot of you.

—He oughtn't, she said sarcastically; where'd he get
another like me? He means well, poor man, but honest, it's
pathetic when we're alone, an' he thries to get goin'. Askin'
me to tell him when he's hurtin' me! She went into a soft,
gay, gurgling laugh, putting a hand over her mouth to
quench the merry sound of it. It's funny to talk of it here,
but maddenin' when I'm with him. I'm often near worn
out thryin', thryin' to coax a little flash of endeavour outa
him. He does his best, but the little sting he once had's
gone with the wind—joy go with it! She now laughed
venomously and loud, making Sean fearful of someone
hearing her. Wait till I tell you, she went on—you'll die
laughin'! You should see Charlie when he's at the he-man
business—are you sure you won't get faint, Nellie? Don't
forget to say if I'm hurtin' you, dearie! One night, when
he was—you know—I jerked him clean outa th' bed on
to th' floor—th' bump shook th' house! D'ye know, honest t'God, he just lay stunned there. Put th' heart across
me. Ever afther, d'ye know, I've had to handle him like

71

a delicate piece of china! No; poor Charlie's style's too shy for me. Not like Jim Achree's. J'ever hear o' his?

She slid down till she was half lying over him, and sang sedulously beside his ear:

Jim Achree's style has a wondherful way with it,
All th' girls' minds are in sad disarray with it;
Whenever they venture to have a short play with it,
Good girls want to stay with it, ever an' aye.
Oh! Jimmy Achree, shure your style is your own,
Amazin' th' way it has flourished an' grown,
With lovely threats shakin,' tense with mischief makin',
Knockin' poor women flat like a gorgeous cyclone!

—Looka, she said breathlessly, th' least bit o' fondlin' now, an' I'd swoon away, helpless an' benighted.

—In the midst of death we are in life, thought Sean. He tried to turn his head away so that he wouldn't be prompted by the white breast that was like a golden cup with a misty ruby in its centre; but his head refused to stir. Instead, he found his hand sliding over her fair bosom. He felt her arm pushing a way under his head till it was firmly round his neck, while the other pushed the clothes from covering him. He was lost, unless he yelled for help, and that he couldn't do.

—You're a good young man, he heard her whispering, an' would never take advantage of a woman alone in your room in th' dead o' night, with but a loose slip between you an' a swift lie-down on a bed o' meadow-sweet. Don't sthruggle, man, or you'll upset things! Why'r you thryin' to keep me from gettin' the clothes down? You've far too many on you; a little cool air'll do you good. Take th' good things while they're goin'. She whipped the clothes down with a fierce jerk, and lying beside him, pressed her mouth to his. Her big innocent eyes looked frantic now.

—G'won, she muttered, panting, be as rough as you like with me—it's what I'm longin' for for weeks! And half mad himself now, he gripped her like a vice, and sank his fingers into her flesh.

Then they suddenly went still as death, listening; listening to the whine of a motor-engine cruising down the road outside. Then another whine followed that, and another, the last, till they mingled into one shrill, threatening whine that went echoing round the walls of the old house.

—Out in strength tonight, thought Sean; more'n three of them; each of them crooning a song of death to someone. Ireland's modern, senseless Tanshee!

Suddenly the shrill whine lifted into a shrill, quavering scream, the scream fading into the throb, throb of active engines as the lorries stopped outside, or very near, the house.

—They've stopped at this house, or th' next one! said Nellie, loosening her arm from around his neck, and sliding swift from the bed to the door. Who' ha' thought th' bastards would bother to come twice th' same night? Christ! It's this house they're makin' for! And swiftly came a great hammering on the door again. Nellie frantically twisted and turned at the key, but she couldn't get the door of the room open.

—In they'll come, she squealed softly, an' I'll be exposed to th' world as a fast woman. She tugged and writhed till the slip fell from her shoulders, leaving her naked, fuming, at the door. You it was, she half shouted, turning a red and bitter face towards Sean, that lured me into this predicament, never able to let any decent woman pass without thryin' to meddle her!

Sean as eager as she was herself that she should go unseen, leaped out of bed, hurried over, and with a hard twist, turned the key. Snatching up her flowered overall, she whipped the door open, rushed out, and up the stairs, without another word. Shutting the door again, he fled back to bed, digging himself down deep into it once again, listening to hear if it was Tan or Tommy who had entered the house.

The door spun open, and a torchlight shot terror into his eyes. Silently he waited for a blow or a shot, but neither came. He opened his eyes, and saw a young khaki-clad officer just inside the door, a torch in one hand, a revolver in the other. Behind him were two soldiers with rifles at ready. The officer stared at Sean, then slowly returned the gun to a holster, and the soldiers, at this sign, stood at ease, and rested the butts of the rifles on the dirty floor.

—Get up; dress; go out to the street, said the officer tersely; this house has to be searched room by room. Don't try to go farther than the wire cordon ringing the district: orders are to fire on any who do. He watched Sean dressing, and when he saw him clap a cap on his head, asked, Haven't you an overcoat?

—A sort of a one, said Sean.

—Better than nothing; you'd better put it on—it's damned cold outside.

74

—Decent man, thought Sean, putting on his old coat; has an occasional thought for others. Thank God, the Tans are absent!

He went out into the dark hall, and near bumped into a Tan standing there, fingering a heavy revolver. A cold shiver trickled down his spine.

—Where are you going? he asked.

—Outside to street—officer's orders, said Sean.

—What officer? asked the Tan.

—Military officer, sir.

—Oh! Military officer, eh? Well, we give the orders here—understand?

—Yessir, said Sean promptly.

—Are you a Sinn Feiner? he questioned, twisting the gun in his hand.

—A Sinn Feiner? Me? No fear.

—You were one, then.

—No; never, said Sean emphatically. Thank God, thought Sean, he didn't ask if I had ever been a Republican. The ignorant English bastard doesn't know the difference.

—Well, you're an Irishman, anyway—you can't deny that!

—No, sir, I can't deny that: I'm an Irishman, right enough.

—Well, shout To Hell with Ireland, and you can go—no mutter, but a shout the house can hear. Now!

But Sean fell silent. God damn him if he'd do that! He knew his face was white; he felt his legs tremble; but he fell silent, with a stubborn look on his face.

—Go on, you Sinn Fein rat, shout it!

A streak of light fell on them, and Sean saw the young officer coming to them. He stopped, looked at Sean, then looked at the Tan.

—What's wrong here? he asked. Let that man go into the street.

—You mind your own damned business, snarled the Tan.

—I am minding it, said the young officer. I happen to be an Irishman, too. Have you any objection to it?

—I don't take orders from you! said the Tan roughly.

—I'm not sorry for that, the officer said; but this man does—didn't I give you an order to go into the street? he asked, turning to Sean.

—Yessir.

—Carry it out, then, he said sharply; and Sean, turning swiftly, made a quick march through the hall, out by the door, into the street.

It was very cold, and from the timid gleams from a waning moon, Sean saw that path and road were white with a covering of rich rime frost. Groups of people were standing, huddled up against the railings of the houses, while more were oozing sleepily out of the remaining ones, shepherded into bunches by armed soldiers. The women were trying to coax warmth into their tearful and shivering children by wrapping flimsy rags round their shoulders, and tucking the little ones under them into their arms.

Several searchlights wandered through the street, flashing over the groups of people, or tinselling along the walls of the houses. At one end stood an armoured car, the lids raised, showing the heads of several Tommies who were quietly chanting an advice to the shivering people to pack up their troubles in their old kit-bags. Along the road, over the calm, quiet chastity of the white frost, slid a diamond-shaped tank, looking like a dirty, dangerous crawling slug, machine-guns sticking out from slits, like ugly protruding eyes staring at the cowering people.

He saw a commotion round the door of the house he lived in. He mooched over till he was beside the steps to look over the shoulders of a rank of soldiers. A prisoner! Who could it be? He whisperingly asked the soldier in front of him what had happened.

—An awrsenal! whispered the soldier hoarsely. Rear of th' ouse, an awrsenal discovered! 'Nough gelignite to blow up 'ole neighbourhood. A blighter there drew a gun, but was shot through hand afore 'ee could pull trigger. 'Ere's the bawstard coming!

Amid a group of soldiers with rifles at the ready marched a thin forlorn figure, but the lips in the pale face were tight together, and the small head was held high. Peering closer, Sean saw that handcuffs kept the two small hands locked together, and that from one of them red blobs were dripping on to the white frost on the path, leaving little spots behind like crimson berries that had fallen on to snow. In the hall he heard the voice of Nellie shouting.

—That's me husband! he heard her shout; a good man an' a brave one! Yous'll never shoot the life outa Ireland, yous gang o' armed ruffians! Here, take me, too, if yous aren't afraid. Keep your pecker up, Charlie—Ireland's with you!

Sean peered closer. Good God—the prisoner was the timid, insignificant Charlie Ballynoy who took no interest in politics! A lorry, full of soldiers, swirled into the kerb. The handcuffed prisoner was pushed and lifted into it. Standing there in the middle of the soldiers, with the searchlight covering him with glory, he held up his iron-locked hands from which clouts of blood still dripped.

—Up th' Republic! he shouted with the full force of his voice.

The lorry drove off, and the red specks in the rime turned brown and lonely. Heads that had lifted bent again, and all was quiet once more. A bleak dawn at last began to peel the deeper darkness from the sky, and the scene crept into a ghostly glamour, brightened by the pale faces of the waiting people; the pale moon sinking deeper into a surly sky, and the rimy frost on pathway, road, and roof grew whiter. Dirty-yellow-clad figures moved into the whiteness from one dark doorway, to move out of it again into another blacker still; while the brown, slug-like tank crept up and down the road, charring the dainty rime with its grinding treads—the new leviathan that God could ne'er control.

PAX

A LORDLY, laughing sun covered the city with a hazy veil of strident heat; and all that moved through it seemed to lazily dance along, slow, quivering, as if lost to their earthy origin, and were tremulous, but trying to be brave in another world.

Sean was walking slow down the elegant part of Dublin's North Circular Road, where the daintier houses stood, each aloof from the dust of the street; each flounced with a trimly-kept garden; all looking like nicely-reared children, tidied up to go to Sunday school, or to receive their first communion. Along this way George Moore could have safely extended his particular nose to take in the fragrant scent from bush and blossom giving a cooler charm to the molten air.

Passing by the Phibsboro Church, its Vincentian spire thrusting into the deep-blue of the sky, looking like a huge spear left behind on the field of one of heaven's battles with Lucifer and his lost angels, he crossed Blaquiere Bridge to enter into the lower part of the thoroughfare. On his right now was the great high stone wall surrounding the outspread and dour-bodied Mother of Mercy Hospital, while on his left rose the grimly-grey walls of Mountjoy Jail, where a contingent of Black and Tans smoked the pipe of war, waiting for orders to go forth

79

again and give the Irish another lesson in light and leading. No fragrance from the further flowers came stealing down here; a black van went swiftly up the drive to the jail bringing prisoners to their quiet and scanty quarters, while vans as black brought the dead away from the silent and senseless hospital.

Then Sean saw them—an army patrol, dressed in dirty-white drill, filing along towards him, on each side of the road, each man with a rifle at the ready, an officer walking on the pathway, midway between the head and tail of the patrol. As Sean went nervously on, he saw the officer glance at his wrist-watch, turn, and say something to his men, and then he saw the soldiers suddenly squat down on the kerb, leaving their rifles carelessly by their sides; he saw them lighting cigarettes, and stretching their legs gorgeously out in front of them.

The Truce had come. Rifle and revolver wore a friendly look now. Passing people stopped to speak to the soldiers and some shook happy hands with them; some hurried out of the houses near by, and doled out cups of tea to them; a few did a few violent steps of a dance in the centre of the street; but, now and again, men and women passed without looking right or left, going on with a fixed stare forward.

> The fight was over, and the Truce was here;
> The busy quietness seemed lone and queer;
> For ev'ry twisty lane became a golden street,
> Where generals and commandants each other greet,
> Festoon'd with glowing deeds from head to feet;

Talking the tir'd night away ere they arrang'd to meet
When morning came to tell to exil'd fear,
How each, 'gainst odds, with but a questing gun,
And two grenades, made slick from cast-out cans,
Destroy'd three lorry-loads of Black and Tans!

Golden boys in golden streets: there they stood, mid-stream, in a torrent of talk, rambling, delicious and deliri-ous talk, the dust of death still in their eyes,—all that remained of Ireland's tattered, nerve-worn, gallant army; or they leaned against a fence in a country lane, canopied by the sly innocence of woodbine's dangling stems; farm-er's son and farmer's lad, girls listening; shy, white fingers sometimes stroking the faded, maybe blood-stained, cloth of a coat; there they stood, their faces turned from dan-ger—the nerve-racked, exhilarant Fianna Fail.

Free for the time, anyhow, from the danger of a dread-ful night in a barracks, or in a silent room, fitted up for a tomb, in Dublin's Castle, if any of them happened to be taken alive. Free from the searing thoughts of having the toes hammered flat with rifle-butts, cloaking the bones of the feet with a bloody squash; the tender belly punctured with merry bayonet jabs; the face unbalanced with blows; the finger-nails pulled out with pincers, forcing yells from the man who was losing them; free from cords twisting tight on a neck till all the breath was gone. Good to be merry for tomorrow we don't die. Warriors all, for war-riors they were to fight with the bare chance of a restless rest now and again, and the certain chance of an agonising end; to fight against a force outnumbering them a hundred to one, so well armed that each could lose a gun to save his life; while an Irishman would risk his life to save his gun; so well armed that the Black and Tans wearied with the weight of what they had to carry, while the Irish lad often had to beg his quartermaster for another bullet.

Pax. Peace was here. *Pax vobiscum* to all in this fair land, first flower of the earth and first gem of the See. The people dwell now in peaceable habitations. Bread could again be eaten in quietness; people could lounge at their doors to gossip, or lean from a window to throw down a greeting to a passing neighbour. Peace was dropping now from the veils of the morning to where the cricket sang. The wild-rose in the hedge could push her face and fragrance forward without being troubled by the rude and careless hands of hidden gunmen. The busy wren could build a delicate dome over her cosy nest without the uncertainty of having it desecrated by a grim grenade exploding. The last grave had been dug; the last lad buried. The tear at this moment shed is the last one too. Now we can see the sun shine, feel the rain falling, and watch the jaunty corn grow. Three shouts on two hills for peace: on Croagh Patrick, in Mayo, where Irish Christianity was confirmed, and on Cave Hill, in Antrim, where Republicanism was brought to life: three shouts on these two hills for peace in Eire's green, unpleasant land.

The whole country became a rhapsody of bands, banners, and bonfires. Bonfires blazed in the meanest streets, even when door and stairway had to provide the fuel. And God wasn't forgotten—don't go away thinking that, now.

Thanksgiving ascended from every altar; the floor of heaven was lifted with the storm of te deums that swept up under it; and prayers were offered up that the peace might last forever and a day after. In places paraded honour was shown to God. Down in Sandymount, a suburb of Dublin, a parade was held in honour of Christ the King, and trams could hardly hold, without bulging, the crazy-joy crowds hurrying out to line the streets near the church, and watch the guard of honour, specially uniformed, groomed, and belted, to pay military homage to the Blessed Sacrament. Every honest head was bowed as the Host went by, the silver-and-gold encasement standing on a velvet-floored, silk-canopied carrier, borne by Irish officers, surrounded by a thick and glittering fringe of fixed bayonets. Oh, gentle Jesus, alanna, once they came out with swords and staves to take Thee; now they come forth with bayonet and gun to keep Thee safe. What a change for the better!

—A sight worth livin' to see, said Roary O'Bawlochone to Sean.

—It would be, if Ulsther was here to see it, said the tram-conductor.

In and out of the smoky jabber, the generals astroll in their uniforms, the flame of the bonfires, the exuberant prayers of the people on their quiet way to God, and the just hopes of the country, went the long and lone chain-letter of dearsirsiamfaithfullyyoursismishelemeasmor between Lloyd George at home in London and Ayamonn De Valera half-at-home in Dublin, asking how where when why which what when Ireland could and in what way accommodate herself when she sat down or stood up in or out of the Empire, insulated from the association which would hamper and help by being beside or well away from what was canonistically known as the British Family of Nations, with a fine formula in hand to enable Ireland to be the one and a different thing at the same time, to stand on a republican rock while swimming in the sea of imperialism, the juxtapositional problem solved by alternative proposals, one in the hand of De Valera which he read to Lloyd George when he wasn't listening, and the other held by Lloyd George which he read when Dev was busy lilting I'm in my sleeping, and don't Waken Me; each of which and both together was were to tighten things that had been loose, and loosen things that had been tight between Ireland and England for the last seven hundred years *anno domine dirige nos.*

—Looksee, said De Valera, hooking an arm in one of George's, you're a Kelt and I'm another; so we'd better have a stroll, and talk of the first four things first, before we decide everything in the discourse of time.

Away the two of them wandered, not noticing the passage of time, chatting away furiously, but in a real friendly spirit, for both of them were Kelts, thoroughly conscious that God was guiding them, and that He had given them an important place in the cosmopolitan cosmos.

—Over there, and De Valera's finger pointed to the nor'-nor'-west, is Tara, and somewhat further to the west's where Patrick kindled the turf fire that has never gone out.

—Dear me, murmured Lloyd George; a great man, your Sarsfield, Earl of Lucan.

—No, no; I'm talking of Patrick the saint, not Patrick the soldier.

—Of course—St. Patrick, said Lloyd George penitently; pity, though, he was an alien.

—He was more Irish than the Irish themselves, said De Valera emphatically; and I won't hear one word against him. Kelt or no Kelt, you must leave our saints alone.

—All are more than Irish, murmured the British Prime Minister; Anthony of Aghadoe; Ignatius, the Gael from the County Clare; the Little Flower of Lissodell; and Bernadette of Ballyvourney; I crave your worship's pardon.

De Valera, without the slightest fuss, hurried Lloyd George down the draughty Irish corridors of time; up Croagh Patrick, down Slieve Mish, around the Magillicuddy's Reeks, till George was breathless; all the time pouring into his widened ear tales from the saga of Cuchullain, the Ranns round Rosnaree, the Dreams of Angus, the story of the bee in the bonnet of St. Finnbar; taking great care to assure Lloyd George that he personally believed, or accepted, only those records, historic, pre-historic, and preter-historic of Eire's ruins and regulations which were substantially marked and sealed with the *nihil obstat* and *imprimatur* from the downright impression got from the signet of a bishop's ring.

—A knowledge of each of these and all together, George, went on De Valera, may suffice to form, or postulate, the possibility of a condition which might allow us to enter into some preliminary idea as to whether we should consider the status of how we feel, and what we are, in connection with your own consideration of the status as to how you feel, and what you are, in regard to whatever may be now, and subsequently, discussed between the two nations; and to endeavour to attain that desirable end, sir, you must get to know a few of the facts from all the sources I have enumerated, and will enumerate, before we can sensibly begin our talk.

—I don't know that we'll have enough time, murmured Lloyd George.

—We'll have to find enough time, said De Valera shortly; a man's never too young to learn. Another hour's trotting and we'll be in another Irish epoch—near to Avvin Macha, home of the Red Branch Knights; the great city that Macha planned on the plain with the pin of a brooch she took from the neck of her gown; so to this day it is called Avvin Macha, Armagh, Neck Pin of Macha, from eo, a pin; and muin, the neck—see?

—I see, in a kind of a way, murmured the Prime Minister, a little out of breath.

—Here's The Fews, the passage-way to Ulster, said De Valera in a half-whisper; so slow down a bit, for the people yonder aren't too hospitable, as you will soon see; for each householder has three trained cranes perched on the rooftop, the first calling out, Do Not Come, Do Not Come; the second calling Get Away, Get Away; and the third Pass this House, Pass this House; so now you know the kind of fare you're facing.

86

—What's that I'm seeing and hearing? said Lloyd
George, startled, and suddenly stopping in his tracks.

On a fence at the mouth of the Pass they saw a short,
sturdy man. He was soberly dressed in neat black cloth, a
trim bowler-hat on his head, with a blue-and-orange
feather stuck pertly in the band of it. A thumb to keep the
place was inserted into a bible he had on his knees. Time
and again the man would open the book, look at it, then
shout up to the Mountains of Mourne coming down to the
sea, saying Be ye studfust, immovable, always abounding
in th' wurrk of th' Lord! Then, standin' up to attention,
he sang,

> Th' Pope's gut his curdinals all in a row,
> Th' lame, th' blind, the daff, en' th' dumb;
> They're comin' tae Ulsther with saint So-and-so,
> Tae silence th' boast of th' prutestunt dhrum.

> Lero, lero, all so quaro,
> Lut th' domned papists with sucrements come;
> With our guns all akimbo, we'll send them to limbo—
> Says Wullie boy Scutt an' Dickie McCrum!

> King Bully's high up on his lully-white steed—
> Shet up th' bible, an' run for th' gun!
> We'll give th' proud Pope an' th' devil their need,
> An' show how th' Chrustian endeavour is done!

> Lero lero, do an' daro,
> Tae hull with th' Pope's devalerian chum!
> Call all the kind neighbours an' arrm them with sabers,
> Says Wullie boy Scutt an' Dickie McCrum!

—Let's get out of here, said Lloyd George; this fellow is better left to himself.

So the two of them hastened back to safer fields, De Valera stimulating his companion with lurid and entrancing information about Ireland's right and Ireland's wrong; picturing it all so vividly that poor George as he was stepping across the little River Nanny in County Meath, was nearly run down by a troop of Cromwell's galloping Ironsides, the windy swish of their swords taking the puff out of him, before he reached the farther bank in safety. Along at a loping gallop went the two of them to the safer south, though when they had got as far as Wexford, De Valera's revival in burning words of things past was so glamorous that Lloyd George found himself flying for his life from the pike-men of ninety-eight, losing a lock of his bushy hair, while he was swimming the Slaney, from a bullet fired by a hasty Shelmalier, from his long-barrelled gun of the sea, who mistook him for a Yeoman.

—Call it a day, cried the panting statesman; I'm done in entirely!

—We must suffer on, said De Valera. Surely your brain isn't going to conk out that quick? All that we do is but the precursor to peace, and we all want peace.

—Quite, murmured Lloyd George, quite; we've quarrelled often enough; we must have peace now, at any price, almost.

—Well, then, don't be calling a light historical chat of twenty-four hours, a day, man. What has been said is but the point of the beginning: we haven't even got within sight of the Normans landing in Cork and Wexford.

—And what about when I was near cleft in two by a Cromwellian trooper up on the plains of County Meath? queried Lloyd George, halting in his stride; and the tuft of hair whipped from my head by a Shelmalier bullet, and I walking peaceful round the slopes of Vinegar Hill? Didn't those things happen after the Normans came to Ireland?

We're going backwards, said De Valera.

—Looksee, d'ye think I'm going to permit myself to be lost in Ireland's ranns and ruins? said Lloyd George, with the edge of anger on his voice. D'ye not realise that a whole nation's waiting for me over in Downing Street? How far do you want me to follow you back? Do you imagine, sir, that an enlightened man of my dimensions is ready to believe, that, in his voyage to an undiscovered America, your St. Brendan celebrated Mass on a whale's back?

—You could believe a worse thing, sir.

—I couldn't believe a thing more nonsensical, sir. A fairy-tale, a myth!

—A myth, sir, remember, is a thing that may, or may not, be true.

—True, did you say? You make me laugh! Brendan discovered America when no-one knew it existed! Look, he went on in tense tones, listen, young man, listen: if you want to know the truth, and accept a fact, it was Madoc, son of Owen Ap Gwynedd, who first set foot on America; and you can prove this by going to the back parts of Virginia, for there you will find communities and groups speaking the most fluent Welsh to this very day!

—I think if we kept to the point, sir, it would be very much better, murmured De Valera.

—The point? Well, to the point then. He banged his stick on a rock. Everything that has happened in the world hasn't happened in Ireland. Keep to the point! And what about you, De Valera? Haven't you ranged from a point of the present away to an imperceptible point of the past?

—That's different; that's very different.

—How is it very different?

—To get to know Ireland through her history, you must begin at the end and end at the beginning.

—I won't listen anymore, cried Lloyd George; I'm tired with words; I'm perplexed; I'm fairly moidered! He walked rapidly away to a great distance, then turned to shout back. Send a man who you can trust to me, there are too many voices speaking at the same time here. I'm off. Send me a man who's something less of an historical kaleidoscope, and we'll chat over things quietly. And re- member—if you can't come to an agreement, look out for war; immediate and terrible war! I'm going home to Dixie—there now, you see how my poor mind's getting mixed here. He hurried up the slopes of Lugnaquilla. When he got to the summit, he turned, and looked down on the tiny figure of De Valera standing still in the valley below; then he shook his stick in the air, and shouted, Im- mediate and terrible war! Then he disappeared over the brow of the hill, making for the rocky road to Dublin.

Lonely and disturbed, the other wandered about, for he could see nothing but the mists rolling down the bog, and the mists again and they rolling up the bog, and hearing nothing but the wind crying out in the bits of broken trees were left from the great storm, and the streams roaring with the rain. Then he cocked an ear, for the crying wind seemed to be whistling. Thou art not conquered yet, dear land, thou art not conquered yet. He, too, whistled with the wind, and Mick Collins came up, and they both whistled the same thing together.

—He wants someone to go over, said De Valera; and you're the man to go, Mick.

—Aw no, no, Dev, said Mick; you'd be better. You know your own mind well, and everyone else's better; you're the man to go.

—You're the natural choice, Mick. Isn't it all prophesied in the Book of Kills?

—No, you, Dev; you as head of the State should go.

—The place for the head of the State is here in the heart of home, entrenched among the soldiers and the saints.

—But supposin' we fail, Dev?

—Fail? How fail? How could Fianna Fail fail?

These two men, after risking terrible deaths for a long time, heavy prices upon both their heads; worn and very worried with doing more than mortal men should ever be called upon to do; shook hands for the last time; shook hands, and parted; De Valera to his anxious lonely thoughts, the other to England to talk a lot of his life away.

So Mick Collins, this homely, exuberant knight of the green guerdon, fortified himself with many prayers and a splendid communion, before he went on to the boat with his companion, Arthur Griffith, to do battle for Ireland, though both of them were unsuited, either in knowledge or experience, for the fight; went forward for as much as Ireland was prepared to receive; went forward to get as much as they could out of the cunning of Lloyd George and Winston Churchill; to get as much as any man, or group of men, could have got out of things as they were then. And going up the gangway of the boat, Mick Collins wiped the sweat of anxiety from his brow, never knowing that it was the first drops from the dew of death.

And De Valera sat down in the dark valley of the shadow of anxiety, too, and waited; and so did Sean, and all the people with him; wondering when they got their freedom what would happen to the whole of them.

DRIFTING

THE bands were silent, the banners stored away, the ashes of the bonfires had gone in the wind; but Collins and his comrades were still talking under London skies. Summer had gone; autumn twilights had faded into the darkness of winter, and still De Valera pondered in Dublin, while Collins, Lloyd George, and Churchill talked and talked on in London. The people waited in the gloom, while all sorts of rumours flurried them into spreading rumours of their own. They were drifting, even as the leaves still falling from the trees drifted, idly, damp and desolate, from one place to another, the wind disallowing them to continue in their stay for long in any nook or corner where they might whirling seek for shelter and repose. The people, too, went drifting from square to square; uneasy, anxious, and suspicious, they believed this and said that, drifting from corner to square, wondering what the will of God would be. Sean began to sense that the unity of the politicians was cracking. Another split in Irish life would show itself, and then would come again the curse, the blow; and those who had so loved one another, like good Christians, would soon be in the midst of clenching teeth, the spitting on beards, and the hauling down of reputation's flag. He went his own way, thinking and writing, through a gathering murmur of bubble and squeak, listening, watching, and wondering how it would all begin.

93

For quite a time now, he had been working in a job, earning thirty shillings a week. Jim Larkin's sister, with a few others, had risked taking a hall that had been a school, a methodist church, and a parish dispensary. Here they had organised concerts and performed plays, building a stage themselves, while cunning hands had painted some scenery, and stitched together a few fancy and suitable costumes. Countess Markievicz had decorated the walls with a number of bad pictures. A home-made pantomime was presented, and Sean himself had acted the part of the cockney burglar in O'Duffy's play, *Special Pleading*. After more than a year's tiring effort, it was clear that these things wouldn't even pay the rent, so with the clamorous approval of many workers, who didn't care a damn about pantomime or play, a club for the playing of the game called House was started.

It was a curious game: each player bought for a penny an oblong strip of leather on which three rows of various numbers were stamped. A player could buy as many cards as his mind could manage. A caller-out at the head of the hall dipped a hand into a large tin-box from which he drew out a small disk of leather, calling out the number that happened to be stamped on it. When a number was called, each player scanned the strips of leather in front of him to see if the number called was stamped on any of them; if it were, he crossed it out with a stick of chalk. As soon as any player had all the numbers on his strip of leather crossed on the top, bottom, or middle line, he shouted out House, and then received the major part of what had been gathered as payment for the cards; the rest going to pay the collectors and those responsible for the club. The men were remarkably quick in marking their cards. He had seen men with as many as ten cards. Each card had, if he remembered right, fifteen numbers, so that these players had to run over one hundred and fifty numbers every other second, marking with his chalk any number called that happened to be on any of the cards. Sean marvelled at the quickness of the eye, the swift movement of the hand holding the chalk, and the look of embattled anxiety concentrated in the rough faces of the men. A great achievement, which, in worthier circumstances of life, with mightier means of education, would have made some of these untidy, turbulent dockers and carters, unerring in their calculations, into mathematicians of the first order.

Sean's job was to come in at nine in the morning, clean up the medley of chalk, cigarette-butts, cartons, and other rubbish scattered over the hall, wash down all the benches, trim the lamps, and leave everything ready for the night's session when he left at five in the evening. For the first time for years he was able to feed himself regularly, though simply, for he devoted most of what he got in buying a complete set of Balzac, and new set of Shakespeare's Works—all second-hand—a volume of Goya's pictures, and another of Van Gogh's paintings and drawings, as well as giving ten shillings a week for a second-hand typewriter which Michael Foley of Middle Abbey Street was keeping for him till the full amount, twenty guineas, was paid. A great machine! He had had it now for twenty-five years, and he was using it still. Well, God's help, as an Irish proverb says, is as near as the door; and so it proved to be, though it required the help from some hundreds of dockers, carters, and labourers to open the door, and let Him in; and it was often a queer thought to Sean that he owed a new lease of life to the folly and thoughtlessness of these uncultured, uncouth, brave men. From the hard toil of these rough men, dishevelled in body and mind, out of what they earned so hard, he lived, ate of bread and meat, and nourished his sensuous being in art and literature. And, worst of all, in his thoughts, he never thought of thanking them.

A Committee had been formed to help get Jim Larkin released from an American jail, where he had been shoved for pronouncing publicly ethics as common as those in the Pope's *Rerum Novarum*. This Committee worked in union with one in New York, and Sean acted as Secretary. The members as well tried to parry the campaign carried on by some of the official Labour leaders to undermine, for their own ends, the value of Jim with the industrial workers of Ireland. These officials were eager to organise a state of things that would allow them to live in peace, after gaining an increase of a penny or tuppence to wages at odd and irregular times for Union members, so as to keep the workers from breaking in on their peace, and permit them to draw their salaries in a quiet and orderly way. And, of course, the church clericals gave a quiet but definite clapping of hands to their course of conduct. It was an odd attitude for the Labour leaders towards a man whose organising genius had placed most of these Labour leaders where they were.

Some thoughtful soul suggested that a greeting should

be sent to Jim, sent to jail for professing the commonest ideas of Christian charity, and it was decided to send him a card holding a simple greeting to show that thousands still remembered him and wished him back in Ireland. Hearing that some of the Union officials were doing all they could to prevent the men from sending a message of affection to their much-prized champion, Sean was selected to go to see Mr. William O'Brien, the Union's new General Secretary. Sean felt that such an open-minded, fine-hearted man as O'Brien would immediately stop any interference with this effort on the part of the workers of Ireland to spiritually visit a comrade in prison. So, having first written an explanatory letter to Mr. O'Brien, Sean set out to visit him.

As he trod the way there, Sean felt angry and contemptuous that the Head Office had transferred itself from the old fighting quarters of Liberty Hall to an electable house in the gardenian surroundings of Rutland Square; to a house that never had a history for the workers, and never would; where Labour would—as Sean thought— luxuriously allow itself to lie down and doze itself away to death. Official Labour had left the miry murkiness, full of the memorised shapes of battles, the shadow of which some day would take on the tougher glory of bronze remembrance, for grander quarters, where polished peace would have an easy-chair; golden-brown sherry would take the place of sombre, purplish beer; corduroy and moleskin be replaced by the natty dinner-jacket and the black bow.

Strange influence buildings had on the memory and the heart! Thousands of buildings were passed, maybe entered, in a lifetime, but only a few were remembered in the soul and mind. Of all the buildings in Dublin, but four of them remained forever and vividly in the heart and mind of Sean: his home, the Church of St. Burnupus, the Abbey Theatre, and Liberty Hall; and, indeed, they were four symbols of his life. Each was woven deftly and deep into flesh and spirit.

Ah! Here it is! Headquarters of the Irish unskilled labourer. The silence here isn't broken by the sound of a hob-nailed boot; no sharp smell from stony dust of cement, black grime from coal, or yellow dust from cattle-feed, disturbs the scents of lilac or rosebud coming from the sequestered square across the road. The evening-dress suit and the plus-four front of the Irish Labour movement. And the clergy's coy approval.

William O'Brien, General Secretary of the Irish Transport Union, would help all right in the sending of a greeting to Jim, because of his own generous heart, first; and, then, for the sake of old times in the Socialist Party of Ireland; and, lastly, Mr. O'Brien would be the last to hesitate in doing anything to hearten an old comrade now in jail for reminding Christians of the greatest of the three Christian virtues.

A vision of Mr. O'Brien, as Sean had known him, came before his eyes. The set face, like a tense white mask, crossed straight with thin red lips, fringed with a clipped moustache and short-trimmed, pointed beard; brightened by the small, shrewd eyes, like dark diamonds whose fuller light could never be coaxed into gleaming. Now a Director of the National Bank, he had then the younger vision of a great Union for all the workers of Ireland. Everywhere Sean went he saw the gigantic letters of O.B.U., One Big Union, each taller than the tallest man, forcing themselves in front of all eyes, so that he who ran could read them. Many nasty-minded workers said that the big letters really meant Old Bill's Union; and so this little fairy, that came out winged from the brain of O'Brien, danced its way through the land for a season; but died at last, like Tinkerbell, and stayed dead, for the voice of Labour was neither strong enough nor advanced enough to bring this brilliant mite to life again.

A strange man who has left his mark on the Irish Labour movement; a nature that sat at a meeting, still as death, listening; all the little thoughts expressed there, which didn't tinkle with his own, rejected, but not forgotten; for his own were great, born big, and ripe for use. He wasn't a man one would expect children to run to meet, dodge round him, laughing; swing from his hooked arm, or prattle pompous achievements into his listening ear. Too serious a man for that sort of thing. Rather might one say that youngsters would sink into silence when he came near, and reverently let him pass them by, for there seemed to be no echo of a child's voice in his own, as if he had been born ready-made, and ripe for planning. He had put childish things away from him, and was a man's man. Quiet in the crowd, William O'Brien was waiting to see what the Irish Delegates would carry back from Downing Street.

Sean went into the Irish Transport Union's Headquarters. All was business; all working steadily to create the order of the O.B.U. Here was no talk; no glitter of a sudden laugh; no hum of a murmured song; no evidence of hurry or excitement; all bent on building the One Big Union, the clerks bent sedately over what they had to do. Sean heard no beating of a heart here; not even the ticking of a clock. As the door closed behind him, he went towards the counter where a clerk was busy emptying figures into a ledger. His footsteps seemed to make a startling noise, and all the heads were raised to have a look at him. He knew some of them; and the one behind the counter, an insignificant-looking little fellow, with a heart of gold, who had a gorgeous opinion of himself as an actor, exiled among ordinary people through no fault of his own, stared at Sean in astonishment, for he knew Sean had no card of entry into Transport Union Premises since Jim Larkin had sailed away from Erin's shore. This eminent insignificance now came out to challenge Sean. Sliding from behind the counter like a performing flea, he stood in front of Sean, head bent, hands outstretched as if to catch him if he tried to dodge.

—What is the nature of your business, please? he asked in a most efficient voice.

—No business, really, answered Sean; I'm on an errand of goodwill, and I dropped in to see Mr. O'Brien for a moment.

—We have no record of any appointment; Mr. O'Brien sees visitors only by special appointment.

—Just you tell Bill, Casside's here, and he'll be glad to see me, stretching a friendly hand out to pat the opposer's shoulder, but the flea jumped back in alarm.

—We received no notice of your visit. Mr. O'Brien sees visitors only by special appointment.

—He'll see me, if you'll only tell him. I wrote to him, and he knows about the matter enticing me here.

—Mr. O'Brien sees persons only by special appointment.

—You said that before. And don't be humiliating the man by calling him Mister; he wouldn't be pleased. Up to now, he has always been Bill.

Two more clerks slid courageously from where they had been working to reinforce the importantly insignificant. They arranged themselves, one on either side of the performer, a little behind him, so that he shouldn't waver in the discharge of his duty, and that they would be close to help, if the need arose.

—I've come, said Sean, just to ask Mr. O'Brien to help us to send a greeting to an old comrade, lonely in a far-off jail——

—Mr. O'Brien sees no-one, except persons who have a special——

—Appointment, added Sean. Well, my purpose is special, even though it isn't armed with an appointment. Mr. O'Brien is a good catholic; a man strict in his observance of the canonical orders of the church; a Christian in spirit as well as in practice; so he will never refuse, if you will let him know, and would easily agree to help us in this simple act of charity of showing a thought of remembrance to a lonely comrade; especially to the man who had lighted the flame of Labour's revolt in the City of Dublin and Belfast, a flame that showed the workers what they were and what they might become!

—What Larkin himself got himself into, let Larkin

himself get himself out of; and the clerks, moving forward, began to edge Sean towards the door. He found himself out on the cold steps, the door closed, the clerks gone; so the little clerks below, by refusing to carry a message, prevented the greater clerk above from carrying out a simple act of Christian charity.

And so from bad to worse.

The Round Room of Dublin's Mansion House was packed tight with people; hushed and reverent as befitted the solemn and misereal occasion. It was a centenary of Dante, and all who could had hurried to enjoy the charm and refreshment of hearing Count Plunkett, Minister of Fine Arts in the Dail, lecture about all the circles of hell, and the many amazing things that commonly happened there. The people, mostly the middle class, came, too, to show how they loved fine literature, and, also, to show England they were so easy in their minds that they could afford to think of things a long way from Downing Street. Not knowing that the Treaty was burning a hole in De Valera's pocket, they sat firm and quiet.

> Calm as granite to their foes.
> Bravely hope, and wisely waited,
> Toil, join, and educate,
> Man is master of his fate;
> They will have their own again!

They had waited a long time; they were gloomy and doubtful; and all were in a ready mood to furnish themselves with the fear of what Dante had to tell them. The

lecture and discussion lasted for many hours, for all were
anxious to reveal their controlled delight in Plunkett's
knowledge of Dante's hell; and soon in every ear re-
sounded the thunderous twisting melody of plaints innumerable and torment and loud lament and furious rage.
If the fiery speakers had been heard by all the Irish people
at the same time, the Dies Irae would have become the
national anthem of the land. The entire audience was gasping before the entertainment was over, and most of them,
when they had escaped to the outer air, vowed to God and
Virgin Mary that never again would they go to hear a
lecture on anything higher than the poems of Thomas
Davis or Barney McCoy; even though it were to be given
by St. Michael himself, accompanied on a trumpet by St.
Gabriel, with a young Virgil from Cork or Galway tapping
out time on a solar plexus. And from that day to this, no-one
has ventured to offer to give a lecture on Dante to the
patient and long-suffering Irish. Ireland had hurried away
from *mons tria millia* of Cassino to climb the homelier
haunts of the Sugar Loaf Mountain.

Curious, thought Sean, how they couldn't see the hells
out of which there was no redemption, in their own home
town. During school holidays, so that children wouldn't
go without a nourishing meal, spurred by a mood of dismal
charity, a brother of S. T. O'Kelly and his wife, had got a
loan of the hall in which Sean worked, so that corporal
charity could put another feather in its cap. Give the little
lambs a meal. And such a meal! A sack of cocoa, another
of split-peas, some slabs of margarine, a few bags of sugar,
a huge metal boiler, similar to those for boiling cattle food,

and a multitude of chipped enamel mugs, were delivered
to the hall. No white linen, no plates or spoons, no flowers
came. Mr. O'Kelly, his wife, and a paid helper, the wife's
sister, a Mrs. Murphy, came to superintend and help. The
huge boiler was hitched to a little gas-ring which wouldn't
heat the water in a week. Sean and a friend, at the risk of
burning the hall to the ground, built a temporary furnace
with loose bricks under the stage, so that the cocoa or the
pea-soup could be ready before the pampered kids filed
in to take their meal. They sat down in batches, for the
hall wasn't big enough to take them all at one sitting. The
second batch had to drink from the unwashed mugs used
by the first one served, for there was no way of cleaning
them; and no-one seemed to think it mattered. One day
the hall reeked with the smell of cocoa, the next with the
more pungent and sickening smell of pea-soup. A mug of
soup, thick and stifling, and a slab of dry bread, or a mug
of cocoa, with a slab of bread thinly smeared with margarine, were the feasts set forth for the young Fianna. Sean's
whole being was filled with loathing when he stared from
the well-dressed, well-fed, dapper figures of the server and
his wife to the hunched-up, scare-clad kids, every one of
whom, as far as he could see, showed some sign of under-
feeding. There they were: of the one fold, the well-kept
servers and the ill-kept kids, of the one hope, the one faith,
the one baptism; the few amply supplied with corn and
wine, the many gulping down as best they could the husks
shaken from the finer corn. Every day Sean tidied the hall
as well as he could before the hour for the kids to come,
but, after two days of help in the serving, he refused to

have any hand in this villainous way of showing God's love to the young, the innocent, and the helpless. A mug of heavy cocoa today for the main meal, and a mug of pea-soup tomorrow. Even to these young hungry souls these things were too bitter to taste sweet. Beside the blazing fire, near sick from the smell of the soup, which Mrs. Murphy stirred with a broomhandle—a new one, thank God—Sean watched the children file listlessly in, into the soiled hall where the windows were so high that no-one, not on a ladder, could get a glimpse of the saving sun or cleansing rain outside; moving through the benches, one two one two, sitting down with neither sign nor smile on the hard seats, staring at the metallically-grinning mugs set firmly before them on the rough planks stretched on trestles to form tables, dusty with the chalk used the night before in the game of House; Mrs. Murphy patrolling along the benches, filling each mug with the strongly-smelling soup from a big enamel ewer, Mrs. O'Kelly following with a tray of bread from which each youngster took a slab as she passed them by: Pippa passes, and she does the job nicely, though no song ripples from her lips. Bring out the rich and savoury viands for those who have often been faint with hunger at the top or bottom of their street! Watching this through the steam rising from the soup and the smell that filled the hall, Sean felt that this would make as good a circle as any seen by Dante in the inferno of his imagination. Ring the bell, Watchman— ring, ring, ring! Here is something rotten, desolate, and to be destroyed by the sense of decent men and by the workers' red resentment!

Sean closed his eyes, and saw a better sight: The convents of the teaching sisters of Loretto and Ursula; the Catholic Colleges, and the higher schools of the better-off followers of episcopus and presbyter. Green grass, gravelled paths, and flowers in centre and at the sides; playgrounds made for play; clean food, and wholesome on the whole, served decently over white cloths; snowy sheets and healthy beds in rooms where the air flows freely; and, over all, the crucified Christ, in spirit, on the one hand; in actual image on the other: in one place, the hanging Saviour among the lavender; in the other, the hanging Saviour among the lice.

And so from worse to worse.

The morning dawned with a bright sun shining; then the clouds came, and the storm broke. First thing, after breakfast, the Countess Markievicz ran round telling people to be merry, for great was the Treaty brought back by the Irish Delegates. Harry Boland, Ireland's Ambassador to America, hailed it in a speech as the freedom that came from God's right hand; and Coocoo Ulla, Gaelic League President, auctioneer and valuator, put up a blackboard on the railings outside his office, which ordered every passer-by to murmur *Buidheacheas le Dia ar son saoirse*, thanks with God for the sake of freedom, finding out a short time after that he had made a mistake, and had written bad Irish; so he hurried out to take it in again. Many who ran out to cheer, ran in again to curse, when De Valera, with swift indecision, sent a letter to the Press, emphasising that this Treaty, or Articles of Association, with England partner on the one hand, and Ireland partner on the other, was in violent conflict with the wishes of the majority of the people, including the animals in brushwood and covert, and birdies in the trees; that he couldn't recommend it; and that the Minister of Defence and Home Affairs agreed with him; making everyone more bewildered than he himself happened to be, so that thousands were for the Treaty in the freshness of morning, against it in the heat of the day, and neither for nor against it in the cool of the evening. A good chance, when it met to discuss things, thought the Larkin Release Committee, to get the Dail to pass a vote demanding the release of the workers' champion.

It was a cold bleak day in the penitential season of Advent; a grey grumbling sky overhead, with a damp, chill wind erasing the feeling of life from the flesh of the citizens crowding round, when the Delegates of the nation pushed their way through them into the puritan-faced building of the National University. A great cheer went up to God when De Valera stepped from his car, and others rang out and in when Griffith and Collins glided in after their Leader. The people gathered together to wait a decision, pushed closer together, to guard against the nipping air blowing in from the east.

The people were swaying about before the building, murmuring among themselves, murmuring words round what they thought would happen. Sean pushed through to the gate where one of his old club, the O'Tooles, was Captain of the Guard. A handsome young man, with raven-black, curly hair, eyes only a little less dark, a pale, ascetic, but humorous, face, and a very slim buoyant figure. Yes, he told Sean, come along with the resolution for Jim's release; I'll slip you all into the hall, and send in any message you like; but I'm afraid it's little they'll think of Jim, and they the way they are.

Sean slid back into the crowd again, and stood for a time, watching and listening there, for it would be a while before the rest of the Committee joined him.

—It's the loppin' off of Ulsther from the rest of us's th' rough spot, said a voice beside him; yield on that, an' we yield on everything. Th' thing should never ha' been signed without first havin' submitted it to Dev: that goes without sayin'.

—How does it go without sayin'? asked a querulous voice behind the first one. De Valera can teach Mick Collins nothin'.

A venerable old man, a plaid muffler hiding chin and lower part of the nose, was being pushed, now a step forward, now a step backward, by the arguing people. He raised his nose and mouth above the muffler to say—Don't push, please. Isn't there any respect left in the land for the aged? Can't we take pattern by the members of our Dail who are quietly deciding, without any bitterness or blame, the choice the country is prepared to make? Don't push, please. Let us all preserve a decent reticence of opinion, till we learn how things go. We won't have long to wait. The questions before the Dail are simple, and reasonable men can settle them in an hour.

—D'ye call th' takin' of an oath to a foreign king a simple question?

—I refuse to reply to such an irrevelant question, said the old man coldly, hiding his nose and mouth in his muffler, immediately taking them out again, to ejaculate, Oh, don't push, please!

But they continued to argue and to push, and ugly terms of traitor, renegade, and hypocrite, were hissed about among the crowd, forcing the old gentleman to prise his nose and mouth up from the deeps of his muffler to exclaim—This Treaty you are trying to condemn is giving us more than we had any right to expect.

A tall girl, standing beside Sean, gave a bitter moan when she heard the old man's vigorous remark. He had noticed her before, and had thought how good she would be to have beside him, under a hiding hedge away in the country where no-one thought of trespassing. She had a great mass of dark-brown hair rippling over her neck, big grey eyes, a tempting mouth, ripe and red as a finely born cherry; her coat was open, and underneath the blouse, Sean saw that her breasts were lovely enough to make a nest for a hero's head. She had been biting her lips for some time, and he could see that she had been repressing a desire to shout out something to the people around her. She was biting them harder than ever now. Suddenly, tensing her arms and clenching her little hands, this lovely edition of sweet and twenty wheeled around to face the larger section of the crowd, gathering their strict attention with a screaming yell, causing the old gentleman to dive deeper into his muffler as he tried to force himself away; but she had a grip of his arm, and held him close to her.

—Look at him! she yelled; one of Griffith's toadies, mumbling his treachery here when he ought to be down among the dead men! Hear what he said? The Treaty gives Ireland more than she has any right to expect! That's what this old, dried-up palaverer tells us. The Treaty! Here's some of its good points for you, people:

> It takes away Irish Sovereignty forever.
> It gives Ulster away for ever.
> It gives Four Ports away forever.
> It makes a Guest of an English Governor-General forever.
> It makes Irishmen British Citizens forever.
> It asks an Oath of Allegiance to the English King forever.
> It Divides Ireland forever and ever and ever!

—That's what it does, and what it does it does for ever; the young girl paused to pacify the sobs that were shaking her young bosom, that was fit to comfort the head of an anxious and sorrowful hero.

Evening had fallen when Sean and his few companions stood in the shadowy hall of the great University building, waiting a chance to send in their appeal that the Dail should call collectively for Jim Larkin's release; a hallway, cold, severe, and silencing. They had given in notes for Countess Markievicz, Austin Stack, and Tom Hunter to a Republican officer who had promised to see they reached the persons named on the envelopes. They stood there, cold and silent, watching young men clerks and young women clerks and officials, bundles of documents under their arms, coming and going on tiptoe. When any one of the clerks had something to say to another, he whispered cautiously,

as if they were in the presence of some great being about
to die; and so they were, for Irish Unity was at its last gasp.

After a long, long wait, two strong young men came in
staggering under the weight of a gigantic roll of foolscap,
which was borne on a pole, and was covered with writing
of divers kinds, old Irish, middle Irish, and modern Irish,
with a special translation into ogham.

—What are yous carryin' up, misther? asked the tram-
conductor, tiptoeing over to the leading bearer.

—What is it, is it? queried the foremost finn maccoolie;
what d'ye think is it, now?

—I dunno, but it looks important.

—So it is; it's no less than the original copy of Document No. 2.

—D'ye tell me that? An' what may that be now?

—A counther-blow at the Treathy; an amazin' thing.
A document that'll be historical as long as destiny lives and
time lasts. And with a final shake to get it even on their
shoulders, the two carriers went off, and disappeared under
the archways.

It was deeply dark now, and Sean could but guess when
officials were passing by the sound of their furtive whispering. He and the tram-conductor crept over to where they
heard whispering, and touched down on two of the officials.

—Any chance of having a brief talk with the Countess,
or Mr. Stack, or Tom Hunter? Sean whispered cautiously
in the ear of one of them.

—Don't yous know damn well yous can't, and things
the way they are? Yous can't see any deputy for any talk,
brief or breathless, for they're sthruggling in the middle

of Document No. 2. That's the thing'll put the English in a quare dilemma; for they can't accept it and they can't reject it.

—Why can't they reject it, man, if they want to? asked the tram-conductor with a note of contempt in his voice.

—Because, man, if they did, they'd commit themselves to rejecting their own offer, see?

—How reject their own offer?

—Because while preserving Ireland's sovereign status, Document No. 2 provides for external association only in the Empire, with the king as head over the separated conjunction.

—What, head over Ireland's sovereign status, is it?

—No, no, man; for how could Ireland be sovereign herself if there was another sovereign authority over her?

—Isn't that what I'm askin', insisted the tram-conductor? How can you let go of th' hand, if you still hold on to it?

—What hand are you talking about?

—The King of England's hand, of course.

—Dtch dtch dtch! the whisper from the dark clicked its tongue impatiently. Look; the king's hand doesn't come into it at all. Listen: though sovereign status puts Ireland outside of the British Empire, external association keeps her inside of it—see?

Silence encircled them again, as they listened to their own disturbing thoughts; standing in the depths of the lofty hall; thinking in the darkness, silently anxious, feeling forward in a lonely way with whispers; forming a shallow pool of defence between the quarrel of the people outside and the quarrel of the deputies in their secret chamber of open discussion.

—D'ye mean, asked the puzzled tram-conductor, at last, that Document No. 2 shifts the British Empire outside of Ireland's allegiance, while Ireland's sovereign status and external association brings the British Empire inside Ireland's external recognition?

—You see, it's this way: if Document No. 2 gets accepted, Ireland'll be what you could call a sequestered country that is still within the outlines of the British Empire.

—I don't much like the sayin' of within the outlines of the British Empire, and I don't altogether like the word sequesthered either.

—If we don't take the chance offered in Document No. 2, said the whisper, louder now than it had been before, the land'll become an improvised inferno.

All the time, the foolish fight was waging in the secret chamber of open discussion; a foolish fight, for there was as much difference between the document flourished in the upper air by De Valera and the folio of the Treaty spread out on the ground at the feet of the people by Griffith and Collins as there would be between two eggs laid by the same hen at the same time. But every meagre mind, hoodwinked by its own thoughts, praised its own devotion to Ireland, resting from its labour to spit out the charge of treachery against an opposing brother. Vainly De Valera cursed the bitter, maiming bite of politics, holding out a hand to Collins in one impulsive moment of remembrance, to have it knocked down by Mary MacSweeney; while at another moment, Collins held out a hand to De Valera, to have it set aside by the venomous speech of a supporting follower. There could be no reunion. Ireland was there in the midst of the revelling quarrellers, her chaplet of crêpe, worn for the dead who died for Ireland, going askew; there she stood distracted, or ran from Billy to Jack, shouting order order, unity unity, discipline discipline, unheard in the storm of each side shouting at the other, stamping her little foot on the floor for a silence that never came, till she sank, tired and wordless, on to the floor, anointed with the spits dribbling from the angry, twisted mouths of her own devoted children. The Kelleys, the Burkes, and the Sheas were at one another's throats.

The terrible beauty was beginning to lose her good looks.

INTO CIVIL WAR

AFTER ages of talking that threatened to defy Time, and last forever, each delegate denouncing another as a traitor, recreant, or slave, the Treaty was accepted by a majority of a few votes; many, including De Valera, breaking out into tears when the result was finally and forensically known.

Then those who were to become the rulers of Ireland separated into two parties. Most of the coming middle class followed Griffith, and the rest halooed for freedom round the disappointed De Valera. The clergy stood quiet on the right; the labour officials watched as quiet on the left; both waiting to see which would prove the stronger, hoping that some good things could be gathered from the fragments. Not a leader left had the power or personality to check the drift, now flowing swift to an armed fight for dominance. The laundered people of the Big Houses shut-to the gates of their demesnes, locked the heavy doors of the houses, pulled down the blinds, drew cosy chairs to the marble-mannered fireplaces, sat down in them, opened a bottle of wine, drank a health to His Majesty, and assured themselves that they were well out of it all.

The provisional government of the Free State began to cajole and coax the people to the grandeur of their state by sending telegrams in green envelopes, painting the postal pillar-boxes a richer green than the green on the envelopes, crossing out the GR, and printing in the mystic symbol of SE, while tailors worked night and day making green uniforms for the new Free State Army. Erin was becoming the green isle in fact as in figment. Clap hands, clap hands, till daddy comes home, for daddy's got money, but mother has none.

Here and now, the slick slogan of the clergy that civil war and all deforming crimes were in the mind and way only of those who forgot God, was to be mocked at by catholic murder, catholic gun-fire, and catholic torch set-ting flames to the homes of catholic people. Here were those, now on the threshold of battle, who had not for-gotten God; who went to Mass as regular as clock-work; who had deep-cut circles in the flesh of their fingers with the never-ending twisting of rosary beads. What atheism, the clergy said, had brought to Russia, catholic Christianity had brought to Ireland. Catholics who had been steeped in the Faith from the very cradle; who had listened to every papal encyclical and episcopal pastoral; who could find their way to confession blindfolded; who acknowledged with a bumper of bows the divine headship of the See of Rome; holy men who had excuse of neither atheism nor paganism; yet here they were, feverishly getting ready to shoot one another in forehead and back; to torture oppo-nents when they got a chance; to hurry a different opinion from a hasty court-martial to a quick end by a firing-squad. Righteous Catholic Irishmen were about to get busy mak-ing their land a nation once again; showing, if it ever needed to be shown, that good practising catholics are very much as other men are, and sometimes a damned sight worse; that all the countless supernatural and spiritual advantages they boastfully possess do not give them any lead in grace over others, and do not fix on catholic natures any spiritual or natural bridles than those which check the desperate anger that may try to assert itself in the heart of any common atheist or communist. The Papal yellow and white rage is worse than the rage of the red, for it is tireless in its enmity, and its revenge is swift as lightning, or as slow as the crawl of a snail through a thicket of tough grass—according to the chances conditions may put before it.

Judging by what the two parties were saying of each other, there wasn't an honest, truthful, or semi-Christian left alive in the land. Ireland's magenta sky was dark with the cloud of venomous words, hot and steaming, that came from the mouths of the delegates reviling each other. Most of them kept awake at nights pondering on the bad things they could say of the others when the sun rose in the morning. Each day it grew worse, till half the hands fingered the triggers of rifles; the other half of hands tightened on the butts of revolvers; and those who had neither, nursed a hand-grenade in every pocket. To God and Ireland true; for they still went to Mass, to confession, and recited their rosaries, *ad lib*.

In the midst of this seething, senseless conflict between the Treaty and Document No. 2, the Black and Tans were withdrawn in sealed vans, and crowds looked curiously on, while British cavalry cautiously cantered out of the Curragh Camp; and Sean stood to watch the infantry marching stolidly down to the docks, a band playing *Come Back to Erin* to keep their hearts from failing; watching the cannon, too, as it lumbered through the streets, seeming to look, that as they had lived so long in Ireland, they didn't want to go. Well, thought Sean, as he watched them pass, at least, the Irish now will have the expansive liberty of biting each other without let or hindrance from low law of Dublin Castle or high law of heaven.

So right through this tear-up of catholic composure, the British kept quietly dribbling out of the country, puzzled as much now as they were when they first landed in Cork and Wexford near a thousand years ago. Captain Heslip, of the Free State Army, spoke a few encouraging words to a Major of the Worcestershire Regiment, a plump man with a look of heavily-controlled bewilderment on his furtively-staring face, as he handed over the sacred Bank of Ireland to the wild Irishman in an officer's uniform. It was all beyond the major. It had been all so sudden. The British Government had lost its nerve. The Bank of Ireland gone, and all that therein is. Is it a dream, or are there visions about? This was more than God had fitted the major to understand. Beside the major, like a free and uneasy guardian angel, stood a Director of the Bank, in tall hat and top-of-the-morning coat, to see that everything was done according to the statutes made and provided.

And, a few steps away, in another street, Sean stood among a quiet crowd, a grin on his gob, watching the Earl of Fitzalan step from his car in a half-dazed way, not even noticing the grand salute given by a nearby police inspector; Sean watched the catholic Earl step out and trot over

the pathway to hand over the place known to all as Dublin
Castle, in a circumspect and affable way. Fitzalan, the Earl,
seemed to be doing it all in a dream; things were turning
tipsey-turvey; the dragon had conquered the knight; the
lion was roaring like any sucking dove. Fitzalan happening to be a catholic in full bloom, the astute British Government naturally thought the Earl would be able to en-
dow the Irish with a sense of order, and that the catholic
Irish would yield him the respect due to his quality; but
the poor man found that it was even hard to get Mass
quietly, and that his catholic Irish brethren penned him
up in his Vice-regal Lodge as they had penned up his
protestant predecaesars. So here was the belted Earl, plundered of power, bowler-hatted now, bent at the knees, head
down, slipping into the Castle quick as he could, a wist-
fully-reluctant look on his face, such as the face of St.
Peter might show if compelled to give up the keys of the
kingdom; slipped in to hand over the keys of the Citadel
to the ungrateful Irish, so long the waifs and strays of history. Gone forever the knights of St. Patrick, with their
orders dangling from light-blue ribbons: *Quiz seperrabit*
had lost its meaning: Skibereen and Tuberneering were at
home in Dublin Castle. Come all ye in. Sit down, boys,
an' I'll fill your can.

—Here's the key of the Throne Room, and this one's
the key of St. Patrick's Hall, my good man. A long, long
trail from Fitzhenry to Fitzalan, Alpha and Omega. Goodbye, all. Farewell, but whenever I welcome the hour of the
flight of the Earl, I feel kind of sad. The last glimpse of
Erin with sorrow I see, regretting the time I've lost in

wooing; 'tis gone, and forever the time when first I met thee, warm and young, a bright May moon was shining, love; but the dream of those days when first I sung thee is o'er; 'tis gone, and forever, the light we saw breaking, and no longer can you come to rest in this bosom, my own stricken dear; so, farewell, and go where glory waits thee, where the harp that once can function again, and the min-strel-boy will be your well-known warrior. From henceforth you will have your own disorders, surrendering the order of Macha's Brooch for that of Armagh's Red Hat; order of the Black Peeler and the Green Goat; order of the Old Turf fire; Order of Knights Hospitallers of the Clean Sweep; Order of the Little Greyhound in the West; the Sublime Order of Excommunication for Catholics i Collegio Trinitatis; Order of the Banned Books; and many such, and many more. There's nothing to stop ye now!

In spite of the cool meetings held under the care of Dublin's catholic Archbishop; the dear pleading of Dan Breen, Eire's No. 1 Guerilla; in spite of pact and promise, broken ere they were understood, the day came when General Tom Ennis, a fawn trench-coat mock-modestly covering a neat green uniform, with brilliant yellow tabs on the lapels, goads his unwilling men to swing a heavy gun swiftly, so that its angry snout may point towards the Republican enemy barricaded deep in the Four Courts; hurries them into pulling the lanyard that opens the cannon's mouth to send a British shell over the walls, send it screaming over, to spread a shattering shower of sharp steel against her greying dignity, darting hither and thither in its effort to bring maiming death to angry comrades be-

hind the walls on the far side of the river Liffey; while a
great crowd of excited civilians crouch behind corners near
Richmond Bridge to listen to the crack of the cannon, and
watch the smoke and flame of the bursting shells. Rory
O'Connor, chief of the Republicans, steadied with a few
doses of phospherine, taken to tighten his nerves loosened
from lack of sleep, tightens his belt, and waits; waits for a
closer attack, for he has no bullying guns to answer the din-
ning onslaught of shells sent over, minute by minute, by
his one-time comrade, Tom Ennis, hidden behind the
houses on the other bank of Anna Livia Plurabelle. Thick
dust hides the body of the building, and dark smoke en-
circles the huge dome, making it look like the great
globe itself trekking the sky through a way of stormy
clouds.

The Free Staters having expended their shells, advanced to the building in a sharp trot, murmuring holy
acts of contrition, finger on trigger and bayonet fixed; advanced, till a land-mine exploded under their passing feet,
and brought the charge to a stop for a while, so that they
could watch all the foolish wigs and gowns of Dublin sailing up into the sky; with all the records of the country,
processes, cases, testimonies, bills of exchange, and sales of
properties to church and private person, and all heredita-
ments chronicled since Strongbow came to Ireland, flying
up after the wigs and gowns, to come fluttering down,
scorched and tattered, into every Dublin back-yard and
front garden.

Defeated in the Four Courts, the Republicans fortified
themselves within a long portion of O'Connell Street; and

Business and Banking hurried everything valuable into their safes, before retiring to the country to wait till things settled down. Once more, machine-gun and rifle-fire, rising and falling and rising again, shivered the air into a sharp and bitter moaning, pierced now and then by the strident bark of a ten-pounder gun sending snarling protests into buildings housing the deadliest marksmen among the Republicans. Occasionally, the shrill squealing of the gun-fire was relieved by the gentle and more musical tinkle of falling glass, splitting away from trembling windows that now began to send out flickering tongues of flame growing swiftly into steady streams of burning destruction, till the smoky skyline was changed into a rosy and tumultuous lake of fire.

At night, when the sky was nowhere, and the stars were being suffocated by an acrid smoke pall, and all beneath them was a bewildering furnace, out from the sparks ascending, as roofs crashed in and walls tumbled down; out from the spouting flame and the grey veil of powdered rubbish, came Cathal Brugha, running; shooting at the dim, green-uniformed men bobbing about in the curly clouds of smoke; shooting at what he thought to be enemies of Ireland; shooting, till he himself was shot, to become a ghost among the ghosts of those who had fallen before him. Well, here you lie, Cathal Brugha, dying under the battle-banner of smoke-fringed flame, your couch a street of crumbling, blackened buildings; a big torch, too, lighting your last few tired steps into that unsearchable darkness reserved for life when life has ended. However strict you may have been in the holding high of an abstraction, you were a Republican; a very brave man; generous in a large way; and too honest to find comfortable companionship in the lesser men around you. Many will be carried out of life, feet first, covered with an Irish tricolour that will be too big for them; but you the flag fits well, exchanging honour for honour with the gallant dead beneath it.

Stretching himself on the old stretcher-bed by the wall that separated his room from the hall outside, Sean halted his mind from thinking out the new play he intended to write. The Abbey Theatre had accepted one, after long consideration, and he had reason to feel elated. Idly he looked around the room, while he half listened to gun-fire in the distance, or the whine of rapidly-moving lorries on the street outside. Free Staters out for a raid on the home of some old comrade-in-arms. Lift your heart up, mother Erin! Well, for the time being, he was fairly nice and snug here, if it weren't for the never-ending commotion of the families who lived in the house. He glanced round to see how he was placed: the fireplace was big and clumsy, but when a fire blazed there, it was cosy and alluring. A fine settee, to hold two comfortably, stared at its dying embers now. A large mahogany table, on which he could spread out his work, undisturbed by scattered books, a yellow-varnished desk, with a few nests of file-cabinets, gave the room a look of a shy office not knowing what to do with itself. Beside the bed was an open two-shelved locker, one of thousands cast away by the Government when the war ended, and bought by Sean for half a crown; on the shelves were his soap, shaving-kit, face-flannel, and washbasin, all discreetly hidden by a coloured print curtain. On each side of the huge windows, shelving held his many books, and the windows themselves were draped with long, creamy-coloured curtains of good twill. On the table stood the lamp that gave light to him when darkness came, and, in the centre, stood a mimosa plant, faded and dry now; never likely to show its delicate yellow blossoms again. He hadn't the gift of his mother in keeping flowers friendly and responsive. No picture hung on the wall yet, for he didn't care for the cheap ones on sale in the art shops, and he couldn't afford a good one yet. On the mantelshelf was a framed photograph of Thorwalsen's *Venus*. On one side of the fireplace was a press in which he kept his crockery, coal, sticks for kindling, and a few saucepans. Beside this stood the small table holding his typewriter, and beside it, a suitable dignified chair to sit him straight up at his work. Not a lot to brag about, but enough for his present needs. A good nest, if it were not for the noise. The room to his right held a father, mother, and five children; the room over his head, the same with one more child: seven in the room beside him, eight in the one over head—his was a haven of peace, a palace of dignity compared with either of them.

—There's that damned shooting again! as a volley rang out, followed by a sharp, scattered firing somewhere near the house, on the street outside. Kelt was killing Kelt as expertly and as often as he could; catholic Kelts, too. Not a freethinker among them. As diligent as the Black and Tans themselves. And just as clever. Men were shot down while at business, on pleasure, even when they whispered

to a girl. A young man was swung up to a beam; as much
castor oil as he could hold was poured through a funnel
into him, and he was left hanging there to mutter rosaries
as best he could without being able to tell his beads. And
that was a merciful method.

For when Griffith and Collins had escaped into the
grave, the rest of a frightened government, left breathing,
ensconced itself behind the thick wall of a building near
Kildare Street, protected by a generous border of barbed
wire, itself defended by a running mound of sand-bags;
safe nowhere, for all militant Ireland was crawling round,
creeping to country hedge or street corner; prowling about
to get a chance for a sure and pure shot at anything they
didn't like. From their hide-in, the Government in embryo
sent out warrant after warrant for the orderly execution
of those caught with arms in their hands; and even those
from whom the arms had been taken long before. When
General Hales and Patrick O'Maille, descending from a
jaunting-car to enter a hotel for dinner, fell by Republican bullets, the Provisional Government, fanged by fear,
shook from sleep three prominent Republicans who had
been in jail for months, led them out to a quiet corner,
and, after providing them with a few moments for private
prayer, separated them by rifle-fire forever from everything they knew and loved and hated in this world. As a
reprisal. Rory O'Connor, the Republican, sleeps long now,
like Michael Collins, the Free Stater. Collins, fooling
about in the south, just jumped to death when a random
bullet fixed itself firmly in his brain. Here the Free State
and all Ireland suffered a loss. Collins wasn't a great man,

but he was the makings of one. He was human in a way that Griffith couldn't even try to be; he had a laugh Griffith couldn't reach, stretch he never so high. He was tolerant, and ready, even at a moment's notice, to forgive a blow, and, more difficult still, to forget about it too. Collins could never have hated militant Labour as Griffith did; nor could anyone think of him as jealous of high things in others, as Griffith was of the higher things in Yeats. One could never conceive of Griffith dancing a reel, even in the privacy of his own home; but one could easily imagine Collins doing a wild dance in the courtyard of the Castle, or of him singing a song out loud in the porch of Parliament House.

After the capture of Dublin by the Free Staters, ambushes began to blossom red from many a street corner; and the joyful killing spread over the whole country. Houses went up in flames, exploding often with a wild hurrah, and bridges sank sullenly down into the rivers they spanned. Republicans put land-mines under road barriers so that when the Free Staters tried to remove them, they ascended into heaven; and when Free Staters captured Republicans, they fixed up barricades of their own, laden with land-mines, compelling the Republicans to remove the road-block, so that they too were blown to pieces. As a reprisal. The splitting of the atom. And for what? For Document No. 2! Not to abolish poverty. No; just for a spate of words that Alice in Wonderland wouldn't understand. While poor Yeats, having climbed up the winding stairs of his Thoor Ballylee, looked out of a high window over the land, and wondered what it all meant. And to

explain some of it, the Republicans blew up Thoor Ballylee's ancient bridge as they were leaving, shouting quite
politely up to Yeats, Good night, sir, and thank you, as
though he had given them the bridge.

Well, such good deeds were common to Christians.
Ever since catholics were catholics, fire and sword became
their common courtesies. The Hundred Years War that
made of Europe a great grave; the Inquisition that made
torture and death holy orisons to God; the Conquistadores
slaughtering tens of thousands to make the holy Faith a
living thing in the hearts of men; the Crusades which so
often showed the noblest killed, the meanest killing; and,
now, the protestants of the north driving the catholics out
of the province by bolt, bullet and bar; while the good
catholics in the south were at one another's throats, spray-
ing death and disillusion in the minds of men. And yet
these glib, imperturbable prelates, from the oldest Pope to
the youngest bishop, were sloganising the lie that commu-
nistic atheism alone brought these evils upon the life of
man. And has it not been recently said by one of the Pope's
famed champions, a mighty man in apologetics for the
Catholic Faith, that the really important thing happening
was not the conquest of France by the Nazis, but the
downfall of the Freemasons brought about by the fall of
France; even though this Papal champion had to admit
the great stand these very Freemasons had made for education, freedom of the Press, and freedom of thought in
their own land. However rapidly and decidedly these prelates and apologists might pull mitre, biretta, or cap down,
well over their foreheads, the mark of Cain showed

through—the black cross of pure indifference to the plight of a brother. Politics has slain its thousands, but religion has slain its tens of thousands; and the church must coax a change into her own heart before a call or a claim can be made for a change in the hearts of others.

—There isn't a room in this very house, thought Sean, as he lay awake, alert to every sound in the street outside, that hasn't a picture of the Sacred Heart hanging around somewhere; that hasn't a votive light, however tiny, burning to St. Anthony of Padua, but the house shakes with fear just as it did when the Black and Tans were howling. Look at poor Mrs. Moore, living above in the two-pair back, with her gentle, even handsome, face, that hovered unsteadily over the rushing, unreasonable agitation of the times like a trembling star in a turbulent sky. Her finely-made hands, their grace peering out even through the deep seams of age and toil, had lighted candle after candle to St. Anthony, the flickering flames mutely begging, throughout the day, throughout the night, for the safety of her little household. But St. Anthony busy with higher things, hadn't bothered his head about her; for her two sons, who were Republicans, had been thrown into jail; their sister had quickly followed them; then this girl's sweetheart, a Republican, too, had been found on a lonely country road, more than just dead, for his belly had been kicked in, his right eye was a purple pulp, an ear had been partly shot off, and, now, jagged and red-edged, stood out like a tiny fin from the side of his head, his mouth a cavity of bloody fluid, floating bits of broken teeth, while to make sure that there would be no chance of escape back into the everyday world, his body had been systematically punched full of gaping bullet-holes, so that the boy gave a lively insight and outsight of what can be done when the twitching hands of the killed twist a rosary in harmony with the twisting of companion rosaries in the hands of the killer.

So worn out, in the end, with a life daily tested to the full, the kindly soul of the old woman found rest only in restlessness. One night, while her old husband slept, she had wandered out into a windy, sleety night, to be found the morning after, stretched calmly out, indifferent to the stinging rain and the bustling wind, on the streaming pavement of a windy turning, in a last, long sleep.

Everything was embedded in a damp, dark-grey mist, spitting out a contemptuous shower of pointed sleet now and again, when Sean and a few neighbours walked beside the old man, behind the closed-in hearse, carrying the body of what had been his wife from the mortuary to the church. Sons and daughter were refused a parole from prison by the Free State Government, so they couldn't come to mingle their excited sorrow with the old man's bewildered grief; and, unable to do more, Sean and four or five neighbours had turned out to act as guards and hedge the old man's sorrow in between them. The driving, sleety rain polished the hearse into a more gleaming blackness; and Sean and his neighbours thrust themselves bending forward so that some of the showers might slide over them, slantwise, and so fail to give them a fuller drenching. They pulled their caps well down over their brows, and thrust up their topcoat collars as high as they could make them go. Glancing up, Sean saw that the hearse-drivers were crouching forward, too, rain pouring from the rims of their top-hats, and falling with a splash on the horse's haunches.

The old man walked by himself, shaking his head with annoyance when the neighbours had surrounded him to try to shield him from some of the worst weather. He wore no overcoat, not even putting up the collar of the light jacket that held out against the rain for a few bare minutes. He carried a newly-bought bowler hat under his arm, and with head held up, seemed to be gladly taking any discomfort the rain and wind could give him. Sean saw that the rain had seeped through his thin clothing, and must by now be trickling down his skin. The few white tufts left on his head were saturated, and Sean watched the globules of water gathering at the ends, their stems slowly lengthening till they parted suddenly from the edge of the tufts, now one, then two, two again, then one more, to go swiftly coursing down the nape of the old neck to disappear down inside the collar of the old man's shirt.

—You should ha' brought an old overcoat of some kind with you, Mr. Moore, said Sean.

—I wouldn't ha' felt easy if I hadda', Sean, said the old man; not after what happened the other night when who you know lay so soaked an' dead chilly the live-long night on the hard road, an' no-one mindin'. If I only hadda' known.

—Well, put on your hat at least, advised Sean. It isn't good for a man of your age to go uncovered this weather.

—No, not yet. It's the one way I can show her I'm sorry I slep' while she was dyin'; the one token of respect I can offer her now.

130

—But, insisted Sean, if she knew, she'd be the first to tell you to do it.

—She does know, the old man said, knows well. An' by standin' up to what I'm standin' up to now, she knows I'd ha' willingly laid down with her on the cold ground in all the sleet fallin' an' all the wind blowin', the time she was dyin' alone, if only I'd known; if only I hadda' known.

The whole of Ireland's following a hearse these days, thought Sean, and Ireland herself's driving the horses.

A lorry carrying two Republican prisoners, surrounded by Free State soldiers, went swiftly by them, and Sean saw it wheeling into the drive that led to Mountjoy Jail. The governors had changed, but the prison stayed there still, as brazen, as bitter as ever. As the hearse passed the gateway of the drive, Sean saw the heavy gates of the prison swing open, and the lorry pass in; saw the gate swing shut again, so that soon those two prisoners would be with the two sons of this old man whose gaze never sought the jail, but stayed fixed on the hearse moving ahead in front of him.

Why this sudden fever of killing each other on the part of the catholic Irish, so deep in the Faith, so close to God? Some there were who fought and fell, like Brugha, in the dazzling white light of their nationalistic immaculate conception. And Brugha fought openly and fair. But the others? It wasn't for want of religion—they were soaked in it from the cradle up to now. Even Ferguson, the poet, wrote that God having made the Irish brothers, and joined them in holier rites than wedlock, would never suffer them to draw opposing brands; for if He did—

Oh, many a tuneful tongue that Thou mad'st vocal
Would be cold and silent then;
And songless long once more, should often-widowed **Erin**
Mourn the loss of her brave young men.

What God had joined together, let no man put asunder.
Poor, unhappy, futile words! Erin hadn't time even to
mourn them, now, for too many were falling at the one
time in different places. A gala day of death. The terrible
beauty that was, is not. Like the grass, yesterday Ireland's
terrible beauty had the green freshness of spring, the bright
dew of the morning; to-day it is withered, and well in the
fire. Bring out the prisoners and the firing-squad: ready!
one, two, three! Fire that house! Blow up that bridge!
Tighten the noose round the bugger's neck! Oh, Mary,
the very thought of thee with sweetness fills me breast!
Sure 'twas for this that Emmet fought, and Wolfe Tone
sunk serene! Oh, young lads of Eireann, who know so
little, but are so warmly wrapped up in the songs of
Thomas Davis, join the Irish Republican Army, and take
the chance of a death-time! Bring your own rosary beads.

But a sensible, hardy plant was rising in the place once
held in Ireland's cabbage-patch by the terrible beauty's
sweet pea. Sturdy stalks of petty power were springing up,
and blossoms of privilege would soon be bright on them,
petalled with scarlet thorns to keep envious, pulling hands
away.

They stopped at Berkeley Street Chapel, took the coffin
from the hearse, carried it into the church porch. A priest
in cassock, surplice, and stole came dashing out, carrying a

bucket and brush, muttered a few Latin invocations with bored celerity, scattered a few swift drops of water over the coffin and ran swiftly back into church again. If the pathetic, careworn body in the coffin had been a countess, hells bells wouldn't have kept an archbishop from sprinkling the holy water sweetly, saying the prayers slow, giving the reception an elegant and ornate look—God giving the lady value for her money and rank. Hurry up, hurry up; they carried the coffin into the church, sacristan pointed hurriedly where to put it; ran off, then; for the look of the mourners promised no tip. Hurry up. Then they went out, the old man staying behind to pray, and keep her company for a little longer. Hurry up. Sean and the rest climbed to the top of the hearse, and sat around it, their legs dangling, looking like a freak-frieze of grotesques, set in black marble, broken away from a main design.

—That old man'll catch his death in those wet clothes, said Sean.

—What's the odds, if he does aself? asked a neighbour. His children are so busy with themselves that they have time only to notice now and again that he's still there. If he catches it bad, the wind an' rain'll after be doin' him a good turn.

A tiny vignette of the Civil War: the big church, with the light on the altar; the chalky statues of glum saints, green, blue, and brown, gawking down at the figure of an old man kneeling beside the coffin that held what remained of one who had been his lifelong comrade.

COMRADES

Ah! The bould Sean! A hand clapped down on Sean's shoulder, while on his way to a sit-down in Stephen's Green, where he could dreamily deny the tale of a God existent, and test the woe of the world with thought. Sean turned, to see a wide, comradely grin on the broad, innocent face of Mick Clonervy, a rancher's son from the County of Kiltoran, whom Sean got to know when he came with cattle to Dublin, prodding hundreds of the frightened animals on to the boats for the English markets.

—Ah! me bould Sean, an' how is every bit o' yeh? asked Mick Clonervy again, his two little grey eyes agleam under the wide-peaked cap.

But Mick was Michael now. A colonel in a fine new army, one of Ireland's Own. The superfine green cloth of his uniform, the gay, dignified strip on his shoulder-strap, denoting his rank, the highly polished brown leggings guarding his sturdy limbs, or the splendid, saucily peaked cap took away no sign of the man's clumsily patterned nature. No matter how smartly he might be saluted, or how often, Colonel Michael Clonervy was Mick Clonervy still. His wide, fleshy face now beamed with joyous embarrassment as he noticed Sean scanning the prim richness of his uniform. There wasn't a button astray on it. Even the ugly-looking holster, where a gun was nesting, was neatly latched by a tongue of leather linked to a button of gleaming brass. But the wearer of this glory was ill at ease. The smart, elegant uniform fitted the body, but it failed to fit the spirit of the man. He would have felt himself happier in the old clothes spattered with cow-dung to give them taste and character. Even in the Free State Army a sergeant's job would have been a little difficult for the kindly, heavy-limbed fellow. His eyes, grey, cunning, and bright, peered at Sean from under the officer's cap. The soft, swelling, childish cheeks, red as ripe apples, the unsteady mouth, circled by thick, leechy lips, told Sean that here was a young man without a chance of ever being other than he had been years and years ago. No garment, however rich, no dignity or brightness of uniform, could make this fellow be other than Mick Clonervy who so efficiently manœuvred his father's cattle on to the boats, heedless of the sickening steam from their distended nostrils, or the slippery patches of their dung through which his hob-nailed boots had one time so safely and so merrily splashed.

—This new corps of officers, thought Sean, will never do. Utterly unaware of the elements of a military life, and has no desire to learn them. How are things, Mick? he asked, hardly knowing what to say.

—Merry enough, ould son, responded Mick. Don't fret—the Republicans are finished forever. But wait till you hear: Standin' with two C.I.D. boys, guardin' a big house in Donnybrook, an' questionin' one o' them about his goin's on with a maid in a house down further, gettin' her in the family way while he was on duty—a big breach

o' discipline; an' th' damned liar thryin' to make out it
was all an accident; when who d'ye think comes sailin' up
th' steps on a visit but the long-haired poet, Yeats himself. You should have heard th' click o' me heels as I
gave him a firm salute!

—Did he take any notice?

—Why wouldn't he take notice? 'Course he took notice;
Yeats is no fool. An' he noticed that th' other two go-boys
didn't budge from their loungin' against th' door-pillars,
one o' them with a cigarette stuck in his ugly mouth, puffin'
away. No manners! Goodmornin', General, says he—
general, mind you! Only a common colonel, Misther
Yeats, I says, Colonel Clonervy; just plain colonel, I
says, sir.

—Yez are heirs to a great thradition, says he, while he
waited for th' door t'open; th' Fianna Fail.

Sean's glance followed the Colonel's eyeing casually a
young man cycling smoothly past them, his face turned
towards the Green, away from them, humming *Home to
Our Mountains* from *Il Trovatore*, the cyclist's head moving emotionally to the gentle swing of the tune.

—A great thradition, says Yeats, went on the Colonel,
his eyes following the quietly-moving cyclist; th' famous
Fenians, says he—McCool, Oisin, Oscar; thruth on their
lips, sthrength in their arms, an' purity in their hearts, says
he. You're tellin' me! I says to him. Them was th' days,
sir. An' listen, Misther Yeats, I says, we have as much to
do today; for we have to demonsthrate a good example
now to th' whole o' th' livin' world! Then th' door opened,
an' th' house swallied him up.

Silently, their glances followed the lilting cyclist going along the side of the Green. When he came opposite to a tall house where Free State troops were quartered, he glided gracefully to the path's edge, guiding his machine between other cycles resting against the kerb. Still mounted, but resting his left foot on the pavement to balance himself, they saw him glance swiftly round, whip with his right hand something hanging from his waist, swing the object fast, let it go, and send it flying through the air, smashing a pane of glass, and lobbing into the room beyond.

Half deafened by a swift explosion, tempered by screams of agony from the room where the bomb had burst, shrinking from a flying shower of glass, a spear of it slicing in two the ear of a passer-by, Sean saw Clonervy snatch the leather latch loose from the holster, pull out the gun, level it, and pull a trigger that responded only with sharp derisive clicks.

—Th' ignorant, lazy lowser of a skip's forgot to load it! he shouted, red rage masking his wide, innocent face; th' bastard sent me out helpless as a kid! Then the Colonel rushed off towards the tumult as the thrower of the bomb launched himself forward on his bicycle with a swift push of his left foot, and went tearing down the street as fast as his feet could turn the pedals.

Sean saw two plain-clothes men come running down the steps, through smoke that curled from the broken windows, to join the Colonel; saw him load his empty gun with what he got from one of the plain-clothes men; saw them spring on to bicycles resting by the kerb, to launch for-

137

ward, each with an angry push from the left foot, and go careering away in the direction taken by him who had thrown the bomb.

An ambulance came tinkling up to sort out things; while Sean hurried into the Green to sit in serenity beside the lake to try to sort out things, too, among the indifferent ducks and drakes.

The bomb-thrower had dodged and twisted down, through, in and out of the lowliest streets in the district, meeting no-one showing a sign of suspicion. He could go easy now. He entered a long street, cycled slow to the end, and, as he was turning out of it, glanced back to see, in the distance, three men on bicycles coming along, one in the Free State uniform and two in civvies. He pedalled furiously up the street into which he had turned, and, at the end, glanced back again, and saw that they were still coming steadily behind, a long way off. Then he knew they were after him.

He raced along the Waterloo Road, down the Appian Way, down, and out of Belgrave Road, and whirled into Rathmines. The lady-nurses out with their lady-children, when they saw the speed of the cyclist and the speed of those who followed him, pushed their pompous perambulators into a canter away from where they were, for they knew not when shooting might burst out upon them. Passers-by hesitated, halted, then slid to a house's shelter till the panting danger had gone from view. Out of Rathgar, into Dartry, went the riders; on and on through devious ways along the river Dodder, into Rathfarnham, heading on fast, fast, faster for the Dublin hills; the lonely leader glancing back, with sweat trickling down into his eyes, murmuring, murmuring as life rolled off behind him like thread unwinding from a turning spool:

—They'll get me yet; they'll get me yet! He pedalled hard, he pedalled harder, children playing near stopping to cheer him as he shot madly by them; cheering again, after some time, when the three following, body-bent, went headlong past them, too.

—Wondher who th', who th' bugger is? jerked out one of the plain-clothes pursuers.

Lanehin, panted the uniformed officer, Clonervy, leading; seen his gob, an' he turnin' th' corner. Lanehin. Captain of the crush I was in when we were fightin' th' Tans. Lanehin—a bastard!

—Seems as if he's not got a gun on him, either, panted the plain-clothes one.

On the top of the pensive lake a modest brown duck came swimming shorewards from a pursuing drake, his brown coat, dabbed with velvety black, ashine; his glittering green head and neck stretched designedly. She climbed the shelving bank in a hurry, shook a shower of moisture off her, and made a waddling run for the grass beyond the path. He climbed calmly out, shook himself free of the clinging drops, his curly twist of a tail quivering, then waddled, slow and determined, after her.

—George Moore's Anatidean lover and his lass, thought Sean, envying the drake's comfort in having to solve but one problem at a time.

Rougher and rocky the road grew. Upupuphill now, all the time. The man who had thrown the grenade had to stand on the pedals to force them round. Sweat from thigh, chest, and back was seeping through his clothes. No; he hadn't made a good get-away. He should never have come to the frown of these lonely hills. Better to have stayed in the busy streets. Jesus, Mary, and Joseph, he was in a bad way. And he only twenty-two. Not even that, for there was a month and more to go yet. Christ, me heart'll burst if I have to keep this up!

He slid from the bicycle sideways, letting it fall to the ground, leaving it there, while he dashed into, and pushed through, a hedge on to the rising slope of a hill, tangled with the spiny gorse, and roughly pompous with patches of purple heather. The cycle-clips had been dragged from his ankles, and the bottoms of his trousers streamed about like sombre ribbons worn by visitants to a mournful fair. Blood trickled down his legs where thorn and spine of gorse had torn the flesh. He ran on, crouching, trying to shelter his flight behind every bush, every clump of heather; he climbed in a tearing way over rocky mounds, never minding the bruising and breaking of his skin. He splashed through noisy, gurgling brooks, the gentle flow of the water cooling his aching feet and weakened ankles, now twisting under him from the stress of the fierce and long run from the terror and death following behind.

—Good God! he murmured as he raced unsteadily over the tough grass, through the thorns in bush and brake, look at the state of me trousers!

He could go no further. He was stumbling about now like a drunken fool. His legs were getting numb. He could go no further. Not another step. His whole mind encouraged his panting body to take a rest. How often he was angry when his mother used to say, You look dead tired, Kevin; you really ought to go to bed. Oh, God! If he was only at home now with the old woman urging him to go up and lie down and rest and have a good sleep!

A few more staggering steps brought him to an old stone wall, standing somewhat higher than his waist. Get behind this; lie down; sleep. He leaned his hands on the top of it, and tried to spring over; tried hard, but no spring was left in him. He leaned heavily on it, and tried to drag himself to the top and over, but no strength remained in him to do it. He spread his arms out along the top of the wall, rested his breast against it, closed his eyes, and stayed still. He'd wait here. Here in the hills. Just as he was, he'd stay. He had no gun, no gun. He had thought that after the grenade had been thrown, if any cordon was flung round where he might be, he'd have a fine chance of getting through without a gun. A mistake; a big mistake. Well, it should soon come now. Unarmed, he'd just have to take it quietly. Pity he couldn't take a chip or two out of one of them before he passed out. Couldn't though; he had no gun. Not a ghost of a chance now. Damned fool, that O.C. of his who advised him to go on the mission without a gun. *He's* all right—curse o' God on him! He shivered at the thought of sudden death. Soon now. Creeping up to him, maybe, to take him unawares. Slowly and steadily, he turned his throbbing head to see whether they were near or far or absent altogether. They were there. Only thirty feet away. The three of them; sitting ten yards apart, in a semicircle, on a grassy mound watching him; each with a cocked gun in his right hand; the uniformed man in the centre. Jasus! sitting down, resting, and staring at him! Mick Clonervy, Sergeant of his company when they had both fought the Tans; a colonel now in the Free State Army; promotion sure. Sell his own mother for a yellow tab.

There were the two of them again! The brown duck, like a maid hid in a Franciscan habit, spurting forward when she felt the pursuer coming too close; waddling swift from the temptation following her obstinately and unerringly in the desire of the drake, brilliant as a courtier in a gay king's garden. Sean's glance followed them till both were hidden behind a curtain of flowering currant.

—Turn right round, Lanehin, shouted the Colonel; right round till we all get a full look at you! Sthretch your arms out each side of you, along the top of the wall, and rest like that till we're ready for you. Stir an inch, and we'll plug you full of holes, you creeping, cowardly, murdhering bastard!

Lanehin did as he was told, stretching his arms along the top of the wall, and leaning his back where his breast had leaned before. He watched them through half-closed weary eyes. Watched them resting there, calmly; eating something from a paper bag and drinking from a flask. Good thing they didn't come for him at once. They'd feel better after having eaten; and they'd have time to think better of what they may have thought of doing in the heat of the chase. Give them time to cool. He saw the Colonel throw away the paper bag, and one of the others putting the flask away in a breast-pocket. Now he'd see. No, not yet; they had taken cigarettes from a packet, and each was now quietly smoking, while they chatted together. The Colonel broke off a sprig of blossoming heather and slowly and carefully fixed it in the side of his cap. Suddenly, he to his feet, saying sharply, Come on, boys, let's get going; we can't stop here all night.

He advanced with his two men towards Lanehin; advanced without a word, till they were so close, Lanehin fancied he felt their breaths tickling his cheeks. They stood as they had sat—in a closer semicircle, staring curiously at him. He stared back at them for a little; dropped his gaze; lifted his head again, knowing not what to do, for his mind overflowed with prayer, and he felt his bowels turning to water. They were quietly gazing at him, saying nothing, not lifting a hand.

—I surrendher, he said plaintively at last; what are you going to do with me? I surrendher.

—A wise thing to do, said one of the civilian-clad men.

—After all, went on the frightened man, there wasn't a lot of damage done.

—Oh, not a lot, said the Colonel; you're right there; only one of us had an eye knocked into a jelly, and another got his chest rieved asundher.

—What are you going to do with me? Make me a prisoner o' war; I surrendher.

—What are we going to do with you? echoed Colonel Clonervy. Bring you home, sit you on our knees, and nurse you? Would you like us to do that for you, eh?

—And let him sleep late in the morning, added one of the civilian-clad men.

—Make me a prisoner, murmured the unhappy lad, the hoarseness of fear darkening his voice; a prisoner of war—I surrendher.

—You asked us that before, said the Colonel; but it's easier said than done. The house at home's too crowded to take another soul. What are you sweating for, man? Are you afraid of what's coming to you, or what? I thought all Republicans were above that sort of thing.

—I'm an old comrade of yours, Mick, the young man pleaded.

—Sure I know that well, said the Colonel heartily, and I'll say this much—for the sake of oul' times, we won't let you suffer long.

—Jesus! whimpered the half-dead lad, yous wouldn't shoot an old comrade, Mick!

The Colonel's arm holding the gun shot forward suddenly, the muzzle of the gun, tilted slightly upwards, splitting the lad's lips and crashing through his chattering teeth.

—Be Jasus! We would, he said, and then he pulled the trigger.

—*Looka Ma! shrilled a childish voice behind Sean; looka what th' ducks is doin'!*

Sean turned swift to see a fair young mother, her sweet face reddening, grasp a little boy's arm, wheel him right round, saying as she pointed out over the innocent lake: Look at all the other ducks, dear, over there on the water!

The drake had reached his goal, and he was quivering in the violent effort to fulfil God's commandment to multiply and replenish the earth.

THE CLERGY TAKE A HAND

The clergy take a hand, the clergy make a stand,
With bell, book, and candle O,
All over Spireland!

THE bishops now decided to bless one side by cursing the
other from the Maynooth valley of squinting windows.
For a long time they had been cautious, dubious, wondering which party had the bigger power behind it, and which
of them would be the more amenable. They now realised
that a good many of the people wanted anything that
might bring peace; that Britain's power was behind the
Free State; and that in this Free State a free people would
have a dog's chance of saying a word, or a byword, against
the clergy. So one fine morning, as Sean roved out, an
episcopal declaration appeared in all the morning papers,
fresh with dieu, condemning Unauthorised Murder on
the part of the Republicans, implying to many minds that
the same kind of progressive activity, on the part of the
Free State followers, came within, according to the clergy,
the shadow of canonical condonation. They seemed to be
investing it with a kind legal validity. But the outcry
against it was so loud and clear that the clergy withdrew
the manifesto the next day, shoving out a more slyly-
written one in its place. So from the bishops the minor
clergy got their cue: the priest followed the bishop, the

deacon the priest. The holy catholic church was against Republicans, and the Republican cause was lost. The odour of piety was mixed in with the fight where bayonets were plunged into bosoms, and brains scattered with blows from rifle-butts, so that Eire was kept busy writing down the deeds of her sons, in fair, legible characters, in the big book of death. The number of executions mounted higher; but everything was done in a rather nice way. One of the Free State ministers told us all that—"the men who were executed this morning were, perhaps, uneducated, illiterate men, never meaning, perhaps, to get into a situation like this; men, perhaps, of no political convictions. We provided for these men all the spiritual assistance we could muster to help them in their passage to eternity. We are people who realise that man is made in the image and likeness of God, and we treat man as such. When a man is going to his death he always gets a priest."

Now could anything be more Christian, more catholic, more decent? What nicer combination could there be than rope and cross—a natural blend. Religion, religion, what crimes are done under thy cloak of light! The jails were full, and the executions, before done to a minuet, now advanced to the quicker steps of a jig-tune.

The venerable Bishop of Blarney became so hostile and bitter to Republicans that the following letter, signed by the Officer Commanding for and on behalf of Republican prisoners in Cork jails, appeared in the Republican Journal, *Eire*, on Saturday, the 23rd of June, 1923:

"This Bishop of Blarney, who, when the Black and Tan terror was at its worst, excommunicated the Irish

Republican soldiers, and thereby nerved the British to carry out the Executions in Cork County, has now so far forgotten the principles of the religion he professes as to incite the Free State troops to murder prisoners. This incitement he uttered when addressing little children at the sacrament of Confirmation. The Catholic Faith has stood many assaults in Ireland. Its latest trial is to withstand the action of a Prelate of the Church who incites bloody-minded soldiery to further atrocities in the hearing of little Irish children at a religious ceremony." The following letter [the paper goes on] was sent to this man by the prisoners in Corca Dorcha jails: "To the Most Reverend, Dr. Cockadoo, Lord Bishop of Blarney; My Lord, we have read your infamous and vindictive outburst in Wednesday's *Cork Examiner* at an address given by you at the Confirmation Service in St. Peter's and St. Paul's Church. It would be a misrepresentation of fact to say that we were surprised, for we all know too well the source to be surprised at anything that emanated therefrom. We have, on previous occasions, endured outbursts in the same vein, but they were treated with the contempt they deserved. But your latest invective, however, considering the implication that runs through it, and considering the occasion on which it was spoken, calls for a response.

"We wish you to understand that your opinion does not weigh with us in the slightest; the principles for which we stand are immune from such petty outbursts as yours, actuated as they are by deep-rooted imperialistic and slavish tendencies. Your incitement to murder, however, calls for strong comment, and we intend to make it. It is nothing short of scandalous that you should have chosen Confirmation day to annunciate a doctrine of pure and unadulterated murder, and endeavour to inculcate the children's receptive minds with that venomous antagonism to freedom and all it stands for, which animates your own speech and action. It is appalling to think that the Altar of God is turned by you into a political and partizan platform, from which you give free run to your own personal opinions, leaving them open to be interpreted by the uneducated as the word of God. That you would go further, and imply that the Imperial Free State troops were very lenient for not shooting all that stood for Irish independence, and that we should have been very grateful for being flung into evil-smelling, foul jails, instead of being summarily executed, is outrageous. Moreover, that you should have chosen for audience little children, many of whose relatives were doubtless imprisoned, is unprecedented.

"We have too long had foisted upon us, without protest, as the teaching of our Divine Saviour, the political opinions of one who was always thoroughly unnational, and who always endeavoured to impede progress towards freedom, even to the extent of denouncing and excommunicating those who had the slightest leaning towards that holy cause. On Tuesday you surpassed yourself, and definitely implied that, had the Free State soldiers chosen to fill the graves with the bodies of Republicans, their methods would have received your commendation. You instilled into the minds of your juvenile hearers, at one of the more solemn moments of their lives, that to fight for National freedom is a crime which fully merits to be punished by death, and that such punishment would have the full sanction of the Church. That such a murderous doctrine should be preached in the house of God to innocent children, would give grounds for doubting the sanity of the preacher, were he other than your lordship's self; but we quite realise that your venomous mind is perfectly capable of it. You are now what you always were.

"You are *now* an expressed exponent of the will of the people. When the people elected an overwhelming Republican majority, it did not enter into your slavish mind to recognise it, although the Republican Government was then, *de jure* and *de facto*, the government of Ireland. Now, however, that the settlement, dictated by England's Government, has been accepted by some of your countrymen, behold you are a stout champion of the will of the people. We will not accept our politics from you, nor do we intend to allow you, unchallenged, to allocate to yourself the power of deciding our fate, even though you may have chosen to become the champion of a much bigger opinion, which leads us to believe what we have for some time suspected—that the campaign of executions received the tacit approval, if not the official sanction, of the Bishops of Ireland. O/C Prisoners. Signed for and on behalf of the prisoners in Free State jails."

The bishops again! The Men of Ninety-Eight; the

Fenians; Parnell; and now the unfortunate Republicans in the Irish jails recommended to the hangman, or to a firing-squad. A way of thought that seems to be nothing new to the Vatican bishops. No episcopal voice raised, nor word spoken, asking even the executioners to go slow. Republicanism had in it the seed of anti-clericalism, so let it be banished by rifle-fire, or dangle dead at the end of a rope. St. Patrick'll see they get their strict due wherever they may have to go. Let their denouncing voices be smothered in the coldness of inanimate clay. Maybe shamrocks will grow over them. Recite the Office for the Dead; pray for the sweet repose of their souls: they can do no harm to us now. Don't be stingy or mean to the poor dead chaps. *Requiem aeternam dona, eis Domine* to all the dead of the Lost Legion of the Republican Rear-Guard. They can do no more harm to us; no more harm to us now. Another one? Two more? Ah, well, we'll soon be used to it. *Requiem aeternam dona eis, Domine.* What? The very ones who had thrown them into jail, or who had sent them to the firing-squad, were often the very fellows who had encouraged them, had persuaded, had even put them under oath to uphold the precious ideals for which they were now perishing? No! D'ye tell me that! Poor boys! Well, that's not really our business. Good will come out of it, never fear. Authority comes from God, and we must approve it, even though it makes Eire's eyelids dark with the shadow of death. No sigh for mercy from a single bishop for these misguided young men and women, though they were, with these clericals, of one faith, one hope, one baptism; yet, many years after, the bishop of bishops was to send a finely-polished plea of mercy for a saurian-souled ruffian who had slain thousands and had tortured tens of thousands, with satisfaction, and in great glee.

And Sean, alone on a Dublin pathway, thought that since they could pass by so sedately on the other side while young members of their own flock were going through the agonies of execution, how rancorous, how cool and bitter they would be in handing over to death the Socialist, the Communist who might deny their importance and ignore their power in those lands where the bishop and the priest had in their white, jewel-circled hands the keys of the kingdom of life as well as those of the kingdom of heaven. Well, he had done his best to get a word in edgeways. He had written a one-act play, satirising the contesting parties and putting official Labour against the wall for its stupid and selfish pursuit of jobs, instead of flinging themselves between the opposing guns, calling out the question of which of you will fire first! Sean could never hear a word about his little play, though he had sent it to *The Plain People*, and though he asked many who were connected with the distribution of the journal. It was ten years after, when he was living in London, that a priest from Kerry visited him, and reminded him of his play, *The Robe of Rosheen*, which had appeared so long ago in the Republican paper, though ne'er another soul, apparently, had ever noticed it.

He had shifted away from the active Ireland, and was growing contentedly active in himself. Instead of trying to form Ireland's life, he would shape his own. He would splash his thoughts over what he had seen and heard; keep

eyes and ears open to see and hear what life did, what life
had to say, and how life said it; life drunk or sober; life
sickly or sturdy; life sensible or half demented; life
well-off or poor; life on its knees in prayer, or shouting
up a wild curse to heaven's centre. His first play, *The
Frost in the Flower*, which he had sent to the Abbey
Theatre, had been returned, with a note saying how interested they were in the play, which was promising, but one
of the main characters had been too critical, reminding
them of various characters in Abbey plays, a characteristic
that tended to become tiresome and irritating.

Sean guessed that this comment was wrong, and a little
ridiculous, since he had been in the theater but twice, and
had seen only *Blight*, by Gogarty, *Androcles and the Lion*,
by Shaw, *The Jackdaw*, by Lady Gregory, and another
one-act play built up on a short story by James Stephens.
He had seen nothing that he could try to imitate. The
play dealt with a young man, a lay teacher in a Christian
Brothers' school who, though full of confidence on
gigantic questions he was never called upon to touch, was
timid as a new-born mouse over simple questions concerning himself. He got a very small salary from the Brothers,
paid to him quarterly, mostly in sixpenny pieces and three-
penny bits. A teachership in elementary mathematics and
elementary English fell vacant in a Technical School, the
gift of a Dublin Council Committee, and Sean's timid
friend, certain he hadn't a chance of getting it, applied for
the job. To his frightened dismay, he was elected by a
fine vote, and everyone in the parish brought him all kinds
of books to help in preparing him for the work he would

have to do. Though he had the ability, he hadn't the will-power; and the play ended in the midst of a party given in his honour, at which it became known that he had resigned from the job, to become the scorn of his family and the joke of the parish. The second one, called *The Harvest Festival*, dealt with the efforts of militant members of the unskilled unions to put more of the fibre of resistance to evil conditions of pay and life into the hearts and minds of the members of the craft unions whose gospel was that what was good enough for the fathers was good enough for the sons. The action took place in the busy preparations made by a church for holding the annual harvest festival, which the Anglo-catholics sneeringly called the Feast of Saint Pumpkin and all Vegetables. The play brought back to Sean a letter saying that the work was well conceived, but badly executed; with an added note from Mr. Lennox Robinson, then the Manager of the Abbey Theatre, saying that he liked very much the character of the clergyman in the play,—which was something, though not enough for Sean.

A shadow showing a familiar figure passed by the window, and formed a memory in his mind: of Father Michael O'Flanagan. An unselfish man, with more than a little courage to make him a marked man; a brilliant speaker, with a dangerous need of more respect for bishops dressed in a little brief authority; a priest spoiled by too many good qualities. He had been priest of the poverty-stricken parish of Cliffoney in Sligo, and when, one cold ice-proud winter, he saw his people shivering for the lack of fuel, he said to them—go ye even unto the boglands where there is turf and to spare, and gather all ye need; and they said to him—How can we venture to do this thing, seeing that the bogland is owned by one who got the place from God? And he answered them, saying—Let him, of his plenty, give unto you of your need. They answered, saying—We have gone to him, and, behold, he turned us away, using us despitefully, setting the dogs on us, and saying—Begone, for none but those who can buy are welcome here. And Father O'Flanagan, raising his hand to heaven, saith unto them—Go, and take what ye need, for it is written, The earth is the Lord's, and the fullness thereof; so go again, for the Lord will not refuse ye in your extremity; and take what ye need, and the Lord will bless the doing of it. And they went, and took of the turf every man, according to his need; and the owner thereof was afraid, for he was but one, and they were many.

But it came to the ears of the righteous bishops whose deep affection and profound respect for the common people, the children of God, could not be denied by any fair-minded person. The bishops knew that this sort of thing would not be good for the people; that the finest way of keeping them close to God was to disencourage any attempt to cock them up with any kind of comfort. Their flock came first to them. So they laid hold of the foolish Father Flanagan and drove him from his parish. Time to do it, too, for in a few places held by the Republicans, red flags were fluttering over the roofs. God Almighty, what was catholic Ireland coming to! Another priest was sent to replace Father Flanagan; but the poor people locked the chapel door, and so the poor man had to climb in through a window to celebrate Mass; but lacking any support of thought or action, the poor people of Cliffoney soon had to submit, and resume their old pilgrimage along the way of hunger and cold. If they were cold for want of fuel and had no money to pay for it, then they must remain cold; if they were hungry for want of food, and had no money to pay for it, then they must remain hungry; and all these light afflictions would work for them an exceeding weight of glory in the world to come. So Father Flanagan wandered here and there, subdued, beaten, making odd speeches that became calmer and more reticent as the days passed, till he died in a quiet corner, forgotten by almost all, save the kindly bishops, who shook their mitred heads and murmured—poor misguided man whom we could not help to a higher honour than a quiet death.

With a shake of his shoulders, Sean banished the memory of Father Flanagan's decline from a hawk to a hernshaw, and thought again of the plays he had written, and of those he would write. He had a fight of his own to make. There had been a good chance of his third play, *The Crimson in the Tri-Colour*, being produced, for Lady Gregory had written that she was very interested in it; that it was evident that the author had something in him; that Mrs. Rosebud was a delightful character and Mr. Rosebud a fine foil to her. A play that was somewhat confused, but one of ideas might be made from it. But it could not be put on till the Revolution was over; and it must be typed by the theatre, for no-one could possibly attempt the reading of such written manuscript a second

time. And then came a letter from Mr. Robinson saying—
that in moving from Clare Street to Foxrock, he had mis-
laid the play, and would Sean please furnish them with a
copy. And Sean had clenched his teeth, for there was no
copy; not even notes from which a copy might be built.
So his last state was as bad as his first. A double jolt—one
to mind and body, for a sick stomach followed a disturbed
mind. So much hard work had gone for nothing.

There was nothing to do but forget, and go on; forget,
and go on. He had made up his mind years ago that the
Abbey Theatre curtain would go up on a play of his; and
up it would go, sooner or later. First decide slowly and
deeply whether it is in you to do a thing; if you decide
that you can, then do it, even though it kept you busy till
the very last hour of life. Maybe, too, the play would be
found again; and, so, in the meantime, he would go on
writing another play. A year after, or more, when he was
just finishing the play he was working on, news came that
the play was found; that it had been typed; that each of
the Directors had read it, and that rejection was their final
decision. Well, refusal wasn't so bitter now, for the new
play was all but done. Now that he had another to offer,
he felt no grievance; his heart was calm and steady. It was
years after, when he had left Ireland forever, that bitterness, mingled with scorn, overtook him, for he began to
realise that the plays refused by the Abbey Theatre were a
lot better than many they had welcomed, and had played
on to their stage with drums and colours.

The young girl below was coughing again. He could
see in his mind's eye the bed in which she lay, a heap of

clothing, confused with the restless tossing and turning of one in an advanced state of consumption. A basement dweller, she lived with an old mother, a brother who was a plumber, and a little girl, child of a sister, who, too, had lived with consumption for years before she had died. They lived in a basement set of two rooms, one a bedroom, the other a kitchen. Two days before, the young brother had shown Sean the floor of the bedroom that had rotted under the oilcloth till the boards were of the texture of rainsoaked wallpaper. Sean and the young man had pointed this terrible condition of the room to the sanitary inspector, and now the family were living together in the kitchen while the landlord took his time to put in a new floor. Sean had advised Peter, the sick girl's brother, to get her into the Hospice for the Dying, since there was no hope of recovery, and grave danger that the rest of them should be infected with the repulsive complaint. The cringing girl had screamed an outcry against going, saying she was not as bad as that; she would rise out of it; she already felt her strength returning day by day; so they let her lie on, mixing their poor life with a poorer one still. Answering an appeal by the mother, Sean had gone down to try to persuade the sick girl; but she had turned her face to the wall, had cried the whole time, and screamed occasionally while he was there, so he had returned to his room without a word spoken. He had left her there in the glory of dying diseased, for, it is written, whom the Lord loveth, He chasteneth.

Anyway, it surely was the priest's job to get the dying girl to dimly realise the inevitable end of this illness in a tenement. But the priests, as far as Sean could see, were chary of crossing the border into the hidden horridness of a slum—the hidden Ireland! Usually, they'd hurry in to fortify the dying with the last rites of the church, and then hurry out again. No priest, as far as Sean knew, had ever visited this dying lass to say even the Lord be with thee. There wasn't much to be got out of these places. So the lass lay there, all that had been she, diminished now almost to the bones; animated now only with the large rich eyes, luminous with the glare of feverish fear, and the long silky, black hair coiling from the ridged skull down to the withered shoulders, and flowing mockingly over the bony breast. How often in the stilly night had he listened to the sad symphony of her coughing on her lonely bed in the miserable room below, unheard by mother or brother enveloped in the thickness of a tired sleep.

A knock sounded quick on the door, the door opened— as it usually did—before the last rap was given, and young Peter came into the room, fervour in his eyes, and a curious defiance shown in the stiffened contour of his shoulders.

—Look Sean, he said, rough and ready; look, I'm fed up! If she isn't taken out of this, we'll all be goin' to the grave together. The sisthers have a snug place for her in the Hospice for the Dying, an' I can't see why she's not willin' to go.

—No-one's willin' to go there, said Sean; we all take the last few steps to the grave as slow as possible. But, Shamus, she'll be far more comfortable there than she can be where she is, and she won't die a second sooner.

—Amn't I tired tellin' her that! She's so damned selfish, she won't listen. She can't walk, an' she wouldn't be able to sit in a cab, so the only way is to get hold of the Fire Brigade Ambulance; but where the hell's th' fee to come from?

—From me, thought Sean; that's why he came here. He's asking for it round the corner. Aloud, he said, I'll lend the money, Peter. You can pay it back when things improve; though Sean well knew they would never improve enough to pour back the money jingling into his pocket. Six or seven new books gone west he sighed. Look, he said aloud, don't tell her anything. Let the ambulance men come suddenly down on her, so that she won't have time to know what's happening when she's being whisked from the festered dusk of her bed to be brought away from the world forever.

—I'll go ring up the Hospice from the pub outside, said Peter, after Sean had handed him thirty pieces of silver, to say she's comin', an' then the ambulance to come an' take her off at once. I won't whisper a word till she's on the way. Thanks, Sean.

Another knock at the door, and before the two could look towards it, the tram-conductor, quick and excited, hurried into the room.

—He's found! he said breathless; found at last! Young Captain Wogan: away in a lone counthry lane, beyond Finglas, half-hidden in hemlock. Taken out an' murdhered! Near unrecognisable; his belly kicked in, ears frayed, an eye gouged out, and the nose broken, with a bullet through his brain as an amen. The bastards only left a batthered memory of him! He sank down on the sofa, and wiped warm sweat from his brow. There's Irish freedom for you!

—But Wogan shot a man before he himself was shot, said Sean.

—Ay, in fair fight, though; and it was a clean shot; not like what made the thing I saw. Sweet Jesus, have mercy on th' poor lad's soul.

—I'm goin', Sean, said Peter at the door, to settle things finally, and he closed the door softly behind him.

The conductor pulled a chair to the fire, and sat down to brood. Sean saw that the years were weighing heavy on his crouching shoulders; that the mane of hair was very grey now; and that the seamed hands shook slightly while he lighted his pipe: the model of an ageing *semper fidelis*.

They're lavishin' contracts on each other, said the conductor suddenly, a Senathor gettin' more for eggs, with cheaper tendhers for eggs, as good, refused, making as much as fifty quid a week clear; an' th' same with butther; an' I know a lamp-lighter who's a Free State Quarther-masther now, gettin' a lift for givin' th' contract to a friend for the fittin' out of his battalion. Holy God! what's catholic Ireland comin' to!

Sean heard the engine-whinge of the ambulance stopping beside the door; heard the heavy tread of the men carrying the stretcher through the sullied hall, heard the heavier, more carefully-planted steps going down, one two three, the basement steps, seeping with rottenness, on their errand of mercy—the love of God among the mildews. Then came silence, to be broken soon, Sean knew

160

well. There it goes—a frightened, weary wail; frenzied too, like a soul descending, vanishing, before it ended, in a hurried, hacking fit of coughing.

Sean went to a window, and looked out on the street. The bright, green leaves of the sycamore sapling were weaving patches of scarlet and gold into their quiet loveliness. A fine, fair evening, with a touch of a chill in the shining of the sun. Boys were playing at Free Staters and Republicans, their voices imitating the sound of bomb-burst and rifle-shot; shouting the slogans of each party at each other that were to bring peace and goodwill to Ireland. These had halted now from their mimic work of death and wounding to stare at the dull, dread ambulance, waiting with expansive bosom to receive a dying body. Sean heard the thud of the heavy feet again, walking this time slow and in unison through the hall, carrying what was now but the life of a lung-cough. He saw the red-shirted men go down the stone steps, on to the pathway, out to the wide-open door of the ambulance, carrying on the stretcher a flicker of life away from where a ruddier life had at last refused to live along with it. All Sean could see was a thin, frail hand, white as snow, clawing timidly at a brown blanket tumbled over the stretcher; a thin, white hand paying its last respects to the life it was losing.

—What's up, what's wrong? asked the tram-conductor, trying to stiffen the shoulders that had crouched too deep to straighten, and half turning towards where Sean stood.

—A citizeness being brought to the Hospice for the Dying to hand over a life that has lived too long.

—What's amiss with her?

—Consumption.

—That's not much to get excited about. We have more stringent things to think of today than a case of simple consumption.

—She was very young—just on the verge of woman-hood; and, one time, she was handsome and gay.

—Aw, what signifies that, Sean? That sort o' thing's a daily occurrence in these places. You ought to be well used to them things be now. She's a lucky lady compared with poor Jack Wogan. Looka, he went on, tapping Sean's knee when Sean had sat down again by the fire, I'll betcha anything you like, the clergy'll never raise a hand or say a word to stop this quiet, cool killin' of our poor best boys. As men—I say nothin' again' them as priests, mind you, Sean,—as men, it's poor Saint Pathrick himself must be woebegone lookin' down to see the clergy dumb, while th' counthry's becomin' a murdherin' fiasco!

Saint Patrick, thought Sean; holy Saint Patrick, pray for us! Dear saint of our Isle; the isle of bullets, beads, and bombs.

Beads round every rifle sending a bullet to kill a man; beads twined round every rope, prepared to hang another.

Upon the dear children bestow a sweet smile. The tear and the smile. The tear was there, all right; so what we want, now,

Saint Patrick, is a smile, a sweet smile. So Saint Patrick, jewel of the Gaels, pack all your troubles in your oul' kitbag, and smile, smile, smile.

BLESSED BRIDGET O'COOLE

THERE she was before him. The lean, wand-like arm of
Lennox Robinson had waved her out of her chair in a dark
corner of the Abbey Theatre office; waved her out to meet
Sean, whose play, at last, had been accepted for production.
There she was, a sturdy, stout, little figure soberly clad in
solemn black, made gay with a touch of something white
under a long, soft, black silk veil that covered her grey
hair, and flowed gracefully behind half-way down her
back. A simple brooch shyly glistened under her throat,
like a bejewelled lady making her first retreat, feeling a
little ashamed of it. Her face was a rugged one, hardy as
that of a peasant, curiously lit with an odd dignity, and
softened with a careless touch of humour in the bright
eyes and the curving wrinkles crowding around the corners
of the firm little mouth. She looked like an old, elegant
nun of a new order, a blend of the Lord Jesus Christ and
of Puck, an order that Ireland had never known before,
and wasn't likely to know again for a long time to come.

The first night was very disappointing, for few came,
and only thirteen pounds worth of tickets were bought; the
second night was much better for it was more than half-
full; and the third capped the previous two, for the house
was packed. Going to the theatre early, Sean enjoyed a
look of ecstasy on the Old Lady's face as she stood to

watch the people gathering round her little theatre. She ran to him when she saw him, caught his hand in hers, and led him out to see the queues forming a long, long trail right round the famous building. Well, he had done what he had set himself to do seven or more years ago: he had mounted a play of his on the Abbey stage. Odd, he felt no great elation; no more than he would have felt in the middle, or at the end, of a speech in Irish delivered before a crowd of Gaels. He felt, though, as he stood quiet in the vestibule, that he had crossed the border of a little, but a great, new kingdom of life, and so another illusion was born in his poor susceptible soul. He didn't know enough then that it was no great thing to be an Abbey playwright; and, afterwards, when he knew a lot more, he was glad he had suffered himself to feel no jubilation to mar his future by thinking too much of a tiny success: life remained a mystery to him. He thought, not of what he had done, but of what he had to do in the form and substance of his second play; realising, though unaware of it at the time, that to be a great playwright was a very different thing from merely being one who had had one, two, or even three, plays produced by the Abbey Theatre. Coming out of the theatre, however, he shook himself, thinking in himself that sufficient for the day is the good thing thereof. Some time after, he sent in two one-act plays, *Cathleen Listens In* and *The Cooing of Doves*; the first a skit on the Irish politics of the day, the second full of wild discussions and rows in a public-house. The first play was taken by the Abbey, the other returned, and later was used to form the second act of a later play. This was the first shock given

to Sean by the selective committee of the theatre, for the
second work was definitely better as a play than the first.
This was the first jolt he got, but he was to get many more
before he was much older, and from the same source, too.

The third play was the biggest success of all, for the
theatre was booked out in a few days for the whole week.
Lady Gregory began to get young again, for all the weight
of her seventy years and more. Hands everywhere were
shaking Sean's. After his first play, during the recess, the
Abbey Company had engaged the theatre to produce a
play of their own selection, to keep themselves from the
sin of idleness. The play they choose was Ervine's *Mary,
Mary, Quite Contrary*; and Sean went to it as a token of
his thanks for what they had done for him in the performance of his two works. He was damned glad he did. There
he saw, for the first time, an actor, Barry Fitzgerald, glorifying comedy on the Abbey stage. He had never met the
man, and no-one had ever mentioned his name to him.
Seething with excitement, when the play ended, Sean ran
behind the stage to pour out his enthusiasm into the unwilling ears of the other actors. Fitzgerald's not bad, he
was told, when he gets a part that exactly suits him. Not
bad? echoed Sean; why he's a born clown! And, when he
went with his third play, he had a suggestion for the cast:
Fitzgerald was to play the chief comedy part in it. Mr.
Robinson demurred, and mentioned the name of another
fine actor, F. G. McCormick, for the part; but Sean held
firm for Fitzgerald, knowing in his heart that he, and he
alone, could get the arrogant, boozy humour from the
character. Fitzgerald, himself, was very hesitant about

taking it on, and Sean, with another member of the Company, Gaby Fallon, who had a very fine understanding of acting, stage and production, spent a long time arguing, demonstrating, and cursing, before Fitzgerald finally could be convinced he would do well in the part. The first night showed Dublin that Fitzgerald stood in the front rank of comedy actors, and Sean and Lady Gregory were delighted.

Letters came asking for his autograph; he was stopped in the street by levelled fountain-pens and pencils held firm by persons demanding his signature on scraps of paper; notes, bearing dignified addresses on their summits, came from others, announcing that They would be At Home on a certain day, at a precise hour, with a hope, in letters of purest gold, that he would be found among the number knocking nicely at Their big hall doors; and, lastly, a letter from Mr. Robinson inviting him to a monthly dinner furnished by a Thirteen Club (or some name of that kind), with a gilded addendum that W. B. Yeats would be there. The ritual was held in a well-known Dublin restaurant bearing a sturdy poetical name. This invitation couldn't be set aside, for it was one conferring real honour; so, trimly dressed and neat as he could make himself, Sean hurried off to mingle with the elect people of Ireland in a ceremonial meal.

Hiding his nervousness, Sean quietly greeted Mr. Robinson and Arthur Sheilds, brother to Barry Fitzgerald, who gently led him, the first before, the second behind, to a table for three, hedged safely in a corner of the room. Away in the dim distance, a far larger table served a number of persons whom Sean did not know yet, though, through a murmur of submissive conversation, he heard the booming voice of Yeats chatting in a lordly lilt about Utumara, Brahmin Mohini, birds born out of the fire, the two inflows to man's nature—the one common to him and all animals which is natural; and the second, which is intellectual, coming from the fire. Yeats murmured about coming through the fire as if it were but coming through the rye, going on from that to chatter about *anima hominis* and *anima mundi* and spirits that walked only once on a Sunday, while his listeners cocked their ears and bowed their heads, murmuring, *Lord, Lord, thou hast the words of infernal life.*

It was all very mysterious to Sean, and he realised that he had not yet entered within the veil of the temple, but still was allowed to but stand reverent on the doorstep. So he did what he could to ingratiate himself with his hosts, eating what he thought was a badly-cooked meal as delightfully as he could; answering questions put to him as wisely as possible; but discovering that he knew nothing about writers that were common names in the mouths of those who sat beside him. No, he had never seen or read *The Life of Man*, by Andreiev, or *Falling Leaves*, by Giacosa, or *Monna Vanna* and *Joyzelle*, by Maeterlinck; no, nor Benevente's *Passion Flower*, or Pirandello's *Right You Are (If You Think So)*; while Sean whispered the names of Shaw and Strindberg, which they didn't seem to catch, though he instinctively kept firm silence about Dion Boucicault, whose works he knew as well as Shakespeare's; afterwards provoking an agonised My Gawd! from Mr.

Robinson, when he stammered the names of Webster, Forde, and Massinger. So Sean hunched his shoulders, and sat silent, while the other two went in and came out with arguments about them and about the works of playwrights whose names Sean had never heard of, much more read. He shut an ear to the talk nearby, and cocked the other to the voice of Yeats blossoming into a fuller booming about Megarithma who had told him he must live by bread and water and avoid woods, because the woods concentrated the solar rays; afterwards asking himself why woods concentrated the solar rays, and deciding to reject that part of the counsel as an error (Petrushka deciding to fight rather than to run away); though Sean wondered if he didn't know why the solar rays did, or did not, concentrate in woods, how he could decide what Megarithma said must be an error; but the voice went on booming about the divine spirit of the path Samekh, the golden heart that was the central point of the cabbalistic Tree of Life, corresponding to the Sephiroth Tippereth. The rest round the round table bowed their minor heads, murmuring *This same is a voice that is more than the wind among the reeds.*

Sean was awakened out of the booming by the voice of Mr. Robinson asking him if he had enjoyed the dinner, Sean dazedly and innocently replying with The Rhubarb and Custard were Fine, thanks, but the rest of the things were badly cooked; to be startled by Mr. Robinson ejaculating What a Terrible man you are to bring to Dinner! Another shock for Sean, and he felt his face go red. What was there terrible in saying food was badly cooked? He

168

based his remark on his mother's skill. Whenever she and
he had anything worthwhile, steak, mutton, liver, or fish,
garnished with vegetables, they were always sure to be
handed up in simple, but first-class style of cooking. And
all done on a plain open coal fire. Seldom it happened, but
when it did, there was always the next thing to perfection.
To this day, he remembered the soiled, sloppy look of the
greens and the tattered dry look of the meat, served in the
poetically-named restaurant. A ceremonial meal to Megarithma, or any other deity, wasn't going to make him say
what he felt to be badly-cooked food was good and appeti-
sing. There was make-believe here, he thought, in spite of
the solid aura of Keltic twilight that envelops the group.

Well, he'd take things easy; but he wouldn't be let
take things easy. Some in Dublin hated Yeats, official
catholics feared him, and a group of younger writers dis-
liked his booming opinions on literature and insubstantial
things without any local habitation or name. A number
of these last, headed by F. J. Higgins, the poet, Liam
O'Flaherty, and Brinsley Macnamara, the novelists, and
Cecil Salkeld, the young painter, had started a Radical
Club to nourish the thoughts and ambitions of the young
writers, in opposition to the elderly and wild speculation of
Yeats and the adulatory group that trailed longingly after
him. Some of these wanted to hook in Sean so that his
newer influence might be useful in putting Yeats in his
improper place. As a preliminary, O'Flaherty brought
Edward Garnett to the tenement where he lived, and
coaxed Sean to tell Garnett a good deal about the play he
was then trying to write, for foolish, innocent Sean had told

O'Flaherty something about it. Garnett said he was delighted with the description given, and O'Flaherty bravely
simulated the happiness of his companion. On the strength
of this praise, O'Flaherty built a hope that Sean would do
anything he wished; and so for long, and continuously, he
argued against the influence of Yeats on literary thought
in Ireland and elsewhere, saying Yeats was too damned
arrogant, too assured of the superiority of his own work
over that of all the others. Sean, however, had no bubbling
desire to be O'Flaherty's gillie, so he countered the arguments used, for he saw clear enough that O'Flaherty, in
the way of arrogance and sense of being a superior being,
was worse than Yeats without the elder man's grace and
goodwill; while the cloak worn by the story-teller wasn't
near so fine or colourful as the fine, silken mantle of
poetry draping the shoulders of the poet.

Afterwards, when the play he had been writing then
appeared on the Abbey stage to merge into conflict, the
gnashing of teeth, and fearful outcries, Sean found he had
to pay for his refusal to join in the campaign to make
Yeats a little humbler. F. R. Higgins sent a letter to *The
Irish Statesman* that emptied reproaches over the head of
the defiant poet for his daring advocacy of Sean's play.
Higgins referred to the play as *a technique largely based
upon the revue structure, in the quintessence of an all-
Abbey burlesque, intensified by diversions, and Handy
Andy incidents with the more original settings offered by
O'Casey. That aspect of comedy so gushly over-portrayed
from Dublin artisan life, as seen only by this playwright,
merely affords laborious bowing on a one-string fiddle.*

O'Casey in his new play entirely lacks the sincerity of an artist. Austin Clarke, the poet, joined in the fight, gently, but none the less bitterly, indicative of what he thought about the play, saying, *The playwright seemed to be trying to exploit the poor;* and O'Flaherty, full of zeal and national righteousness, in a letter to the Press, said emphatically that the play was a bad one, protesting loudly, as he strutted about in his crying, that Yeats was a pompous fool; while an Englishman from a pleasant residence in Kingston-on-Thames, out to defend the workers and proletarian art, shouted out as far as his lungs could lean that this O'Casey was nothing but a dramatic Pontius Pilate; though poor Sean, almost at that very moment, had parcelled up the books of the plays published by Macmillan's, and had posted them off to the Soviet Union, filling the first leaf of the book with fervent good wishes for the future of the great Socialist Federation of States.

It all bewildered Sean for awhile; but, afterwards, he became certain that the attack was born of no sudden impulse, but was thought of long before the cry came. In it there was no tint of fear for Ireland's honour, the integrity of art, or the dignity of the Irishman. It was aimed at Yeats, and if it obliquely hurt and bothered Sean, all the better. It revealed to Sean for the first time the divisions in Ireland's family of literature. But these things were still in the womb of the future, and, for the moment, Sean knew peace. He had entered places unfamiliar; he had done things he did not yet fully understand; and he was quietly excited about it all. Anyway, he was quite at ease with the Old Lady. They got on grand together. They

had many things in common besides the theatre. He loved
pictures, and she was brimful of what her nephew, Hugh
Lane, had done to diamond-clothe the walls of precious
buildings with fair paintings of the men of the day, and
with those done by their fathers in the old time before.
She loved good books, and Sean felt that he was a little
ahead of her there. She saw humour sparkle from things
thought to be dead, or dull, and so did he; and they often
talked and laughed together over tea in a hotel that over-
looked the fair form of Stephen's Green; Sean trying to
look at home in the posh place, and succeeding in a way;
she eating bun after bun, murmuring that she was very,
very hungry; and saying that their talk was lovely;
though, best of all, she rejoiced that his plays were forcing
queues to stand outside her little theatre, ringing a chime
of cheeriness into all their chat. So here was Sean, sober
and thoughtful, reading a warm invitation to come and
spend a week or two in Coole Park, in Galway; eager to
go, but a little nervous at the thought of setting out to visit
foreign parts.

The Galway Express left Dublin at 8 A.M. He was to
get out at Athenry, the King's Ford, where she would be
there to meet him so that they could go together to Gort,
and on to Coole Park on her own side-car—she had carefully planned it all out in a previous letter to him. He
booked a Dublin jarvey to call for him at seven-twenty so
that he could have plenty of time to get his ticket and take
a seat in peace. He rose at six, made and ate his breakfast,
and was well ready for the car when it came. Off they
went, helter-skelter, for though they had lashings of time,

the jarvey drove furiously—makin' th' animal earn her keep, he said. Sean planked himself in front of the tiny arched window of the booking-office, and waited impatiently for the shutter to be removed, his money for the ticket ready in a closed fist, his suitcase at his feet—the first his life had known. Keeping an eye on the clock, he faced the window when the hands were twelve minutes before the hour, for in two more, the shutter would fly open. It didn't. Thirty or forty people had gathered when the clock showed it was five minutes to eight, with the little window as tightly shut as ever. He grew anxious, and a number of tongues behind him were clicking viciously with impatience.

—Thry a rap on th' shutther, there, said a voice in the background; aw, a sharper one than that, man! for Sean had knocked gently.

—There'll be a holy rush, now, when it does open, complained a second voice.

—Ay; that's if it ever opens! said a third voice with the sound of anger hopping off it.

There in the centre of the wide door, leading to the platform, stood the guard, glaring at them, green flag in hand in readiness to wave the train away.

—Is it out again he is? queries the guard maliciously; yez are wastin' your time waitin' for that fella. He glanced at the grinning clock, and then looked at his watch. Yez have got four minutes left, so make th' most o' them, an' get your tickets, an' hurry up, an' take your seats; and he hurried off to his van.

Several fists now battered an angry tattoo on the shutter

of the booking-office window, but no answer came to the knocking, though the hands of the jeering clock crept close to the unhallowed hour. Nice experience for Sean, and he a respectable traveller for the first time in his life. And getting up so early in the morning to be in time!

—Is it there yez are still like a lot o' frightened crows! blared in the voice of the guard on them again. Don't yez know that the ticket-givin' boyo's undisturbed be the thought of a given thrain havin' to leave a given station at a given hour? D'yez know th' time it is? Isn't there one among yez with brains enough to guess that the boyo's curled up in a warm sleep in a warmer bed, regardless of thrain or tickets?

—Can we take our seats without possessing tickets? asked Sean politely.

—What a gaum y'are! answered the guard sarcastically. What are yez waitin' there for, if yez haven't to have tickets? Yez are not goin' to get me to advise yez to do what yez shouldn't do. An' don't batther down th' place, either—yez are to demand your tickets in an orderly, sensible way.

—Then what are we to do? plaintively asked a voice from the crowd.

—Now how do I know what yez are to do! retorted the guard angrily. All I know, an' all that I need to know, is that th' thrain starts in a minute or two. D'ye hear that now? Th' thrain's got to set off in another minute, so make up your minds. Are yez goin' to thravel to Galway, or are yez goin' to stay where yez are? I'm warnin' yez, mind, that th' thrain'll go empty, if yez don't get your tickets an' take your seats. A shrill blast from the engine told the guard that it was time to go. There y'are—hear that now? Have yez decided to settle down where yez are, an' die there, or what? He clicked his tongue viciously; dtch dtch! An' we're supposed to be an educated people! Half a minute more's all yez have, an' if yez aren't where yez ought to be, I'll leave yez where I found yez to make your minds up in your own sweet way be tomorrow mornin'; and he walked away in scorn.

Sean seized his suitcase, hurried on to the platform, and jumped into the train. Ticket or no ticket, he'd be in Athenry to meet the Old Lady. He was astonished to see the whole crowd follow his example. Sheep, he thought, sheep. In his seat, he thought it odd the way fear took people. He had noticed two priests in the crowd who had been just as fearful and agitated as he was himself, or the old agricultural labourer on his way to Galway, who hadn't maybe, more than his bare fare to bring him there. These would surely have defied the Black and Tans, and yet they shook at the thought of venturing a journey without a ticket, through no fault of their own. When the tickets were collected, Sean found he had to pay seven and six more than the ticket would have cost; and the labourer found the fare he had only enough to bring him to Athenry. There he would have to get out, and walk the way to Galway. Sean started help by offering two shillings, and the rest of the kindly passengers added enough to permit the old man to travel on in peace.

There she was waiting for him—a trim, stout, sturdy

figure, standing upright and still on the platform, ready to guide him safely down to Gort, grimly patient in the midst of the talkative, quickly-moving crowd. A strange, lone figure she looked in a third-class carriage, stuck tight in a mass of peasants and small farmers, and they with baskets on their laps, or live fowls clutched in their hands; while one woman, young and lively, had a big goose, its legs and wings tied with cord, at her feet, so that it could only gabble, mixing its comic cries with the eager, animated chatter of the crowd.

—Der, said Lady Gregory, suddenly pointing out of a window, der's Craughwell where the police were always half-afraid to stir, eating, drinking, and sleeping behind iron doors, thick walls, and steel-shuttered windows. We'll pass Ardrahan later on, remembering what Davis sang,

> And fleet as deer, deh Normans ran
> Tro' Curlew's Pass and Ardrahan.

—An' will again, please God, murmured a quiet voice from a corner.

She has a bit of lisp, thought Sean, and I only after noticing it now. Look at her there, with all her elegance, well at ease among the chattering crowd of common people; so why shouldn't I be steady in my mind at coming to a Big House, among rare silver and the best of china, sleeping in a bounteous bed, and handling divers tools at food never seen before. And he took heart, and felt strong, looking at the calm, handsome, old face, smiling at the chatter of the people and the frightened cackling of the fowl. In the main, silent they had to sit, for she was at one end of the carriage and he at the other; so he had time to sort out his tumbling thoughts, watching her, and wondering by what devious ways she of the grandees had managed to come so close to the common people. It's little she's said herself of her younger days, dropping a bare hint, here and there, of what she thought and what she did between residence in Roxborough House, where she was born and lived her youth; and Coole Park, where she lived when she married; and Tullyra Castle, where Edward Martyn, spouse of terror, lived, told his beads, and spent most of his life like a colourless moth, fluttering between the finger and thumb of a friar.

Lady Gregory was the younger child of a large family and held a small corner in the activities surrounding her sisters, the clever Elizabeth, the musical Gertrude, and the beautiful Adelaide, afterwards the mother of Sir Hugh Lane. To the pulsing, piston-beat of the hurrying train, Sean pictured her dissolving her own life into the life around her—as we all do—, but religiously preserving to herself a secret seed of thought that was to grow into a fine and sturdy understanding of literature; into a shrewd and germinant companionship with Yeats; into a wise and firm Dame Halbardier of the Irish Renaissance; into a lively prop that kept the shaky Irish Theatre standing; into the humorous dramatic writer whose plays will do their devoirs freshly on many a stage, here and elsewhere, for many a year to come.

It is most likely that she played games, went to church

twice on Sundays—dwindling into a visit once, if the day happened to be very wet; committed to memory innumerable woeful and winning texts of the Bible; looked over photos of trimly-dressed relatives and friends, set down safe in the thick and gilded pages of an album; some sitting on marble or brocaded chairs, others standing beside Doric pillars, with the whole world behind them; the women floating upward out of balloon-like dresses, beset with a forest of flounces, the men denoting manliness by husky beard or oratorical moustaches. He could see her, at the end of the day, saying her prayers, before she climbed up a ladder on to a heavily-curtained bed, to try to conjure sleep out of stuffy and most respectable air. Perhaps, some night or other, she slid aside the tremendous curtains to get a glimpse of the moon whose golden disk was telling a story of loveliness to the lass of the tenement as well as to the lass of the Big House.

No Peter Pansy came flying in at her window—the curtains were a little too thick for that young mab man—to whisk her off to a never, never, forever land, turning things that were into things that were not; no Winnie the Pooh gambolled in her garden; instead, her fancies were formed from the brown wind of Connacht, in summer soft and sensitive; in winter sending the foam flying frightened from the waves, beating the Galway coast, carrying the spindrift over the land to cover her window with its healthy, bitter brine. And in the midst of the breeze or blast, she learned of the deeds of Cullen's Hound; listening with a wide-open ear to her nurse, Mary Sheridan, telling tremendous tales of him who swore by the oath of his people that *He would make his doings be spoken of among the great doings of heroes in their strength.* So he did, so did she. Has it not been all written down by her in the fine, gay book called *Cuchulain of Murhevna?* It's well Sean could see her, she sitting up in her big bed, her hair chained up for the night, her firm lips half open, her eyes intent on fancied glories that Mary Sheridan's seeding words set out before her: warriors, sages, stately queens, trancing the young girl into seeing Maeve herself, great queen of Cruachen, fixed, fine, and haughty, in the great red-repp chair of Roxborough, and she listening to the rich-bronze chariots of the Red Branch Knights thundering by in the woods outside.

She lived her young life, and rose out of the red repp and yellow plush life of the time: plush-covered photoframes, plush-covered bodies and furniture, plush-covered souls full of plush-covered faith in God. That she questioned these things is certain; and that she felt another life, wider, harder, and mightier than her own around her, is certain, too; for of all those who were with her when her busy literary and dramatic life began, she alone sat among the plain people, safe at ease, while they sat safe at ease with her. With all his scented, elegant Tony Lumpkin life, George Moore rarely had the heart to stray far beyond the border of his Aubusson carpet; and when he did so, got lost, and hurried back to its soft terra firma, giving thanks for a happy deliverance before his holy Manet icon hanging on the wall. Poor, old, clumsy-minded Edward Martyn, lurching round in the shadows of his ta ra ra Gothic house, pumping *Palestrina* out of a harmonium, try-

ing to clap a friar's cowl on the head of life, tried to hide
himself in the dim light from a holy candle clamped to his
damp and pudgy hand; Yeats, who went through life with
ears cocked to hear what no-one else could, heard something strange at times, shown by his letters defending the
locked-out workers; didn't like what he heard, shuddered,
and turning aside, chanted,

All things uncomely and broken, all things worn out and old,
The cry of a child by the roadway, the creak of a lumbering
  cart,
The heavy steps of the ploughman, splashing the wintry
  mould,
Are wronging the image that blossoms a rose in the deeps
  of my heart.

Shocked he was by this creak and cry, so he started to
run, chanting,

Come away, O human child!
To the waters and the wild,
With a faery, hand in hand,
For the world's more full of weeping than you can
  understand.

But Lady Gregory wasn't afraid of the child's cry or the
creak of the lumbering cart; and she stayed to speak warm
words to the ploughman splashing the wintry mould. She
trotted fearlessly beside all these things, sad or merry;
listened to their tales, sang songs with them when they
were merry; and mourned with them when a silver cord

was sundered or a golden bowl was broken. The taste of rare wine mingled with that of home-made bread on the tip of her tongue; her finely-shod feet felt the true warmth of the turf fire, and beside its glow she often emptied the sorrows of her own heart into the sorrow of others. Out of her plush and plum, she came to serve the people, body and mind, with whatever faculties God had given her.

WHERE WILD SWANS NEST

A LONG, sweeping drive, left and right, gave a ceremonial pathway to Coole House, which shone out, here and there in hand-broad patches from between majestic trees, ripe in age, and kingly in their branchiness. The House was a long, yellowish-white Georgian building, simply made, with many windows, while a manly-looking entrance— tightly shut now for a long time—faced what was once a curving expanse of lawn, smooth as green enamel in a rajah's brooch; but was now a rougher, but gayer, gathering of primrose and violet, making themselves at home where once prime minister, statesman, and governor, with their silk-gowned and parasoled women, strolled over the velvety green, their grace, charm, and power manœuvring the poor world about to their own sweet liking.

Lady Gregory was a Connachtwoman, knowing every foot of the province; every story told by every bush and stone in the counties of Galway and Clare; and she showed her Connacht rearing by compelling her seventy-odd years to climb down, like a stiff gazelle, from the high seat of the side-car, running to the threshold of the house, turning, and stretching out her two hands to say, with a beaming smile, One and twenty welcomes, Sean, to the House of Coole!

Mistress of a grand house, dying reluctantly, filled a

little too full with things brought from all quarters of the
known world; some of them bringing into his fancy the
ghosts of a Victorian age, and others, more modern, that
would send these ghosts away again, moaning; a huge
gleaming marble figure of Andromeda in the drawing-
room, brought in from the terrace when it had shocked the
finer feelings of the people with its clean, cold, nakedness;
the really glorious library, walled with precious books in
calf and vellum, forgotten, the most of them; unheeded,
too, though they still murmured in Sanscrit, Greek, and
Latin, against the changing tempo of the reading world.
Here was a house that for a century and more had enter-
tained great people as well as tinkers and tailors, for every
old or young fiddler, passing through south Galway, came
to patronise Coole, receiving praise and largesse after
playing, maybe, *Blue Butterfly Dancin'*, *The Soft Deal
Board*, or, *Pulse of the Bards*, *Awaken*: and as he went up
the stairs (the walls covered with engraving and mezzotint
so that you passed by, without knowing it, half of England's history), he fancied he heard the dancing notes of
The Red-capped Connachtman flowing from an old fiddle,
mingling with the sonorous voice of Yeats chanting out of
him about the wild swans of Coole.

In the Library o' nights, heavy curtains pulled taut, a
blazing log fire in a huge open grate, Sean stretched out
cosy in a deep settee, while she, from the gentle aura of soft
candle-light, read him Hardy's Epic-Drama of the war with
Napoleon, in three parts, nineteen acts, and one hundred
and thirty scenes; read and read till he found himself
battling sleepily for dear life to keep himself awake, and

be polite to the Spirit of the Years, the Spirit of Pity, the Spirit of Rumour, the Spirits Ironic and Sinister. The poem seemed to have been begun in the dark ages, and he felt that it would roll on till the light of the sun gave out; though he murmured it was all lovely when she paused for breath, cutely conjuring her not to tire herself too much with the dint of the direful reading. But, night after night, she pegged away at it, till the very last word was spoken, and she could murmur, half exhausted, Dat's de end! Two great achievements: one for her—that she survived the reading; the other for him—that he kept awake, though feeling old and grey and full of sleep when she was finished. But later on, Hardy came to him a far, far greater man than Sean had thought him then.

However, the gentle lady made up for the strain by reading him *Moby Dick* and Hudson's fine *The Purple Land*. Once only did he burst out into protesting: when she, full of enthusiasm, and certain of pleasing him, read a Labour play called *Singing Jail Birds;* to Sean, then, to Sean now, the worst play ever written signifying its sympathy with the workers.

Oh, stop, woman, for God's sake! he had bawled, forgetful of where he was, rising, and pacing to the far end of the room: the Labour Movement isn't a mourning march to a jail-house! We are climbing a high hill, a desperately steep, high hill through fire and venomous opposition. All of those who were highest up have dropped to death; lower down, most of the climbers have dropped to death; lower still, many will drop to death; but just beneath these is the invincible vast crowd that will climb to the top by the ways made out by their dear dead comrades!

Perhaps you're right, Sean, she had said hurriedly putting the book away, something ashamed at having so delightedly praised such an insignificant work.

One evening she came in, aglow with a surprise for Sean —a new petrol lamp into which air was pumped so that, she said, we'll have a light that makes the night even as the day of a sunny summer morning. She stood the lamp on a stand on a high table; and a lovely thing it looked with its silver-like stem and opalescent shade. Lady Gregory's maid, Bridget, hovered round while her ladyship pumped air into the petrol bowl, anxiously watching, and murmuring, Let me handle that, leave it to me, now, me lady, to be answered with the angry and impatient retort of Doh away doh away, woman; it's twite simple, and I tan handle it myself. Turning to Sean, she added, and now you'll soon see a light dat never was on sea or land.

She was right, too, for as soon as she put a light to it, the thing gave out a mighty hiss that was half a scream, a bluish-white flame shot up high as the ceiling, the old lady's face, panic in her eyes, became as opalescent as the lampshade, and her wildly-puckered little mouth began to send frantic and harmless puffs of air towards the soaring, hissing flame, the agitated mouth suddenly opening wide, between the puffs, to shout at Bridget, Bring a blanket, bring a blanket, Bridget, before de house does up in fire! Sean whipped up a rug from the settee, and placed it between their faces and the flame for fear it might explode; and behind this safety-curtain the three of them juggled, blew, and smothered the thing till the fire died down; standing round it on guard till it cooled, and Bridget could safely carry the soiled silver bowl and cracked opalescent bowl out of our sight into the kitchen.

—Oh! murmured her ladyship, sinking down to the softness of the settee, a buñishment for my banity; tinking I could do it alone; tinking I knew too much. Back to de tandles dat bring peace and surety to men of dood will.

It was strange to see that white, frightened look flash across the face of a brave soul; that fine firm face shrinking from physical fire, though she walked calm through the ordeal of spiritual and mental fire when she fought the good fight for the freedom of the theatre against priest, peasant, and politician, howling loud and long for the putting down of Synge. Against them all she stood, fighting it all out victoriously in Ireland's heart, and dipping deep into the battle again throughout the mighty cities of America, choosing strife that was good rather than the loneliness of a false peace. Again, later on, she defended *The Showing-up of Blanco Posnet* against Dublin Castle, its robed Lord Lieutenant, its pursuivant, its equerries, men-at-arms, scrolls, parchments, laws and crests, archer Shaw beside her, shooting many a broadcloth stinging arrow of wit into the squirming enemy, making them fall back, and yelp, and lower their banners, and seek shelter in the hollows of the hills of silence.

Again her banner of courage (a gay one, too) had gone up on a day that brought Yeats, Florence Farr, Arthur Symons, and others, to take dinner with her in London.

Seeing a letter from home on the table, she took it to another room to read it quiet, finding that every line told of a new disaster, caused by the Big Wind of that year— great lime trees laid flat, oaks, elms, pine, and larch, the calm growth of near a century, had come tumbling down, shattering demesne walls, impeding the public roads; and a tremendous and lovely ilex, the pride of the place, had fallen, given up the ghost, and was no more. But not a word did she say of all this to her guests, but sedately read the play, *Riders to the Sea*, that they had come to hear.

When she got home again, she didn't sit down to wail, but set out on a journey seeking a sawmill, and picked up a second-hand one somewhere; found suitable and unsuitable men to get it going, making all sorts of things for the comfort and convenience of the local people; selling them at cost prices, so cleverly turning an evil into a good thing; the good stretching far, for when Sean came to Coole, the sawmill was still working hoarsely and jerkily, turning out things from the remnants of the fallen timber. And so this brave old Commissar of Galway turned the *Keening of Kilcash* into a busy, surging song of work, though still retaining some of its sadness for the loss of so much upright elegance.

He hadn't been ten minutes at the table before he felt he had often been there, to eat soberly, and talk merrily of books and theatre, and of the being of Ireland; she in simple and most gracious ways showing how things were handled; pointing out that dese things were done, not because of any desire for ceremony, but because dey made one more comfortable, and made things easier to eat. So he was soon at rest, she, when she wanted something from the kitchen, snapping a finger against a tiny Burmese gong that gave a soft, pensive, penetrating note, holding in its quivering sound the muted song and sadness of Burma. Once, after such a meal, they passed through a room where the blue mountains of the Barony of Loughrea nodded in at the great bow-windows; and halting his steps, Sean paused in front of a picture of a young, broad-shouldered man with an open and courageous face.

—My dear son, she murmured softly, my dear, dear son, lost leading his air-squadron over de Italian battlefield. For months and months I had dreaded it, for I knew de German planes were well ahead of ours in design and swiftness.

He wished he hadn't paused before the picture. What the hell could he say to her. He gave a quick glance, and saw that holy tears were racing down the wrinkled channels of her cheeks. He touched her old arm softly.

—Dear lady, dear friend, he said, a little savagely, the falling into death of a young, hearty man is a common thing, and may be a more common thing in days to come. The death of youth has been glorified in the damnable beauty of the belief that They will not grow old as we grow old. That is the heresy of age comforting its conscience in its own comfort and continued security. I am, and always will be, against the death of the young. It is for us who are still standing to fight for the deliverance of the young from a youthful death; from the cruel and wasteful banishment of our younger life, with all its lovely and daring visions barely outlined, becoming, when they go, a tinted breath of memory. To the old, death comes as a fair visitor; to the young, death is a savage intruder.

—We must be brave, she said, forcing her head higher; we must fence our sorrow away so that no shadow falls on those left singing and dancing around us. Come, let us doh for a walk in de woods.

The Seven Woods of Coole with their many winding-paths, so many that it behoved a rambler to go warily that he be not lost in the mazes among the trees. These were among the beloved walks of Yeats, though Sean never cottoned to them, disliking their gloom, with the weight of gorgeous foliage drooping down, sombre, full of sighs and uneasy rustling, as if God had made them plaintive. Sometimes, what Lady Gregory called a badger, cut across their path, and red squirrels shot up the trees at their coming, moving on to the ones nearer the orchard so that they might be close to the fruit when the workers went home by the evening star. In her working overalls, which were an old black dress, an older, wide-brimmed, black straw hat, leather gauntlets over her able, wrinkled hands, one of which clutched a keen, chisel-edged stick, the Old Lady walked beside him, or a little before when the going got bad. Here, in the Wood of the Nuts, right in their way, callous and impudent, rose a mighty thistle, fully eight feet high, thrusting out its savage barbs towards their breasts, daring them to come on. Then, with the fire of defiance in her eyes, her ladyship charged down on the foe, hissing angrily, one gauntleted hand seizing a spiked branch, while the other stabbed the main butt of the thistle with the chisel-end of the stick, till the branchy spikes tottered, bent back, and fell to the ground, the victory celebrated by an uplifted stick and fierce muttering of So perish all de king's enemies!

Occasionally, through the lusty leafage of hazel and ash, they caught a silver glimpse of Coole river flowing by, a river that bubbled up suddenly from the earth in a glade, a lonely corner, alive and gay and luminous with a host of pinkish-blue and deeply-blue and proud forget-me-nots; a secret corner that Lady Gregory had challenged Sean to find, and which had suddenly surrounded him on his third day of searching; a place so lovely in its blossoming loneliness that he felt he should be there. Not a note from a bird disturbed its quietness; no lover and his lass, even, had passed through this glade; no breeze brought the faint lowing of far off cattle to his ears; the blue of a serene sky overhead mantling the blue of the flowers at his feet; no sound save the musical gurgling whisper of the water calmly gushing out of the earth; so still, so quiet, so breathless, that Sean thought God Himself might well ponder here in perfect peace; and the merry Mab, in her mimic wagon, might journey home there through the tangled forest of forget-me-nots, without disturbing thoughts of things remembered in tranquillity. This was the river, which, after leaving the quietness of God, ran swiftly to widen out into a lovely lake on whose soft bosom wild swans settled and wild swans rose, lifting up the noble head of Yeats to watch them,

> Scatter wheeling in great broken rings
> Upon their clamorous wings,

possibly a little envious of them, and wishing, faintly, he
was one, because

> Their hearts have not grown old;
> Passion or conquest, wander where they will,
> Attend upon them still.

But Yeats grew old, and cursed the dread handicap of
age; but passion lingered with him to the last, and conquest went before him till he laid himself down in rest
to leave us.

Books and trees were Lady Gregory's chief charmers:
the one nearest her mind, the other nearest her heart. She
laboured long and lovingly in the woods of Coole. She
hated rabbits and squirrels only when they nibbled the bark
from her young saplings. It was she who first taught Sean
to distinguish between the oak—the first dree dat Dod
made,—beech, elm, hazel, larch, and pine. She marched
along telling their names, the way an eager young nun
would tell her beads. Away in a sacred spot of the garden,
a magnificent copper beech swept the ground with its ruddy
branches, forming within them a tiny dingle of its own.
This was the sacred tree of Coole. On its trunk were carved
the initials of famous men who had come to visit Coole, so
that they might be remembered forever. The initials of
Augustus John were there, and those of Bernard Shaw
and Yeats were cut deep into the bark that looked like
hardened dark-red velvet.

With all her bowing down before the mystery of poetry
and painting, she never left the sober paths trod into
roughness by the feet of the common people. One very

wet day, she was busy helping to make what was called a
Gort Cake. When she and Sean returned in a day or so to
Dublin, the cake was to be the centre of a tea given in the
Green Room of the Abbey Theatre. She usually brought
one up for the actors when she visited Dublin. A lot of the
actors and actresses elected to regard the cake with contempt; but they ate it all right, and when the tea was done,
though the cake would feed a regiment, he had noticed
that there was little left behind. The cake was a rich thing
of spice, raisins, and currants, but rarest thing in its make-
up was a noggin of brandy to help to damp the dough.

Sean was standing before one of the great bow-windows,
watching the rain slashing down in silvery sheets over the
saturated lawn, and listening to the sighs of the big lime
tree bending discontentedly before the sharp and bitter
wind blowing its branches to and fro. Suddenly, through
the mist of the rain, he saw a dark figure, crouching to
fight the wind and the rain, battling his way up the circling
drive to reach the Big House.

—Derrible day, Sean, said Lady Gregory coming in to
have a look out of the window; derrible day!

—Whoever's coming up the drive, Lady Gregory, must
feel what you say to be true.

Oh! It's Sammy Mogan toming to det pension papers
signed, she said, staring gloomily at the figure struggling
onwards. De foolish man to tome on a day like this; de
foolish man!

She was gone in a second. He heard the bell of the side-
door ring; heard someone entering the hall, and then a
long silence came. Tired of watching the rain, he strolled

about staring at the pictures hanging on the stairway wall. Out comes an old man to the hall, muffled up in a big coat, eyes and ears only apparent, a bundle of soppy clothes under an arm, and he bidding her ladyship goodbye at every step.

—You must never tome out on a day like dis aden, Sam, murmured her ladyship.

—What signifies it, me Lady? What's in it for a day but a harmless sup o' rain? Goodbye, now, me Lady. Penethratin' though th' rain is, it treats th' skin quietly, like th' tendher touch of a mother bird's wing reachin' over th' nest of her young ones. Well, me Lady, goodbye now. An' isn't th' cordial you've just given me afther liftin' me into thinkin' th' heaviest rain on the cowldest day to be no more than the tired leaves fallin' from the high-born branchy threes. Goodbye, me Lady, for with the form signed safe in me pocket, it's whistlin' I'll be all th' way home, intherspersed with prayers for seven blessin's seven times a day on you and all your house. Goodbye, me Lady.

—Whisper, Sean, said Lady Gregory, as they went back to the fire in the library, de Gort cake will lack its warm life dis time. Sam Mogan was so perished wid the wet and cold that I poured the naggin of brandy into him to bring him back to life.

Sitting in the long and handsome garden, he saw the sun going down behind the grey garden wall and beyond the Hills of Burren, giving Coole a crimson and gold salute before it went. He realised that Lady Gregory, in the midst of her merriment and mourning, was ever running round, a sturdy little figure in her suit of solemn black, enlivened by gleaming eyes and dancing smile; ever running in and out of Yeats's Keltic Twilight, which she could never fully understand; turning his Rose Alchemica into a homely herb; and turning the wildness of his Red O'Hanrahan into the serious steady dancing of a hornpipe on the Abbey stage. In her humorous and critical moods, swinging a critical lantern, she trespassed into A.E.'s amethystine no-man's land where A.E. became delirious with quivering peacock-tinted visions, seeing things innumerable and unmentionable, beings plumed, from pituitary gland to backside, with red, white, green, blue, and orange flames. There he sat, with notebook in hand, taking down divine orders of the day from brother-selfs, master-souls, ancient-beauties, elfs and faeries, madly dancing a rigadoon a dad a derry o. Here she'd trot forward impudently, pulling aside A.E.'s twilight curtains, half hiding the Pleroma, gone today and here tomorrow; disturbing the dusky grandeur of the Great Breath's breathing, and frightening away the dim moths of twilight trees, twilight hills, twilight men, and twilight women, by crying out in her quiet, determined way, through all the mumbo jamboree of twilight thought that there were things to cook, sheets to sew, pans and kettles to mend.

It was hard for Sean to single out the best work done by this old woman, flitting through life like a robin with the eye of a hawk; for she had as much to do with what she did not do as she had with what she did; whether it was the writing of plays, or the lofty encouragement (not forgetting the blue curtains for the windows of his little flat) given to Yeats, making the poet at home in the dignity, comfort, and quiet of a fine house; soothing him with a sunny seat under a spreading catalpa tree in a flower-lit garden, where a summer evening was full of the linnet's wings; whether it was the warm determined will that gave her little theatre a local habitation and a world-wide name; for not Yeats, nor Martyn, nor Miss Horniman gave the Abbey Theatre its enduring life, but this woman only, with the rugged cheeks, high upper lip, twinkling eyes, pricked with a dot of steel in their centres; this woman, only, who, in the midst of venomous opposition, served as a general run-about in sensible pride and lofty humility, crushing time out of odd moments to write play after play that kept life passing to and fro on the Abbey stage.

On a stone wall surrounding what was once, maybe, a meadow, Sean sat one day simmering in the sun. All over the heath, the crowds of wild waste plants were covered with wide mantles of brilliant-blue butterflies. Never had he imagined such a host of blue evanescent divinity. In the formal garden, here and there, one, or maybe a pair, flew about from this flower to that one, but here they were in tens of thousands. As they settled and rose, they looked like a multitude of tiny blue banners carried by an invisible army. Or the bright blue mantle of St. Brighid down from the sky, fluttering near the half-remembered things of earth. How delightful the sturdy black figure of her lady-ship would look doing a slow, graceful, if a little stiff, minuet among the brilliant-blue fluttering things. Sean wondered if Yeats had never set eyes on these. Hardly, for they were off the beaten, formal track of his strolling: garden, lake, woods were as far as he got; and so the gurgling rise of the river, and these brilliant-blue angels of an hour were denied the lyric their loveliness commended.

She loosened the tautness of her own work by taking too much time helping others, Sean thought as he sat on the wall, encircled with the cloud of blue butterflies. She became foster-mother to some plays of Yeats, weaving in dialogue for *Caitlin ni Houlihan* and his *Pot of Broth;* helping in the construction of *The King's Threshold* and *Where There Is Nothing,* throwing in, for good measure, scenarios from which Douglas Hyde made *The Poorhouse* and *The Marriage.* In the theatre, among the poets and playwrights, herself a better playwright than most of them, she acted the part of a charwoman, but one with a star on her breast. Ay, indeed, this serving eagerness of hers was a weakness in her nature. She thought too much of the work of others, foaming with their own importance, leaving her but little time to think of her own. So signs on it, a good deal of what she did shows hurry, hinting in its haste that no matter if mine be not good so long as that of others be better.

Once troubled with the pushful realism of the younger writers, she started to write a romantic play around Brian Boru, called *Kincora.* She made many false starts, but kept hammering away, in spite of Yeats' advice to give it up; and, though the play got its share of applause, it wasn't in itself, she says, the success it might have been, and so hindered a welcome from critic and audience. Give it up! No wonder it wasn't the success it might have been. Why didn't Yeats mind his own business! A pity the woman was so near to Yeats while she was writing the play: he had a bad effect on her confidence in her own creation. She was concerned with him and her play; he concerned only with himself. He had no right to tell her to give up writing the play; but she served so frequently in so many common ways that Yeats easily dismissed from his mind her natural vigour in the creation of imaginative drama. It was a shame that the modelling of the play should have been chilled by a scornful wave of a delicate hand from a poetical mind that so often dismissed everything save what was dissolving in the wonder of his own thought.

Lady Gregory had her own Three Sorrows of Story-telling; three sorrows that were rifling her heart when Sean first came across her, and founded a friendship with Coole. The tumbling, burning death of her son, Major Robert Gregory, on the battlefield of Italy, was but being softened slowly by her transferred devotion to his three young children. His death, too, was a loss to Ireland, for to his many qualities, he added that of a fine and sensitive designer for the theatre. In the play, *Kincora*, the king's Great Hall was shown by the hanging of vivid green curtains; there were shields, embossed with designs of gold upon the walls, and heavy mouldings over the doors. For Brian's tent at Clontarf, a great orange curtain filled the background, with figures standing out against it in green, red, and grey. In *The Shadowy Waters*, he made the whole stage the sloping deck of a galley, blue and dim, the sails and dresses were green, and the ornaments all of copper. When Robert Gregory fell on the hilly soil of Italy, Ireland may have lost an Irish, and more colourful, Gordon Craig.

The Second Sorrow was the Atlantic weaving with her

waves a winding-sheet for Sir Hugh Lane, her nephew, when he went down in the *Lusitania,* almost within view of his birthplace in the county of Cork. He it was, who through heavy opposition, gave many gems of painting to many galleries, scattering these lovely things all over Dublin, as another would scatter rose-petals about in the heat of a carnival. A loss he was, a great loss to his people, though only a very few felt it, besides the lonely woman in her home at Coole. To Sean, then, he was none; he felt it not; knew it not; but he knew it well now.

The Third Sorrow was the taking away of the Lane pictures from Dublin by the then British Authorities. A scurvy trick, one of the many done by British authority on Ireland. The lousiest and meanest of robberies ever perpetrated by one country on another. To her last breath, she followed after them, seeking them, seeking them, and often Sean had gone with her. They are still exiled from their native land; but they will be brought back. Though many in Ireland were blind to their beauty, so were others, better placed than the Irish to recognise their loveliness; for one of them, Renoir's *Umbrellas,* lay for a long time deep in the cellar of the National Gallery, too trivial, as the big shots thought, for a hanging on a respectable wall. A scurvy trick, England!

What shall we bring to the place where she now lies asleep forever? Easy enough to answer; easy enough: A promise not to forget the Lane pictures; some of the shining forget-me-nots from the glade where the fresh river rises; a branch from the copper beech that bore the initials of those who had sat at her table and walked in her garden;

an old fiddler to play *The Blackberry Blossom*; a butterfly from the gorgeous blue swarm that clouded the heath,
like the blue mantle of Brighid, behind the House of
Coole; a vine leaf, or two, in token of her gay heart; since
she elected to live and die a Christian, a cross; and the
voice of her poet friend chanting:

> Here, traveller, scholar, poet, take your stand
> When all those rooms and passages are gone,
> When nettles wave upon a shapeless mound
> And saplings root among the broken stone;
> And dedicate—eyes bent upon the ground,
> Back turned upon the brightness of the sun
> And all the sensuality of the shade—
> A moment's memory to that laurelled head.

All the rooms and passages are gone, and saplings root
among the broken stone, for an elevated Irish Government
has broken down the House and levelled it smooth for
nettles to grow upon a shapeless mound. Oh! a scurvy act
for an Irish Government to do on the memory of one who
was greater than the whole bunch of them put together
and tied with string. The god-damned Philistines!

A TERRIBLE BEAUTY IS BORNEO

HERE it was at last—The Irish Free State; or, as it was written down officially, Saorstat na hEireann. A discordant symphony in green. After as many as possible of good men and excellent girls had been laid in the grave, the warring sections thought enough had been done to show the Irish catholic's love for his neighbour; and so De Valera got the Republican bugles to blow the Cease Fire. The I.R.A. dumped their arms, and streeled back to their homes, though many of them never got that far, for the Free State seized thousands, including De Valera, and clapped them into jail. With the exception of a half-sad, lingering shot or two, the Civil War died out, leaving many homes unhappy, many heaps of cold, grey ashes, dwindling ghosts of once fine houses; and a heart in Eire's bosom that had now neither pride nor hope; her courage broken like an old tree in a black wind; the proud step gone that was once the walk of a queen; bent now like the old Hag of Beara, old

> with wanderings
> through hollow lands and hilly lands.

Turn your back on it all, Sean, a vic o! Turn your back on the green and the gold, on the old hag that once had the walk of a queen! What's Ni Houlihan to you, or you to Ni Houlihan? Nothing now. The little brown-backed cow was in the weeds before, and she's in the weeds again.

> *But when the Dark Cow leaves the moor,*
> *And pastures poor with greedy weeds,*
> *Perhaps we'll hear her low at morn,*
> *Lifting her horn in pleasant meads.*

Never! We'll never hear her low at morn in satisfaction, nor see her lift her head in pleasant meads. The weeds, the weeds for her forever!

Ireland held no mystery now for Sean, and what he had learned, joined to all he had experienced, plundered Dublin of its privileges. The city's dignity had strengthened into a bitter and a blasting laugh. Sean no longer wondered what went on behind the imposing portico of the Bank of Ireland. It was no longer royal. Just like any huxster's shop, tossing pounds instead of pennies into a till. He no longer looked with reverence at the blue-faced clock of Trinity College, with its golden hands forever touching up its face. He had been within, and knew that a lot of it was a slum trying to be stately. Late at night, he had helped to cook kidneys and rashers in a cubby-hole of a kitchen, by the light of matches, for the light had been cut off, even from the room of a Lecturer. Professor Rudmose Brown had brought him round the place, expecting Sean to fall down and worship it. The façade of this and of that looked well, but within it was all sourness and gloom. The Engineering School was looked at, entered, and Sean was told it was after Ruskin's own heart; but, to Sean, Ruskin here had fenced away his finer vision, for it showed, in its marble and embellishment, but a tinselled grandeur. It was here, if he remembered right, that the universe was displayed on circling wires, the planets, in due proportion, strung out around a gilded sun perched in the centre—a dead child's dying toy. Sean's own imaginative creation of the universe was a far mightier thing than these poor paupered ghosts of planet and sun.

All the mystery that had illumined his fear had gone, for he had now met many who had curtains on their windows, had a new clock on the stairs, carpets even on the floor, and a frillied maid to hasten to open when a knock came to the door of a house having special rooms in which to eat, to sleep, or rest with a book in one hand, while the other showed the glow of wine in a crystal glass.

Few of the owners of these grand things had shocked him into respect and hesitation. Sean was himself now, serene and careless; as one having nothing, yet possessing most things. They knew no more—a lot of them less—than he did himself. He knew as much as they did about literature, enjoying its fantasy, plunging into its deeps, revelling in its luxuriance; while they wasted a lot of time discussing the articulation of its bones; on which side of its body the heart lay; never putting out a hand to feel the softness of a breast, the gay beat, or the woeful throb of a dear heart. They spent most of the time measuring beauty's body and limb, while he spent all the time he could in her arms. He knew, through feeling and sensibility, more about painting than they did, rejecting their choice, and meeting the praise of the commonplace with critical condemnation. He wanted to know more about these things, and felt that Dublin had told him all she knew.

The Free State was making itself felt in all possible ways. Tim Healy, a catholic and a life-long Nationalist, had been chosen by the British Government to be the first Governor-General, set down, mighty and grand, in the palatial Vice-Regal Lodge.

> *There's statues gracing this noble place in*
> *All heathen goddesses and nymphs so fair;*
> *Bold Neptune, Plutarch, and Nicodemus,*
> *All mother naked in the open air.*

It wasn't long before the Dubliners were calling the Vice-Regal Lodge Uncle Tim's Cabin, for Healy was held in small respect by them. Ireland's figure-head; Governor-General of the Irish Free State—Cosgrave's great conjuring trick to astonish Ireland. A tried and true patriot; a good catholic; the hound that brought down the noble stag, Parnell.

> The old foul mouth had set
> The pack upon him.

Honoured now by all the tricksters, all the holy romans, all who caught the faraway scent of a job; all these, and a few more were soon to be bobbing down before the man who had betrayed Parnell. One whom even the Irish Party had to drive forth as a poisoned bullet. A man who would hardly have been elected for Louth, after that departure, if the ecclesiastical hands of Armagh and Dublin hadn't caressed the hoary head. Just as they had done at the great betrayal, holding Healy out to the people instead of Parnell. The clergy got their way, and all the ruin, the bitterness, the savage hatred of brother against brother, along with their way. The stag dead, the hounds hunted the hounds. But blithely the purple biretta bears the burden, telling all that the woe of the world comes from abandoning God, forgetting the fierce woe, the frightful confusion they themselves brought to Ireland by abandoning Parnell. Now this Tim Healy had become an Excellency, and the red-robed and purple-robed were all around him, meeting him in the doorway of their churches, providing him with a special *prieu dieu*, tucking him up in his car when he murmured Say *au revoir* but not goodbye. Now Yeats's murmur about the dead Parnell shrilled along the streets:

> Go, unquiet wanderer,
> And gather the Glasnevin coverlet
> About your head till the dust stops your ear.
> You had enough of sorrow before death—
> Away, away! You are safer in the tomb.

No, stay where you are, Parnell! Stay where you are, and touch us with your hand! The name of Healy's caught in no man's heart; Parnell's is deep in many and many a one. Your flaming name is woven in and out of Ireland's mind. Where your dust lies will be an honoured and living place forever. But who will turn aside from his way to seek the place where Healy lies; or weave a wreath of laurel for its honour; or cast a sprig of ivy on the grave?

In the midst of it all, the first turf was cut for the Shannon Scheme; and Fitz Braze, one-time Master of Music in the Kaiser's household, was teaching the proper tempo of trumpet and trombone to Irish lads; some of the Free State officials, refusing to let bad alone, paraded in blue shirts, stretched out their arms, and shouted Hail St. Patrick, Hope of the jobless! The Free State Party began to think there was nothing more wonderful in the world than themselves. And in their world there wasn't, though poor Dr. Douglas Hyde has failed to get sufficient votes to lift him even into the Senate; and when Lady Gregory told Sean this, there were tears in her soft eyes as she murmured against The indratitude of dee Irish people. Poorer De Valera and many of his comrades now had their lodgings on the cowld, cowld ground in jails; and those who were still walking the free world were outcast and downcast, trying to buoy themselves up with the rope that their immaculate conception of Irish nationalism, was, and ever would be, the eternal truth. They were in the desert, meditating, till the tears came, on the Treaty that accepted the King as the head of the State, and De Valera's Document No. 2 that accepted him as the head of the family. They meditated, too, on the ruinous Civil War engendered by the difference between a few words in the two oaths—the British oath and the De Valerian one: the one was to be taken in a deep bass; the other to be meekly pronounced in a whispered falsetto.

Only the Countess Markievicz preserved her *sang freud*, dashing round the country as a sound and a fury, pouring the British Empire, the Free State, De Valera's wistful

Document No. 2, and her own mighty misapprehension of things Irish into her little mould of an Irish co-operative commonwealth.

Then, while a host of Irish harps were sounding *Let Erin Remember the Days of Old* at a mass meeting, the new politicians and people decided that they must become genteel, with really nice manners, to show how fit for self-government they were. So all who could, and many who couldn't, spare the money, got themselves fitted adequately for the short black jacket and the black tie and the tailed coat with the white tie for more formal functions. The cruiskeen lawn was rejected for the cock-tail glass, and long, anxious questions of precedence troubled many simple souls. The women employed experts making out blue-prints to see how far their bodice could be lowered, and still be consonant with diocesan doctrine and Dublin's desperate need of attraction. The teachers of up-to-date and old-world dancing were working night and day educating the vulgar hilarity of jig and reel from the joints of the adventists to the new Irish aristocracy, so that grace and a sweet easiness might take their place. Now it became a question of dignity and poise rather than one of enjoyment bred out of gaelic prancing in the dances of the wilder Irish. The ways of the dook snooks were the better ways, so all of Dublin's grander folks were feverishly fitting themselves into the cast-off manners and minor deportment of the English. Every house with curtains on the windows and an old clock on the stairs was a frenzied hubbub of endeavour to find the right way to refined demeanour.

206

But these good people weren't certain of themselves. They couldn't learn everything in a hurry. These things took time. There was an air of uneasiness on most of them at every public or private gathering. They hadn't yet taken root. So a gilt-edged invitation from His Excellency, Timothy Healy, Governor-General, to a levee, caused a flutter of ecstasy, mingling with dismay, to many who graciously got them. What were they to do? How were they to go? They would be facing the unknowable. They were tormented with the thought of what they would be expected to say, and the wherewithal with which to clothe themselves. Too early for evening-dress. Pity, for most of them had, or could borrow, that much. They couldn't go in what they usually wore. That wouldn't be respectful. One had to be suitably dressed to pay one's respects to the Governor-General. But how? Morning-dress? There was no way out of it. But that would cost money; and, besides, one would have to get suitable head-gear to go with it. You couldn't go wearing a cap over it, for instance. Good God no! That would be a revolting thing to do. Well, what then? A taller! That'll cost money, too. Especially with such a sudden demand for them. Black, I suppose? One could hardly go in a green, white, and gold topper. Why not? Why not? Ah, for God's sake, man! It's not right to make a laugh of a serious occasion. Well, a white one then? No; for, as far as I know, them sort is worn only at race meetings or cricket matches. It's a worrying problem. Why not go in me nightshirt? Aw, try to be serious, for once.

As Sean was coming down Sackville Street, a little black

car suddenly stopped, a thin little man sprang out, ran on to the path, caught Sean by the arm, and held him while he was recovering breath.

—Looka, Sean, he said, I've got an invitation to the Levee, and I dunno what to do. You're a friend of Lady Gregory's, and should know what a man is to do to comport himself proper.

—A man who owns a doctorate in a university should always know what to do, said Sean. But what's the gigantic problem?

—Why, what to do at the beginning and the end of a Levee. I've got the tall-hat all right; but where do you put it, and what do you do with it when you get there?

—Well, doctor, if you're any kind of a juggler, you can enthertain the guests when you get there.

—Aw, now, be serious, Sean. Listen: I can't wear the tall-hat when I'm driving the car, can I?

—Why not?

—Why not? Whoever saw a tall-hat driving a car? It would be a laugh for all Dublin. Now what am I to do with it while I'm driving?

—Put it on the seat beside you, or behind your legs.

—I thought of that; but then I'll have to be wearing it when I step from the car, and it wouldn't look decent or sensible to be fishing it from under the seat, with everyone waiting. And then you can't suddenly slap on a tall-hat the way you would a soft one. So what's a fellow to do?

—Why not ask some of the seventy-seven dead men?

—The seventy-seven—what dead men?

—The men executed by your Free State Government.

—Oh, them! I had nothing to do with their executions, anyhow. The dead are dead, and are neither here nor there now.

—They are certainly not here, said Sean with some bitterness. But it seems to me that these men were put to death to afford you the privilege of donning a tall-hat. It won't be long till the gold harp's taken out of the green flag, and a bright, black tall-hat put in its place. The terrible beauty of a tall-hat is born to Ireland.

—Look, Sean, Yeats himself wore a tall-hat at the Horse Show, and this is far more important. I've got to wear one whether I like it or no; so tell me, like a good man, what you'd don under the circumstances?

—Me? Oh, if I was going, I'd go as I am.

—They wouldn't let y' in, man!

—That wouldn't trouble me much.

—You see, you're free of the problem, Sean, so you can well laugh. Listen, though: am I to drive to the back of the house, or right up to the front entrance?

—Looka, said Sean, laying a friendly hand on the doctorate shoulder, I can't advise you on these deep problems. They'll probably have a man in another tall-hat to show you where to go, and how to get there. So good luck to you all!

—Hold on, just a second—listen. How're we to display ourselves when we get in? I daresay there'll be someone there to take the hat and mind it?

—Sure.

—Well, then, when I go in, I suppose His Excellency'll

be waiting. Do I just bow; and, if I do, how far down do I go; or do I simply shake hands, saying, Best respects, I'm honoured, or what?

—You simply put a sweet smile on your kisser, bow as low as your head will go, and then ask His Excellency who he was with last night.

—Now, Sean, no coddin'; no double-meaning talk. We're up against it. None of us never did this before. Listen; the whole population's learning how to approach him, and how to get away again. Listen, an' you'll laugh. Paddy Miskell's missus's sprained her ankle doing curtseys at home. An' if you only heard them doing the approach, you'd have a fit. The doctorate lifted his voice into a shrill falsetto: "Your Excellency's servant, most obedient so I am. I hope I see your Excellency in good condition. For an oul' fella of your age, you're wonderful, so y'are." Rathmines is like a fairyland with the number of candles lighted to St. Anthony asking his help in the emergency.

Every mauler of finer things who had his name in a bank-ledger, or hoped to have it there soon, now that Kathleen ni Houlihan had won back three out of her four beautiful green fields, was busy in a quiet, curtained room, the blinds well down, discussing and practising the arts of refinement when making contacts with eminent people, more eminent people, and most eminent people; of walking with genteel steps, of bowing with dignity and caution, of curtseying with confidence, and of addressing the great with decorum and respect; just a few happy sentences to please His Excellency's ear. They were active fitting on trouser and skirt; morning coat and evening-jacket; getting used to the sit of them; a wife here acting the governor-general to her husband; a husband there acting the governor-general to his wife.

—You go too quick, Jack. You're runnin 'like a news boy. Go back, an' come in again. Walk something like the way a judg'd do it, in his robes.

—These blasted boots are cuttin' th' feet o' me!

—You'll have to put up with them. Now thry again, an' thry to take that hump off your shoulders, an' that look of heart-sthrain off your face. I'll count the steps slow—one, two, three; go on—say something.

—Grand evening, Mr. Healy, so 'tis.

—Oh, not Mr. Healy, man! Your excellency, your excellency!

—Oh, yes; your excellency, an' how d'ye do? Grand-gatherin' of excellency—excellent persons here; very, your excellency.

—Don't stick your mug so close to mine, Jack, when you're speakin'. Keep back a little, man. An' you must leave your tall-hat outside somewhere; you can't bring it in with you.

—An' when I come out, supposin' it's gone?

—We'll just have to take that risk, Jack.

The search for beauty had begun. In the midst of the flurry and fury over the proper alignment of clothes, over the tormenting effort to rise sublime in manner and deportment, De Valera pinched and worn and threadbare, studied the question of the oath. He seemed to turn the spiritual side of the question into a mathematical one. His

Party determined, after tremendous argument, that the taking of the oath could be done without taking the oath, provided they made it plain they didn't recognise the oath when they were taking the oath; that an oath taken under duress wasn't really an oath at all, but just the appearance of one; a deceptive thing, an illusion, a shadow, a ghost-oath. If you believed it was there, it would be there; if you didn't believe it was there, it couldn't be there. Just shut your eyes, close your ears, dispel your thoughts, and speak away, and the thing was done, yet not done.

So, after it was all over, Republicans said they had heard nothing; no-one had said a word to them indicating that they had been taking an oath; they hadn't seen such a thing in writing or in print; the officials who were present never explained a thing to them; they stayed dumb. The Republicans saw a booklet on a bench that might have been, or might not have been a testament. No-one said it was one. So there was no reason for them to assume that it must have been one. It was there; lying alone; but no-one picked it up, or said, Gents, this here is a testament; gents, I warn you, this is a testament—anything spoken beside this book, or in the vicinity of this book, must be the truth, the whole truth, and nothing but the truth. In fact, the silence was really oppressive. So though it was recorded that an oath had been taken, no Republican of De Valera's Party could honestly swear to the taking of any oath whatsoever.

They entered the Dail, upright men, their conscience clear, their hearts aglow, for they could now take their

salaries without pain of spirit, and they could fight more
effectively for the dollars, left over from the American
Victory Loan, which the Free State Party was impudently
claiming for its own.

> A terrible beauty is borneo,
> Republicans once so forlorneo,
> Subjected to all kinds of scorneo,
> Top-hatted, frock-coated, with manifest skill,
> Are well away now on St. Patrick's steep hill,
> Directing the labour of Jack and of Jill,
> In the dawn of a wonderful morneo.

And this was the beginning of the end of Cosgrave's
power and his Free State Party. Cronus was to swallow
Zeus before long. De Valera was destined to reign over
Irish Israel for many years, becoming the *in hoc signo
vincit* of the New Gael. In fancy again Sean recalled the
vision of Pearse coming from the General Post Office into
the now silent street, and standing in the midst of the fair
sunshine to read to a few distant listeners, one here, two
there, and three away yonder, the Proclamation of the
Irish Republic, while a tiny tricolour fluttered high away
over his head; but the building had changed, and seemed
now to be half a bank and half a church, and the words
read were different:

Irishmen and Irishwomen, in the name of God, and of
the dead generations from which she receives her old tradition of nationhood, Ireland, through us, summons her
people to her flag, and strikes for freedom. She strikes in
the full confidence of victory for—

The white tie and the tailed coat.

The right to wear a top-hat, grey or black, according to circumstance or taste, when the occasion demands it.

The banning of all books mentioning the word Love, except when the word is used in a purely, highly, spiritually, insignificant way.

The banning of any mention whatsoever of the name of James Joyce.

The right to examine and to settle eternally the question of procedure as to whether Paddy or Mick, Julia or Bridget, shall be the first to shake hands with, or bow to, Tim Healy or Sean T. O'Kelly; first to ceremonially enter a room, or first to sit down to a table.

The right to excommunicate a catholic student who enters Trinity College.

The right to make it known that western rivers are swift and deep to any person, called a communist, who may be thinking of spending a holiday in Connemara.

The right of the wrong to banish even a whisper of the name of Dr. Walter McDonald, D.D., Maynooth's Professor of Theology for forty years in the wilderness.

The right to give the catholic clergy the first word, the last word, and all the words in between, whatsoever they may be, on any and every question, whatsoever, without any reservation whatsoever either.

The right to consider such men (once referred to as Irishmen) as Tone, Emmett, Mitchel, Parnell, Synge, Yeats, and Joyce; and all such women (once referred to as Irishwomen) as Betsy Gray, Sarah Curran, Fanny Parnell, Lady Gregory, Eva of the Nation, and Speranza as non-gaels, non-Irish, and so *non est perpetua*.

214

The fascination De Valera had, and has, over the Irish people is astonishing. There seems to be no streak of joviality, good humour, or of erring humanity in him as there is in the warmer-natured Cosgrave. His speeches are dull, his voice unattractive, and to an independent observer, there is little magnetism in the man. Yet he seems to hold an unbreakable grip on the people, and is loved by very many of them. St. John Ervine once referred to him as the Pinchbeck Parnell. But it was Arthur Griffith who was a Pinchbeck Parnell, for, posing as the great silent man, who hated speechmaking, he modelled his clay to look like the steely nature of the mighty Parnell. Whatever De Valera may be, he is De Valera and no-one else. He certainly has indomitable confidence in himself and in his policy—whatever that may be. During the Easter Rising, he proved his courage and his military skill, far above that of any other of the Leaders. He is an unassuming fellow, there is no doubt about that. Sean could see any old man or woman, and any young fellow or girl, however humble their circumstances might be, going up to him, and hear them addressing him affectionately as Dev. He would encourage them, or comfort them, and give them a delusive satisfaction. Everyone to whom Sean spoke, Irish acquaintance or English journalist, said that De Valera was a most courteous man. The man seems to have in him no malice of any kind, against man or an institution. He is as if he were one who forever remembered that he must forgive the trespasses of another, if he was to get forgiveness for his own. De Valera couldn't hate. He could deny; he could reproach; he could argue, like a duller Gladstone, against a point of view other than his own; but he could neither hate the man nor the man's point of view. There was nothing whatever of the agnostic in De Valera. In this way, he differed from all great Irishmen Sean could bring to his remembrance; from Brian Boy Magee, from Donal MacSean of the Curses, from Wolfe Tone, from Mitchel, from Fintan Lalor, from Parnell, from Davitt, even from Thomas Davis, gentle and all as he was, De Valera's national monitor and pattern. Douglas Hyde was the nearest to De Valera, for to him, from all he said, all life was sweet and varnished. Devotion to the church's curriculum kept De Valera on the steady path, avoiding hell, and reaching heaven, and all that. His kneeling on a stage, in front of a crowded house, as was recorded in the Press, to receive the blessing of a visiting cardinal, was, to Sean, a humiliating thing for the head of a Republican State to do. The pietistic Spaniard in him, Sean thought. But Ireland wasn't any longer a Republican state, either in theory or in practice—she was a theocracy, fashioned by the Vatican, and decked in the brightest sacerdotal array by the bishops of Maynooth.

Well, thought Sean, apart from his personal qualities, how does he manage to keep his grip on the leadership of the Irish people, swinging about with the greatest of ease, like a daring young man on an Irish trapeze? Perhaps because he is the last living leader of the Easter Rising, and because he will never do a thing to make the clergy uneasy. He will do all things, rightly or wrongly, in the spirit of the good, never wavering Vatican catholic. The one, who, out of the smoke and the flame, came safe. The one-time soldier. With the church's *nihil obstat* written on his brow, this patriot is irremovable. His fight against the Annuities paid to Britain; his long contention with the Loud Speaker, J. H. Thomas, then Minister for the Dominions, are to his credit. His great bargain, after a bitter fight, by which the Annuities were bought for ten millions, ended the Economic War with Britain, and at the same time put a high, and well-curled feather in De Valera's cap. His Irish Constitution added a pewter button to hold the feather in its place; not exactly a sparkling ornament, but stamped deeply with the seals in the ring of every bishop. Underneath this pewter button, though De Valera can't see it, is a little red star.

One thing alone threatens De Valera—the rising of the people against poverty; the union of the north and the south, when Labour will become a hundred times stronger by the natural Republican and Socialist activities of the Ulster people. When this happens, all those to the left of his party will swing into pace with the movement and De Valera will no longer feel at home in Leinster House. Then the orange sash and the green sash will show a red star in the centre of each of them.

Then will come the fight against the slums, reeking with rottenness. Down with them! And the tens of thousands of the homeless cadging a night's shelter from the sleet, the rain, the frost, or the biting wind; old men and young women, young men and old women, silent and patient too long; all of them strangers to life; dumb about it; wondering why some who passed by could chat so cheerily, or laugh so carelessly; wondering at Eire's gay-dressed cavalry galloping or trotting to a ceremonial parade of

politician, social-climber, church dignitary and delegate;
the Jesus Christ hidden from the worker by a multitude
of tall-hats, the marshalled catholicism, not of Aquinas
nor of Francis, but of Belloc and G. K. Chesterton.

Time was with the Socialists, and time would push
away the anxious queues outside trimly-fashioned convents, waiting for a penny dinner, when pennies were more
plentiful; or waiting to snatch a loaf of St. Martin's or St.
Anthony's bread from a bustling nun, more interested in
the bread than in the wretches seeking it. Time, armed
with the power of the people, will push away the slow
decay of tuberculosis, the choking fright of diphtheria, the
soiling horridness of typhoid, the rickets that jellied the
fibre in the bones of the growing child; all brought about
by the ignorance of the many, the careless privileges of the
few, indifferent to these many afflictions till some of them
become afflicted themselves; heedless of the fact that the
pyning pox can be equally hidden beneath the cardinal's
robes as well as the rags of the beggar; ignorant that this
disease destroyed Thomas Wolsey in his Cardinal's Palace, as it did Puffing Dick, King of the Beggars, in the
over-hanging horror of the slums.

Often Sean wandered through the poor streets where
these poor poorer houses were; sometimes going in and out
of them, climbing down to see some of the thousands who
lived in the basements, the poorest of the poor rooms in the
poorer house. No tall-hat, no black tie with jacket, no
white tie and black jacket with tails ever went down these
stony ways, damp with the green of slimy moss, a decayed
carpet honouring the feet of those decaying in the dimmer

den below. Nor did anyone, even those happy with the keenest sight, ever see the scarlet or the purple biretta cautiously going down these slime-covered steps. Only when some soul found itself within the dim flicker of a last farewell to life, did some simple, black-coated clerk climb down to give a hasty anointing to the dying soul, indifferently fortifying it against the four last things— heaven, hell, death, and the judgement.

Frequently he wandered, hurt with anger, through these cancerous streets that were incensed into resigned woe by the rotting houses, a desperate and dying humanity, garbage and shit in the roadway; where all the worst diseases were the only nobility present; where the ruddy pictures of the Sacred Heart faded into a dead dullness by the slimy damp of the walls oozing through them; the few little holy images they had, worn, faded, and desperate as the people were themselves; as if the images shared the poverty and the pain of them who did them reverence. Many times, as he wandered there, the tears of rage would flow into his eyes, and thoughts of bitter astonishment made him wonder why the poor worm-eaten souls there couldn't rise in furious activity, and tear the guts out of those who kept them as they were.

But Sean had more than hope now. He had had letters from a Raissa Lomonovska telling him about what was going on in the Soviet Union, enclosing photographs of the people and their new ways. Two of the pictures showed the children of the Caucasus and the Ukraine assembling to welcome the first Diesel locomotive that had come to the Soviet Republics. There they were—a crowd of them, thin-limbed, and scarcely dressed, infant survivors of a dreadful time inflicted on their bodies and their souls by the good, profit-loving Christians of the surrounding states. There they were; free now, and firm, gazing at the locomotive; not yet conscious of what this one locomotive would mean to them in the years to come. The first swallow to be followed by flocks that would brighten the sky.

Sprinkled among the children were some workers and a few Red Army Men, the soldiers dressed in their loose blouses, and wearing their old cloth helmets, decked out in front with a tiny star of red; poverty their companion and bed-fellow, but resurrection and courage in all their aspect; a tremendous destiny before them all. There they stood, giving a firm welcome to Russia's first Diesel locomotive. They had just defeated a world in arms against them, and this one Diesel engine was their first reward from God. These of the Soviet Union were they who did not despise the day of small things, and this one, small gain has since shown to what an amazing magnificence a single engine and firm hearts and steady minds can grow.

In the spirit, Sean stood with these children, with these workers, with these Red Army Men, pushing away with them the ruin they were rising from, the ruin from which all the people would one day rise, sharing the firmness of their unafraid hearts, adding his cheer to the cheers of the Soviet People.

The terrible beauty had been born there, and not in Ireland. The cause of the Easter Rising had been betrayed by the common-place bourgeois class, who laid low the concept of the common good and the common task, and were now decorating themselves with the privileges and powers dropped in their flight by those defeated by the dear, dead men. And scarlet cassock and purple cassock were blessing them and their gew-gaws—the low-cut ball-dress, the top-hat, the tailed coat and the white tie, the foolish wig and gown, and all the tarnished decorations of a dead state. And Christ, the clergy said, was in the midst of it all. *Ecce Homo! Ecce Homo Noster!* Here was their Christ, like unto themselves—morning-suit, top-hat, gold cuff-links, and dud-diamond stud, with a neatly-rolled umbrella in lieu of a cross.

But steady workers, here and elsewhere; steady poor of the poorer places; your day is coming. The Red Star shines over the Kremlin, once the citadel of the Czars. Those who tried hard to shake it down have fled home-wards, helpless against the might and good courage of a half-starved people. The Red Soldiers with their Red Cavalry are on the frontiers, are on the sea-edges of their vast land. Socialism has found a home, and has created an army to patrol around it. The Red Star is a bright star. No pope, no politician, no cleric, no prince, no press-lord can frighten it down now, or screen its ray from our eyes. It is the evening star, and it is the bright and shining star. It is the star shining over the flock in the field, over the mother crooning her little one to rest, over the girl array-ing herself for the bridal, over the old couple musing by the fireside, over the youngster playing in the street, over the artist achieving a new vision in colour, over the poet singing his song, over the sculptor carving out a fair thing that he alone can see hidden in a stone, over the hammer building the city, over the sickle cutting the corn, over the sailor sailing the seven seas, over the dreaming scientist discovering better and more magical ways of life, over the lover and his lass in ecstasy on the yellow sands, coming through the rye, or sauntering through the indifferent business of some city street, over the miner bending in the deep tomb where the sun-embalmed coal lies low, over the soldier guarding his country's life, over doctor and nurse, forgetting themselves that they may coax back health into all sick persons and young children.

Morning star, hope of the people, shine on us!

Star of power, may thy rays soon destroy the things that err, things that are foolish, and the power of man to use his brother for profit so as to lay up treasure for himself where moth and rust doth corrupt, and where thieves break through and steal.

Red Mirror of Wisdom turning the labour in factory, field and workshop into the dignity of a fine song;

Red Health of the sick, Red Refuge of the afflicted, shine on us all.

Red Cause of our joy, Red Star extending till thy five rays, covering the world, give a great light to those who still sit in the darkness of poverty's persecution.

Herald of a new life, of true endeavour, of common-sense, of a world's peace, of man's ascent, of things to do bettering all things done;

The sign of Labour's shield, the symbol on the people's banner;

Red Star, shine on us all!

THE TEMPLE ENTERED

THE bells were ringing an old year out and a new year in for Sean: he was on his way to the temple of drama, the Abbey Theatre, where he was an acolyte now, in full canonical costume. Among his thoughts was none of either success or failure. He knew nothing about these things. What he thought of was how much money he would get from the performances. He would soon be in a position to buy many books, and live comfortably reading them, for a considerable time. He found himself going through the streets without noticing the people passing, or the shops, hearing but faintly even the chatter from the public-houses as he passed them by. It was as if he was on his way to meet a girl. Well, this was Marlborough Street, and further down was the Abbey Theatre, renowned, people said, the world over. There opposite was the Pro-Cathedral, the Church of the Immaculate Conception. An ugly sight. A dowdy, squat-looking imitation of some Italian church, done up in a back-handed Greco style; a cheaply-fashioned souvenir of Rome. No indication that this was Dublin, and that an Irish church, except the stiff statue of St. Laurence O'Toole, standing grim and uneasy-looking on a corner of the entablature. Inside of the church, not a sign of the Book of Kells, nor that of Lismore; or ever a peal from St. Patrick's Bell; or even a painted symbol of the Cross of Cong. All of it imitation, silly, slavish; pomp-

223

ous imitation of the Latin, Italian order of the Vatican. A cheap home for Our Lady of Eblana, a cheap and distressing vase for the madonna lily of the slums.

Here is the church, thought Sean, stopping to look at its brawny and vulgar façade, this is the church that refused to shelter the body of a dead Fenian for a night. St. Laurence O'Toole refuses to allow a ray from the smallest of holy candles to reach as far as the body of a dead Fenian. Here the top-hatted, holy ones streamed sterilely in, on ceremonial occasions, to pay their sweet respects to Jesus. Here at this church, Matt Talbot, a Dublin labourer, full-up of sanctity, stretched himself flat on the pavement to say preliminary prayers, then crawled up the steps on his belly to the big door closed against him, waiting prone on the stones till it opened to let him join in the first Mass, so that he might go merry to work; dropping dead one day as he hurried to another church in an effort to fulfil the obligation he put upon himself to pray without ceasing. But he hurried too fast this time, for his heart gave out before he got there, and he fell down dead. But he died with harness on his belly. Afterwards, in the mortuary, it was found that he was wearing a cart chain round the middle of his body, with another round one of his legs, while a rope was tied tightly round the other one, and all were spangled with holy medals. *A model workman and a model catholic,* the courtly knight, Sir Joseph Glynn, calls him, *and his life points out the only path to true peace for all who labour, a life of self-discipline lived in perfect agreement with the law of God and His church. Ecce hobo sapiens.* Blow, crumpeter, blow! So

224

workers of Dublin, and the world, you know now what you
have to do. Follow Matt Talbot up to heaven. You've
nothing to lose but the world, and you've the holy chains
to gain. Read this Glynn's *Life of Matt Talbot*, then read
Stalin's *Life of Lenin*; and take your choice. Make the
world safe for the bosses. If you do, you're sure to get to
heaven when you die.

Think deep on these things, working-men. Why do
you waste time demanding a living wage? Think of
eternity, and remember there may be none there. Why do
you want to bother about the health and vigour of your
children? Pain and woe and disease may help them upwards. Why do you look for a comfortable home, with
light and heat and colour in it? You fools! Consider Mutt
Talbot, and you'll realise that these poor things are but
vanity. Worse than vanity—burdens, clogs, stumbling-
blocks, impeding your precious way to heaven. Listen, you
dockers and labourers of Dublin! When a boat has to be
unloaded in quick time so that she may catch a tide, and
you get an extra two shillings for the hurried job, don't
take them. Refuse this bonus as Mutt Talbot did, feeling
with him that idle moments waiting for lorries to come to
be unloaded should be set against the extra work. That
was Mutt Talbot, that was! This refusal of extra money,
says the knight of Glynn, *was due to the high sense of
justice this man Talbot possessed*. Oh, how far short do
we come of this man's high sense of justice! Mutt always
thought of his poor boss. Look at all the boss had to do
with his money—keep a big house going, a carriage and
pair, a well-dressed wife, and high education for his little

ones. If indifferent workers could but see the truth hidden in time and eternity, they'd refuse any extra reward of wage or bonus. They'd advance through life on white bread and black tea to the glory of God and rich benefit of their own souls, and so allow the bosses to enjoy their chicken and wine in peace. Do these things, workers, and you'll all be lifted up to heaven with sparkling cords made out of the gold of the rich men. And the sight entrancing you'll all see there—Mutt Talbot and the knight of Glynn shaking hands among the gallant and glittering angels.

—To hell with Mutt Talbot! muttered Sean, glancing up at the cold statue of St. Laurence O'Toole, without the chime of a word from him; we won't give in to the bosses as you, St. Laurence, gave in to the Normans. If any saint is to be preferred, I choose St. Joan, who, at least, prayed with a sword at her girdle. She was a fighter who disturbed great cleric and great lord, and so signs on it, she was burned before she was blessed.

This church was nicely set down, for it was but a minute's walk from Dublin's fairest thoroughfare—O Connell Street; a minute's walk from fine business and great banking; and it was but another minute's walk from the street, where, in tumbling houses, fat-breasted, big-thighed women, clad in brilliantly-coloured calico gowns of crimson or green, sat at twisted windows, calmly drinking down tumblers of luscious stout, frothing over the rim of the glasses. A gentle shake of these gaudy gowns would show bare shoulders and barer breasts, signalling seduction down to any likely man passing by beneath; and many a wayward and unstable Mutt Talbot would lift a wavering but flaming eye to the visions at the windows.

Here was the Abbey Theatre—a red flower in the slum; but a minute's walk from the church, too, so that judgement, heaven, and hell were but a short way from each other. Sean had entered the temple. He had passed under the glass-roofed awning, its iron standards and framework gilded discreetly, showing that, though austerity couldn't suitably don a golden shawl, she could decently wear a golden brooch in a black one. He remembered the first time he had stood in the tiled foyer through which so many fine souls had passed to watch Ireland finding at last her soul in literature and the drama. Sean had come in by the front way, and was now among the gods. To the left were the stairs going down to the stalls where Sean would sit now, to watch the play of another, and to see and help to guide the evolution, through acting and design, of his own. To the right was a door leading to the Manager's office and the stage, and in between these two entrances stood the tabernacle of all theatres—the box-office. Opposite, parallel with a stained-glass window, was a little narrow counter where the audience from the stalls drank coffee, ate biscuits, and discussed the play. Beside this counter, high up on the wall, hung Dermod O'Brien's painting of Barry Fitzgerald in the part of the King from Lady Gregory's *The Dragon*. A poster on another wall told in French when Synge's *Playboy of the Western World* was first performed in Paris.

Inside, Sean saw how small the theatre was, holding only half a thousand. It, somehow, looked smaller now than when he knew it so well as The Mechanics Theatre. The freshness, the red-leather upholstered seats, the shields, bearing on them the armorial signs of Ireland's

Four Beautiful Fields, and the black curtain with its gold stripes, showed up the points of the building, and brought them closer together. Again Sean was treading the poor, narrow stage, its expansion backwards forever prohibited by a slum laneway running from Marlborough Street, where stood the Abbey Theatre itself, to Beresford Place, where stood the Liberty Hall, made so famous by the eloquence and flame of Jim Larkin, the Labour Leader.

He told no-one that he had known this old stage well, that he had even played a part on it; that one of his brothers had often done so; that he had watched, from the pit below, men, with hands tied behind their back, struggling to swallow boiling-hot suet puddings; in their haste, knocking them from the table to floor, and so forcing themselves to stretch there, eating with voracity; for ten shillings reward was to be given to him who finished his pudding first. He remembered the drop-curtain, showing, in fading colours, the lovely Lakes of Killarney; now displaced by the dignified one of sable and gold, but showing signs of fading too. He had drunk glasses of diluted claret, sweet with sugar, with those who had played the principal parts in Boucicault's *The Shaughraun*, in a pub opposite the theatre; in a private room, too, for the pub proprietor had something to do with the venture. All changed now, changed utterly; and here he was now with plays of his own showing themselves off on the very same stage that he himself had trod as a growing youngster so long, so long ago. His brother, Archie, had played the part of Harvey Duff. Archie was a good black and white man with pencil or pen, a splendid carpenter, and a brilliant accountant, but there he was now, up in Liverpool, sweeping the floors of a Dunlop rubber factory. The lad's will hadn't been guided rightly into a fighting, fuller life when he left school; his talents had been left to perish.

The first night of his first play had gone very well indeed, and Sean had been congratulated by all the actors. But he was troubled with vexation of spirit when he was told that the play was to run for three nights only, and this vexation was sharpened when the Secretary of the theatre added the information that there was but thirteen pounds received for the night. However, the second night's receipts jumped to thirty pounds, and the last night to over fifty which meant the first full house for the Abbey Theatre for many a long night. Sean smiled benignly at the Secretary, when he was told the theatre would have no money in the bank till the guarantors sent in their guarantees; but, if Sean so desired, he could be paid from the cash received at the door, instead of in the usual way, by cheque. Full of shy vanity, with a grand wave of the hand, Sean told the Secretary he wasn't to bother, and that he'd willingly wait for the cheque.

When it came, it was less than four pounds. Less than four pounds! And he had bargained in his mind for twenty, at the least. And, if the receipts hadn't jumped up at the end, he'd have had but half of that amount. Dimly he began to realise that the Abbey Theatre would never provide a living. It was a blow, a bitter disappointment. The black stripes in the theatre's curtain were far wider than the gold stripes. Less than four pounds wouldn't even pay his passage to England for a chat about the Soviet Union

with Raissa Lomonovska. It looked as if things would
allow his talent to perish too. What he had got wouldn't
even pay what he owed. The amount didn't extend even
to the purchase of a book. What was he to do? One thing,
and one thing only—go forward. He had put his hand to
the plough, and he wasn't the one to look back. He would
start a new play that very night.

So he had, and he called it *Cathleen Listens In,* a jovial
sardonic sketch on the various parties in conflict over Irish
politics—Sinn Fein, Free State, and Labour. It was a
short one-act work, and was performed after a major play
had ended. Another experience for Sean! The audience
received the little play in dead silence, in a silence that
seemed to have a point of shock in its centre. Not even a
cold clap of a hand anywhere. They all got up from their
seats, and silently filed out of the theatre. He was the one
and only playwright to have had a play received in silence
by an Abbey audience; the only one to be deprived of
even a single timid hand-clap. Indeed, it did look as if his
talent, too, would have to perish in silence and with malice
of afterthought. What would he do, for he was vexed,
and a sense of humiliation discouraged him; what would
he do? Go on, go on! Forever he would go on seeing
through his own eyes, hearing with his own ears, speaking
with his own tongue. No power of influence, no seduction
of wealth, no affection for friend, nor would any love for
woman draw him away from his own integrity. Let that
integrity be right or wrong, it would be a true reflection of
what he felt in his nature from the things he saw and the
things he heard around him.

Going as a patient to the Royal Eye and Ear Hospital, with an ulcerated cornea, the head surgeon there, Mr. Cummins, had come over to him, gave him treatment, and then walked part of the way home with him, Sean leaving him opposite the doctor's own hall door, after refusing an invitation to come in and drink a cup of coffee. But that saunter through St. Stephen's Green was the beginning of a fast friendship which has lasted to this very day. A strangely fastidious man, a very sensitive soul, Dr. Cummins seemed to choose his friends cautiously; but he seized on Sean impulsively, and his efforts glowed with eagerness to make Sean easy in his company. It was an odd alliance. Joe Cummins, delicate in word and phrase and manner, sensitive to a high degree, but a true bohemian, all the same, on the one hand; and Sean, a rather rough and ready-tongued proletarian, well versed in Communism, and a revolutionary by nature, on the other. The calm and lovely serenity of most of the Dutch School of painting, balanced by the fragrant venery and graceful feminity of Fragonard, and the lace-like prose of Addison, balancing against the wildness of Van Gogh, the savage sarcasm and definite lust of Goya, the daring of Cézanne, and the tempestuous writings of James Joyce, mingled together and enjoyed themselves night after night in the doctor's surgery; and, long afterwards, when Sean left for England, he carried with him the doctor's warm rug against the chill of the long railway journey; though Sean had never pulled it from its strap, unable to reconcile the idea of himself with a rug around his legs.

The third work, a full-length play, was, from the Abbey

Theatre point of view, an emphatic success, and Yeats
halted in his meditations to tell Sean that he had given
new hope and new life to the theatre. The house had been
booked out for the first week, and the run of the play was
extended for a week longer. Sean had come into his fortune
of twenty-five pounds, after waiting more than a year
for it.

Books, books, more books! And a step nearer to a trip
over the waters to England. His choice of Barry Fitzgerald for one of the two chief parts had been more than
justified. When Sean had mentioned his name, Mr. Robinson had demurred, had murmured the name of F. J.
McCormick as a better selection for Boyle; but Sean had
insisted on the selection of Fitzgerald, and the choice had
been triumphant. After the Abbey season had ended a year
ago, to give place to a long holiday, the Abbey actors had
taken the theatre, and put on Ervine's *Mary, Mary Quite
Contrary* so as to furnish themselves with something more
in the way of money to tide the holiday over, and Sean
had gone to see it, in a spirit of loyalty to those who had
so generously helped him by their fine acting. He had
known all who had played in it; all save one whom he
had never heard of, whom he had never seen. This new-
comer filled the part of the Anglican clergyman. The play
began, and Sean sat easy wondering who was the new
fellow that had joined the company. Sean soon sat up.
This new fellow could act. This fellow was a great comedian. This fellow was an artist. Sean never looked at a
programme in a theatre because of his bad sight, so he did
not know the fellow's name. He would go behind, and

find out. This fellow was the man for him. He had never seen him before; none of the actors had ever mentioned his name. Well, if they didn't, Sean would, and out loud, too.

When the play ended, he rushed round to tell all of his discovery. It was an unwise thing to do; a foolish thing, a stupid thing to do. But Sean was altogether ignorant of jealousies behind the curtain. He rushed across the foyer, through the doorway at the back, up the stairs, down the corridors where the dressing-rooms were, yelling, Who's the fellow that played the clergyman? Where's the chap that played the clergyman? Michael Dolan's dressing-room door was open, for it was a warm night, and the actor was busy taking the grease-paint from his face. He listened without a flicker of an eyelid to Sean's excited demand to know who and where was the fellow who played the part of the clergyman. A great actor, said Sean vehemently; a grand comedian; an artist born suddenly for the theatre.

—He's not bad, murmured Mr. Michael Dolan, rubbing quietly away at his face—when he happens to get a part that suits him.

—Good God, man, said Sean, it's long since the theatre's seen the like of him! And then there was silence, for Sean began to realise that such things spoken loudly were not wise or welcome. For the future, if circumstances called for it, he would praise what he thought was bad, and censure what he felt to be good—he would, like hell! But his ardent acclaim of what he thought was fine raised the first breeze of coolness between him and the Abbey actors.

Passing by his third play, a one-act work called *Nannie's Night Out*, a play no-one liked, except A.E., otherwise known as George Russell, who thought it O'Casey's best work; an opinion that didn't bother Sean, for he knew A.E. knew nothing about the drama, and felt it a little less; Sean, at length, found himself attending the rehearsals of his fourth one, a full-length drama. He was now taking an active part in a rehearsal for the first time. He had stayed silent and passive during these of his first two plays, and during those of his third play, he had been in hospital with a sharp attack of bronchitis most of the time, finding the play well set when he came out, so that he had very little to learn to do, except to persuade the timid Barry Fitzgerald that he could, and must, play the part.

But Sean's persuasion laboured on, for he saw before him clearly now a fine library and a visit to England where his second play was doing well in the West End of London. He was buying furniture bit by bit, and still had a lot to get before he could be decently comfortable. He wanted to move somewhere else to a place in which he would find fairer comfort, greater space, and a steady quietness. He could do all this in England, but the expense would be great, and he hesitated. If the plays brought in double of what he had now, he would go. If the play on in London really settled down, and if this new play went well in the Abbey, he would hoist his sail, and go. A short farewell to Ireland; a hasty look round the places he had known for so long; a last thought of Irish gods and fighting men, and then he would go.

But he was anxious about the present play. He had fancied that when he had fought his way to the Abbey stage, all his troubles would end. Poor, guileless innocent! He had left old troubles to embrace new ones. He had noticed an odd coldness and an irritant nervousness in the manner of the Caste. He sensed that something was going wrong. A number of the actors were doing their parts lazily, as if the play held no interest for them. Mr. Robinson, the Producer, was inclined to be irritable, and he was at times abrupt when Sean ventured to make a suggestion. Then a whisper in Sean's ear told him that Miss Crowe had decided not to play the part of Mrs. Grogan. Sean went to her, and asked if what he heard was true. She said it was. He asked why she wouldn't play the part, and was told that *The part was not genteel*. Oh, Jesus! A Miss May Craig, an actress little thought of, but very good, was got to fill the part, and filled it to perfection. Miss Ria Mooney, chosen for the part of the prostitute, was bombarded with barbed beseeching to rise out of the part; for, if she didn't, she might no longer be thought respectable, and might risk her future in this world and even the next. Fortunately for the play, she held on, and put more fire into the part because of the opposition. F. J. McCormick was hesitant, and seemed to be responding reluctantly to his part. Then, in the midst of the anxiety, Gabriel Fallon, whom Sean had selected to play the part of Peter Flynn, came stealing up to beg this part be taken from him, and the part of Captain Brennan given in its stead. All this made Fitzgerald more nervous than ever, for he had none of the arrogant courage, and none of the jovial

235

determination, which, under different conditions, might have made a great man of Fluther. And, finally, when Sean had ventured to suggest the kind of instrument needed to simulate a band leading the Dublin Fusiliers to the boat, Mr. Robinson's outburst of Oh, shut up, for Christ's sake, man! I've got enough to do to deal with the Caste! settled Sean into a wondering silence. To this day, Sean isn't sure— for no word ever came to him—that the Caste, or any members of it, had heard of the vigorous opposition the play was to meet with when it came to the stage.

While he had been writing the play, Liam O'Flaherty had brought David Garnett to the tenement house to see Sean, and had persuaded Sean to tell of the play he was writing; so, round a blazing fire, Sean had a vigorous chat with this clever and most amiable writer. Both Garnett and O'Flaherty, probably out of politeness and goodwill, had agreed that the play would be a work to be remembered. Afterwards, O'Flaherty's letter to the *Irish Statesman*, definitely and emphatically condemning the work as a bad play, shoved Sean into taking a vow that never again would he reveal to anyone what he was trying to do; never again, except under curious circumstances, would he speak of work in progress. If he spoke at all, he would talk of something he but faintly intended to do. He would think it quietly out, do it the best way he could, and then send it out in the name of God and of O'Casey.

Coming close to the first night, Sean's eyes filled with inflammation, and in-growing eyelashes made the inflammation worse. Dr. J. D. Cummins, now an intimate friend, did all he could to lessen the searching pain; but on the night of the first performance, Sean found it hard and painful to keep his eyes fixed on the bright zone of the stage. The theatre was packed to the doors; the curtain went up; the play began. Though some of the actors didn't seem to strive very earnestly to swing themselves into the drama, most things went well, and the audience sat still, intensely interested in what they saw before them—the mimic, but by no means unimportant portrayal of a part of Dublin's life and feeling. When the end came, the audience clapped tumultuously, and shouted applause. They shouted for the author, and Sean went on to the stage, quietly glad that the play had succeeded. He took the appreciation of those there nicely, though the flame of pain in his eyes pricked like red-hot needles. But all was pleasant, and the loud applause flowed from the serenity of agreement with, and appreciation of, the play. Tightening the belt of his rubber trench-coat tight around him, he went home settled in mind, happy in heart: the worst was over. He was very much the innocent gaum.

The next night he sauntered into a storm. Holy Murther had come again on a visit to the Abbey Theatre. When he entered the foyer, he was hurried up to the Secretary's Office where W. B. Yeats was waiting for him. Listen to my tale of woe. There he was told that the theatre was in an uproar, and that the play could not go on, if something definite wasn't done; that missiles were being flung at the actors, and that it looked as if the stage would be stormed.

—We think it necessary that the police should be sent for immediately, so that the mob may be kept from preventing us carrying on the work we have set our hands to do, said Yeats. We want your consent, O'Casey, to send for the police, as you happen to be the author of the play.

The police! Sean to agree to send for the police—never! His Irish soul revolted from the idea; though Yeats and others reminded him that the police were no longer in a foreign service, but were now in Ireland's own. That the tricolour waved over their barracks, and that it even graced the big drum of their band. Even so, Sean couldn't see his way to ask them to come. No, no; never! But a wild roar heard in the theatre, seeming to shake the room where they all stood, told him to make up his mind quick; and swearing he could ne'er consent, consented.

The police were summoned, and the play began again—two, in fact: one on the stage and the other in the auditorium. Yeats tore down the stairs, and rushed on to the stage to hold the fort till the constables came. The whole place became a mass of moving, roaring people, and Yeats roared louder than any of them. Rowdy, clenching, but well-groomed hands reached up to drag down the fading black and gold front curtain; others, snarling curiously, tried to tug up the very chairs from their roots in the auditorium; while some, in frenzy, pushed at the stout walls to force them down. Steamy fumes ascended here and there in the theatre, and a sickly stench crept all over the place, turning healthy-looking faces pale. The high, hysterical, distorted voices of women kept squealing that Irish girls were noted over the whole world for their modesty, and that Ireland's name was holy; that the Republican flag had never seen the inside of a public-house; that this slander of the Irish race would mean the end of the Abbey Theatre; and that Ireland was Ireland through joy and through tears. Up in the balcony, a section was busily bawling out *The Soldier's Song*, while a tall fellow frantically beat time on the balcony-rail with a walking-stick. Barry Fitzgerald became a genuine Fluther Good, and fought as Fluther himself would fight, sending an enemy, who had climbed on to the stage, flying into the stalls with a flutherian punch on the jaw. And in the midst of the fume, the fighting, the stench, the shouting, Yeats, as mad as the maddest there, pranced on the stage, shouting out his scorn, his contempt; his anger making him like unto an aged Cuchullin in his hero-rage; his long hair waving, he stormed in utter disregard of all around him, confronting all those who cursed and cried out shame and vengeance on the theatre, as he conjured up a vision for them of O'Casey on a cloud, with Fluther on his right hand and Rosie Redmond on his left, rising upwards to Olympus to get from the waiting gods and goddesses a triumphant apotheosis for a work well done in the name of Ireland and of art.

Then the constables flooded into the theatre, just in time. Rough and ready, lusty guardians of the peace. They filed into the theatre as Irish constables for the first time in their life; mystified, maybe, at anyone kicking up a row over a mere play. They pulled the disturbers out, they pushed them out, and, in one or two instances, carried them out, shedding them like peas from the pod of the theatre, leaving them in the cold street outside to tell their troubles to their neighbours or to the stars. Then the play went on, halting often, and agitated to its end. For the first time in his life, Sean felt a surge of hatred for Cathleen ni Houlihan sweeping over him. He saw now that the one who had the walk of a queen could be a bitch at times. She galled the hearts of her children who dared to be above the ordinary, and she often slew her best ones. She had hounded Parnell to death; she had yelled and tore at Yeats, at Synge, and now she was doing the same to him. What an old snarly gob she could be at times; an ignorant one too.

He left the auditorium where the people were watching the play, subdued and nervous, hedged in by the silver-plated helmets of the police, and strayed out into the foyer, right into the midst of a group of women squealers, members of Cumann na mBan—the Society of Women. They shot remarks at him from where they stood or lounged. They said he was a renegade, a friend to England, and that he would soon have a government pension. They said he had held up Ireland's sacred name to ridicule for the sake of the money he'd get for doing it; that it was he who, sooner or later, would feel the shame, and not Ireland. They said he was one now with those who had always hated Ireland, and that the Union Jack was his flag now, and not the Irish tricolour that he had defamed.

—Yes, said one, leaning against the wall, an' I'd like you to know that there isn't a prostitute in Ireland from one end of it to th' other.

Cathleen ni Houlihan was talking. Drawing her patched and fading skirt close around her, she was talking big. Through these women, she was talking. There wasn't a comely damsel among them. Sean noticed this with some surprise. They were all plain, provoking no desire in him to parley words with them, as a pretty face would have done, had one been among them. So after listening for awhile, and saying a few words, he left them to go up to the office to see how things were going. Yeats was shaking hands with an Inspector of Police who was introducing Sergeant Bantry Bay to the poet. The sergeant had developed into a mood of hilarious nervousness. He bowed to the poet, took off his hat, offered his hand, and when Yeats offered his, shook it vehemently, bending Yeats forward with the power of his hand's pull, blurting out a greeting that he must have been practising all the way to the theatre: *It is to be greatly regretted sir, that I have had the honour and pleasure of meeting you for the first time undher such disthressing circumstances!* The Inspector looked silly to hear this greeting, and its unexpected eloquence stunned Yeats out of his senses for a few moments, so that he stared at the sergeant till he summoned enough thought to mutter confusedly, Yes, yes; quite. It is, it is.

Sean went home feeling no way exalted by his famous apotheosis. He was bewildered, and felt sick rather than hilarious. Slandered the people! He had slandered his class no more than Chekhov had slandered his. Did these bawling fools think that their shouting would make him docile? He would leave them to their green hills of holy Ireland. His play was doing well in London, and the Producer, J. B. Fagan, had written several times to him, asking him to come over. Why didn't he go, and leave the

lot of them? The land of Nelson and of Clive was beckon-
ing to him more clearly than ever before; and he was near
ready to leave the land of Patrick and of Tone.

A few days after he received a letter from Frank Ryan
of the National University telling him that Mrs. Sheehy-
Skeffington challenged him to a debate about the play.
Would he take up the challenge, or would he not? He
would; and he wrote to Frank Ryan telling him so. It was
foolish to bother, but Sean felt that if he didn't take it up,
it would be thought he was afraid, and his pride, stupid
pride, couldn't allow that to be thought by anyone. He
hadn't learned enough yet. He was still a gaum. When
he got to the hall, he found it packed to the door, so
crowded that those in the front were almost on top of him;
so crowded that the air was gone, and a damp heat everywhere. That was one of the things he was never able to
bear—a crowded, airless room always made him sick. And
now that his eyes were full of pain, the sense of breathlessness would be worse, and thinking would be hard to do.
He listened to Mrs. Sheehy-Skeffington speaking against
what she called realism in the drama, and pleading very
cleverly for the continuance of romanticism on the stage,
especially in an Ireland fighting against many odds for her
finest national conceptions.

But Sean knew well that those who had fought against
the British had no interest in, no knowledge whatever of,
the battling difference between romanticism and realism.
What concerned them was the implication of fear showing
itself in the manner and speech of the fighting characters
of the play; and in the critical way their patriotism was

ignored, or opposed by Dublin's poor. Mrs. Sheehy-Skeffington, a very clever and a very upright woman, saw it the other way, or thought she saw it so, and turned the dispute into an academic question, because—Sean often thought afterwards—she wished him to do the same, and so lift the question on to a higher plane that that of roars, fights with fists, savage abuse, and the tearing down of a theatre. But Sean couldn't, and wouldn't, get away from the everyday words and conduct of the common people, and what they thought of the things that had happened among them, adding to these things the thoughts which afflicted him about these same things too.

Ill as he felt with the heat and the thickened air, coupled with the neuralgic pain pressing on his eyeballs, forcing his thoughts into the confusing fear that he would speak badly, Sean watched the figure of Madame Gonne-McBride, seated, like a quiet stone image this side of Mrs. Sheehy-Skeffington, and but a little distance from himself. She was clad in a classical way, with a veil of dark blue over her head, the ends flowing down over her shoulders. She turned slowly, only once, to glance at him; and Sean saw, not her who was beautiful, and had the walk of a queen, but the poor old woman, whose voice was querulous, from whom came many words that were bitter, and but few kind. This was she of whom it had been said that men could thrash out, on a dark night, a full barn of corn by the light from one tress of her hair. This was she for whom Yeats had woven so many beautiful cloths of embroidered poetry. She, too, was changed, changed utterly, for no ring of glory now surrounded that crinkled, querulous face. Shadows now were all its marking, shadows where the flesh had swelled or where the flesh had sagged. This is she, who, as Yeats declared,

Hurled the little streets upon the great.

She had never done that, for her knowledge of the ways of little streets was scanty, interesting her only when they issued from their dim places headed by a green flag. She never seemed to have understood Yeats, the poet. Indeed, she could not, having little of the poet in herself, so that she never felt the lure of melody. She forever sat within the folds of, or stood talking before, a velvet green curtain, and never thought to take a peep behind. Here she sat now, silent, stony; waiting her turn to say more bitter words against the one who refused to make her dying dream his own. There she sits stonily silent, once a sibyl of patriotism from whom no oracle ever came; now silent and aged; her deep-set eyes now sad, agleam with disappointment; never quite at ease with the crowd, whose cheers she loved; the colonel's daughter still.

The sickness, suffocating, seized Sean when he got up to speak after Mrs. Sheehy-Skeffington had ended, and he was forced to sit down to wait till the pain in his head steadied into a droning discomfort; till the giddiness lost its power over his thoughts. He did not know, till more than twenty years after, that silicosis had, in shrivelling a lung, pulled his heart out of its place. Some said, go home, and do not stay, for you look ill, and should be careful. But Sean barely listened to them, for he had come there to speak, and speak he would; and speak he did. But it was a hard fight to get going, and his whole being was strained with the effort, and in his heart he despised, more bitterly than ever, the ones who made it necessary for a writer to defend a work so many hated and so few admired. Weary and scornful at the end of it all, Sean went home to his tenement in the little car of Frank Hugh O'Donnell. He felt very tired, and very sad. He lit the lamp, thanked Frank for giving him a lift, looked round, and saw a telegram that had been thrust under his room door. Must have come while he was out. Write to please the Mary MacSwineys, the Countesses Markievicz, the Madame Gonne-McBrides! Jasus Christ, the very thought was laughable! He stooped, picked up the telegram, tore open the envelope, and read the message. It was from Fagan telling him that his play was coming off at one theatre, but another had been engaged, and the play would go on there; but there wasn't much of a chance of a new success, unless Sean came over for the first night, and so created a little publicity for the newer effort.

—I'll go, he said to Frank O'Donnell. I'll go over to help the play's entrance into a new theatre, and leave the wrack behind me.

When the shouting had died down, and the rowdier captains had departed, the turn of the intellectuals came to cheat Sean from any success he might be expecting. Sean saw another side of Ireland's enterprising malice and envy. He was learning more in a few weeks than he had learned in a lifetime. The intellectuals began to send letters to the Press, and to A.E.'s journal, *The Irish Statesman*, con-

demning and upbraiding the plays. Some of them were
influenced to do this, Sean thought, because he had definitely refused to join them in a Club or Society which was
to be organised to put the arrogant Yeats in his place. He
would argue with Yeats, oppose him manfully, but personally, on any question of religion, politics, and even
literature, if he happened to differ from the poet; but he
wouldn't join any clique to do it, because he thought this
opposition was born of envy of the great fame the poet
enjoyed as the leading man of Irish Letters. He had never
mentioned the matter to Yeats, for, having done, or refused
to do, what was right, or what he thought was right; he
was satisfied in his own soul, and nothing else mattered.

Sean's plays were stoned with many criticisms from the
intellectuals, so that he passed from one bewilderment to
another. *The plays,* said one, *are naught but a series of
Tableau Vivants; O'Casey is purely a photographic artist.
He is striving after a literary quality of speech which is
entirely alien to the Dublin slum-dwellers; the plays have
the structure of the cinema and the revue. They are a
series of scenes rather than a play. The career of O'Casey
induces fear for the future.* All this came from the bracing
brain of Dublin's then first critic—Andrew E. Malone.
Again, as if he felt he hadn't said enough, he goes on to
add, *His plays are phases of Dublin life as abnormal as
they are transient. O'Casey's humour is the humour of the
music-hall without the skill of the music-hall or the
sharpened point of its wit. Is O'Casey a dramatist, or is
he but a combination of the cinema and the dictaphone?*
That was written more than twenty years ago, and the
Irish critics haven't been able to answer the question yet.

Following O'Flaherty's direct announcement (as pompous as anything Yeats could have said) that *The Plough and the Stars was a bad play*, came the young poet Fred O'Higgins's remonstrance and criticism, saying, *A new political quality approved by the arrogance of the Anglo-Irish is the only quality for which O'Casey is offered applause. His is a technique based on the revue structure, in the quintessence of an all-Abbey burlesque, intensified by "divarsions" and Handy Andy incidents, with somewhat more original settings. O'Casey in his new play entirely lacks the sincerity of the artist.*

Another coloured bullet-bead was added to the string by a letter from Austen Clarke, another poet, who said with poise and gentle dignity, that *Several writers of the New Irish School* (himself included of course) *believed that Mr. O'Casey's work was a crude exploitation of our poorer people in the Anglo-Irish tradition that is now moribund.* Still another writer, R. M. Fox, referred to the plays as *The Drama of the Dregs*, adding that *The peasant plays have been followed by slum plays, but their reign will not be long, though as entertainment these slum dramas are permissible. But truth is wanted as well as entertainment.*

So Sean, at first bewildered by the riot, was now puzzled by the Irish critics, for, innocent gaum that he was, he didn't realise then that these fellows didn't know what they were talking about.

He wondered how he could have built on the revue structure, for he had never seen a revue in his life. He knew nothing about the cinema. If any of them had only mentioned melodrama, he would have cocked an ear, for he had seen many of these, and had enjoyed them all. They saw in Sean that of which they themselves were full—the cinema and the revue. Then first began Sean's distrust of, and contempt for, the Irish critics. Knowing all, they knew nothing. Two critics now began to shine on his thoughts—one Irish, curiously enough, and the other American. They were George Jean Nathan and George Bernard Shaw—the two Georges. He had got Shaw's two books of *Dramatic Criticisms* from America, paying twenty-five shillings for them—a big sum for Sean to hand out those days; but he found them to be worth the sacrifice. The books formed a gorgeous episode in Sean's life. Shaw's comments were on plays which—bar Shakespeare, Wilde, and Ibsen—he had neither seen nor read, and which, now, he would never see nor read, for they were all dead, never to rise again; but the criticisms lived on, and gave Sean a candle-light view of the theatre dead, and an arc-lamp view of the theatre living. Another book, Nathan's *The Critic and the Drama*, was a book of revelations to Sean. He was becoming less of the innocent gaum every page he passed. Here was a live man of the drama. As deep in what he wrote as he was gay. A wise philosopher, an undaunted critic, a lover of the theatre with cothurnus and sock attached to the glittering costume of the harlequin who carried a torch in his right hand instead of a lath. The Irish drama critics, even those who were poets, could now go to hell for Sean!

But, soberly, while he was here, he'd have to deal with the critics at home. How? By going his own way. That was the one thing to do, for there wasn't even a hint of guidance in what they said. They were no good. He would have to go a long way from the cliques of Dublin. But how could he escape? By living in the country or by crossing over to England. It was time he saw newer streets than those of Dublin. If he went to the country, he'd still be confined within the ken and den of Cosgravian and De Valerian politics, and well within the sphere of influence set up by Irish rosaries, Anthony's Annals, and all the crowding rolipoli-holiness of the Pope's green island; with Church of Ireland stained-glass windows shining timidly through the mist that does be on the bog. No, not that way. His future connection with Ireland must be somewhat similar to that of De Valera's association with the British Commonwealth—neither in it nor out of it. For him, the land of Nelson, Clive, and Canning in place of the land of Patrick, Tone, and Parnell. Not quite— Tone and Parnell would be forever very near to him.

Some little time after, the Abbey selected Shaw's *Man and Superman* for performance, and gave the play, in Sean's vision, a very bad production indeed. It had its comic side, for all the actors were subdued by the relentless enthusiasm of F. J. McCormick who played Tanner, who seemed to be always hustling them off the stage. Barry Fitzgerald, who played the part of Roebuck Ramsden, could only timidly stare, and sputter out his part in an apologetic and bewildered way, like a man asking questions in a crowd speaking another language. It was a helter-skelter performance, and one would have felt no wonder if the characters had suddenly broken up, and joined together again, in a song and dance assemble. Igno-

rant and innocent gaum that he was, Sean, thinking now
that he was among old friends, ran round when the play
ended to tell the artists what he thought of it all. They
were all shocked, and murmured Hush hush hush. Sean
thought they would all roar out laughter with him over the
production, but they refused. They kept silent, except to say
Hush hush hush. F. J. McCormick came close to him,
and said, "I hear you've been criticising our rendering of
Shaw's play. You've got a bit of a name now, and you
must not say these things about an Abbey production. If
you do, we'll have to report it to the Directors; so," he
added a little crudely, "so try to keep your mouth shut."

Bewilderment again afflicted Sean. Just fancy that now!
After all Sean had gone through; after all his mouth had
dared to say, it was to be kept closed at an Abbey actor's
order. Sean went home, sat down, wrote a long letter,
pointing out the bad parts of the production; why and how
he thought them to be bad; added a note to Mr. M. J.
Dolan, the then Manager, saying that the letter held his
views of what had happened, and that he was at liberty, if
he wished, to read the letter out loud to the Abbey Directors, have it printed in papers, and show it to the world at
large. This letter was shown to Mr. Lennox Robinson,
who, in an ethereal voice murmured, "It's just like Sean!"
The letter was then pinned up on the notice-board for all
to read. Some nights following, Sean was on his way over
the Abbey stage to join the actors in the Green Room for
a chat, when he was stopped by Sean Barlow, a scene
painter, in an old-fashioned way; a maker of properties,
again in another old-fashioned way, who asked what he

was doing on the stage. On my way to the Green Room, replied Sean. There's none but the actors and officials allowed on the stage, said the bold Barlow, with a dominant note in his voice; and we'd be glad if you came this way no more.

No more? Quote the raven, Nevermore. Never again. Nevermore. Ordered from the stage he had trod so many years ago and he a kidger, ay, mouthed the part of Father Dolan in *The Shaughraun* from its boards, ere ever the Abbey Theatre had entered its beginning; the stage on which his brother, Archie, had played Harvey Duff in the same play, and others in *Peep o' Day Boys*, *The Unknown*, *Green Bushes*, and *The Colleen Bawn*. Never again; nevermore. He turned away, leaving the other Sean victor on the field, and never after set a foot either on the Abbey stage or in the Abbey Green Room.

He'd hoist his sail and go to England,

> *Neptune's park, ribbed and paled in*
> *With rocks unscalable and roaring waters.*

DUBLIN'S GODS AND HALF-GODS

SEAN was now walking tiptoe among the gods, but he had begun to doubt the divinity of most of them. His reverence for the opinions of A.E. had begun to decline. He began to question in himself the once-held thought that Lennox Robinson was near to knowing all about things theatrical and literary as any educated man could be. Lady Gregory was still herself in his mind; but Hugh Lane's reputation as one who could always tell a bad picture from a fine one was a wavering one now. James Stephens, the poet, was a hearty laugh in his mind, but a ringing laugh, one with the ring of bells in it, silver ones that sang merry tunes, tinged with the note of pathos, deep in the very centre of their chiming. Austin Clarke and Brinsley Macnamara didn't bother him in surmise or reflection; but Yeats stood majestic still. As he listened to the crowd of the lesser gods, listened long, he began to see that their sneering, lofty conception of what they called culture, their mighty semblance of self-assurance in the most of them was but a vain conceit in themselves which they used for their own encouragement in the pitiable welter of a small achievement. Some of these were imitators of whom Yeats said, when he was asked to praise them,

But was there ever dog who praised his fleas?

He was learning by experience.

He had been told that Patrick Touhy was a great painter, and he believed it at the time. A.E., Robinson, even Yeats said so, so Sean believed it. He was delighted when this man, Touhy, asked Sean to come and be sketched. So Sean went several nights a week to the Metropolitan School of Art, where Touhy was a teacher, to sit for an hour or two, while poor Touhy's timid hand sought laboriously to set down the line and expression of Sean's face.

—Aw, chance a stroke, man! Sean would say, when he saw the timid hand holding the pencil, flickering, flickering over the paper without daring to touch it; niggling a little bit of a line here, then there, tormenting Sean with the idea that this man hadn't in him the courage and dash an artist must have, if he is to do work worth more than a smile.

He had agreed to give Touhy three guineas and autographed copies of his book for the drawing; but before it was finished, Sean saw that Touhy would never be among the named artists. Sean felt sympathy for him at first, but life was too much of a battle to give thought to one cowering before it; and the timid pencil in the quavering hand forced scorn into a fighter's mind. One of the loudest laughs Sean ever had was given when he saw Touhy dressed up as Macheath, with Sally Allgood at his side, gathered into the dress of Polly Peachum, on their way to the Dublin Arts Ball. There he was, stuffed into the most gorgeous of velvets, sword and all, a man clothed with timidity as with a garment. But Sally Allgood, as plump as he was meagre, fair smothered in a flowing tide of savage peplus, silk, ribbons, and lace, hooked her arm in his, and led him on to the wild adventure of the dance.

When he had varnished the drawing, Touhy sent a letter to Sean telling him to come and get it; but after he had seen what it was like when it appeared as a frontispiece to one of his books, he took no notice of the call to come. Looking at it close now, for before he didn't like to do this while Touhy was drawing it, he was staggered to see how badly it had been done. Later, down in Coole Park, Lady Gregory had got a grip on his arm to say more effectively, "You must be tareful who you det to draw you. Touhy has made you look like a butcher." Later on still, Augustus John praised it by saying, "It was a damned fine drawing of someone else." When he had settled in London, he got a letter from a relative asking him to what place they would send the picture, but he did not answer. The thing had no merit; he didn't want it; so he left it wherever it was. It was odd that the Ireland Sean knew had no great painter. Not one tended to seal a soul to a picture whenever a soul came to gaze. Even Lavery or Orpen didn't seem able to do this much. In Ireland there wasn't even a shadow coming through the sun of work done by such men as Renoir, Manet, Picasso, Cézanne, or Van Gogh. All the Irish painters had halted at the half-way house of art; and most of them hesitated to take the first step from the beginning; though each had a mighty opinion of himself, backed by a very poor one of all the others.

But Ireland was full of folly, seeking, probing even, for a good opinion. He remembered once when he was in

Coole, sitting by the huge fire in the library, the great logs throwing up lusty golden and scarlet flames, doing a fine dance on the coloured bindings of the books marshalled around the walls, with Lady Gregory sitting opposite chatting away; while she, at times, prodded the logs with a brass poker into greater energy and glow. In her smiling chat she had told him how shocked she had been to discover that Yeats had read nothing written by Dostoievsky; how she had cried shame on him for his neglect of so great a man; and how she had given him *The Idiot* and *The Brothers Karamazov* only a week ago to take away with him so that he might read them, and be delighted with the images of a great and spiritual mind. Then she told Sean how Yeats had written to say he had read one, and how great the work was, and how he enjoyed it. Just then, Sean had had his third play taken by the Abbey, and it was to go into rehearsal in a week or two. When he got back to Dublin, he was told that Mr. Yeats wanted to see him to talk about the play.

The next day he set out for the poet's home in Merrion Square. This will be the second time, he thought, I have set a foot within a house in this place which still treasured the secluded brocade and perfume of the past. An awesome place, for the top achievement for many years in Dublin had been a residence in Merrion Square. The glory of living here was next to the glory of living in one of the Big Houses of the country: a glory reached only by the lonely few. As he came closer to it, the streets became more refined, as if aware of their greater neighbour; and those that were closest to this elegant dot of life began to assume an air of importance, and bravely tried to look imposing.

He entered the Square, and halted to stand and stare at the gracious houses. The Square looked as if it had been knighted by king exclusion and queen quietness, separating it from the lumbering, trade-tired streets of Dublin. He entered it with a bow and a murmur of Yer servant, Sir Merrion; for it was a holy place, to poverty unknown; unknown, save by name, to the distant proletariat of the tenements. If a proletarian ventured to pass through it, he would go quiet and quick, without lounging, or sending a disparaging spit into its kennels. He would lift his passing feet carefully, and set them down intelligently, so as to provoke no noise from the footway. He would pass through with the circumspection he'd show while passing by a rich bed in which a noble or a bishop lay sleeping; pass by slyly and rapidly, without commotion, eager to get to a place where he could walk with ease, hands in pocket, and spit in comfort, the poorer world before him, ready to fulfil his hardier will and lustier pleasure.

How stately the houses looked with their gleaming windows, the brightness of them muffled in the brief modesty of costly curtains, concealing secrets of private life from the eyes and ears of the street outside; their cleverly-painted, highly-polished front doors, each side pillared stiffly, as if petrified footmen stood guard there to see that no dirty hand was stretched out to soil a dazzling knocker, or imprint a slum-speck on the bell-push, that shone like a brassy jewel on a cheek of the opulent doorway.

—Here, the houses would quiver in pain, thought Sean,

if a hawker went by chanting, Strawberries, penny a leaf, penny a leaf, the ripe strawberries! And the houses would swoon in shame if the cry changed to, Fresh Dublin Bay herrin's, thruppence a dozen; thruppence the dozen, the Dublin Bay herrin's fresh from the say!

Sean mounted the wide steps to the door, which was Yeats's dwelling-place. Two Free State C.I.D. men stood in the shadow of the pillared doorway, planted there to prevent the assassination of the senator-poet by some too-ready Republican hand. Guns guarding the poet, thought Sean, though he knew that the Republicans had as much idea of shooting Yeats as they had of shooting Lady Gregory or the Catholic Archbishop of Dublin.

—Are yeh goin' in to see himself? asked one of them who knew Sean well; but as what he asked was half a statement, he went on, I don't envy yeh, Sean, for I wouldn't like to be alone with him long. His oul' mind's full of th' notion of oul' kings and queens, the half of us never heard of; an' when he's talkin', a fella has to look wise, pretendin' he's well acquainted with them dead an' gone ghosts. It's a terrible sthrain on a body whenever he stops to talk. Wait till yeh hear, though, and his hand put down Sean's as it stretched out towards the bell-push; yeh know Jim Errishcool, don't yeh? Yes, well, of course. Well what d'ye think th' bugger's done, an' him on guard over Senator Fedamore's residence, some doors down? What d'ye think he done, disgracin' th' whole of us. The second time he's done it, too. Guess what th' boyo done?

—Fired at a shadow he thought a Republican?

—Aw, no, not that. What d'ye think th' goboy done but got acquainted with th' upper housemaid, an' when th' genthry were away, got into th' house quiet, an' lo and behold yeh, he gets th' girl in th' family way as cool as bedamned through th' medium of th' best bed in th' best bedroom. Now, what d'ye think o' that! A cool customer, wha'? Th' best bed, no less, for a fella, only just up from th' bog, in Fedamore's own house, mind yeh, an' th' upper housemaid, too. They found th' bed all knocked about an' th' girl on it in a half-dead daze, cryin', an' murmurin', He's after nearly killin' me! An' th' boyo come on duty th' same night to take over guard, cool as you like. Now you'll be talkin'!

—Oh, well, he could do worse, said Sean.

—Sure I know he could, said the guard impatiently; but what about us? Everyone of us is misthrusted now. Th' way they look at us when they're passin' as if we all had th' same failin'.

—And I'm afraid we have, said Sean.

—We know all about that! snappily said the guard; I know we all have th' failin', but we all haven't got it in th' direct fashion of a fallin' thunderbolt overthrowin' an innocent girl!

When Sean stepped by the neatly-dressed maid, who held the door open for him, and entered the study, he was met by a blast of heat that nearly downed him. He had entered a den of heat. Never before had he experienced such an onslaught of venomous warmth. The hot air enveloped him, made him sink into a chair, to silently gulp for breath; and it was soon forcing him into an unpleasant

sense of sickness. On the chair, he wrenched his will towards trying to breathe easy. There it was, at the end of
the room, the devil of heat, a huge, squat, black anthracite
stove, belching out its invisible venom quietly, threatening
Sean with an embarrassing display of faintness. Over-
crowded or overheated rooms tended to make Sean's brain
buzz, and his stomach feel queer, and already he could feel
everything in his belly trying to turn over; the power of
his will alone preventing it from happening.

And what was that sound of piercing shrillness, like the
ear-splitting scream of a hundred fifes playing in a room
at the same time, in dire disharmony together? Birds! A
golden-barred cage, half filling a big window, swung there,
swung and fluttered there with the shrill tuning of half a
hundred canaries. Rich yellow ones, some of them streaked
with creamier lines, some with dark satiny patches on
them; active, alert, darting from side to side of the cage,
from top to bottom, and back again, over and over again,
never stopping, singing without cessation, singing, singing
all the time, splitting the thick and heated air of the room
with a mad, piercing melody of noise! These were the
canaries that Lady Gregory had called Dose derrible birds!
And through the heated air, and through the savage whistling, the noble voice of Yeats boomed out a blessing on
the new play.

What was he saying, what was the man saying? Could
Sean fashion the words from the booming, disentangle
them from the violent chittering, mould them from the
heavy air, and fold them into making sense within his own
mind? No. Surely Yeats wasn't saying what he was say-

ing! But Sean's will caught the words, and made sense of them, out of the heat, and through the mad fifing of the canaries; and he listened with an exquisite desire to laugh out loud, as he listened to the voice, the deep, fine voice booming out through the sweating air and the jeering whistle of the uncalmable birds; the majestic voice of Yeats, as he paced up and down the room through the moist haze, came booming to the din-dulled ears of Sean: O'Casey, you have written a great play; this play is the finest thing you have done. In an Irish way, you have depicted the brutality, the tenderness, the kindling humanity of the Russian writer, Dostoievsky; O'Casey, you are the Irish Dostoievsky!

Moving homewards, gasping into him the cool air of the street, faint still from what he had suffered in the red, ruthless heat from the anthracite stove, his shirt sticking to back and breast, Sean felt ashamed of Yeats and ashamed of himself. Wait, now, till he grew a little cooler. Sean had worked within the airless chamber of a boiler, helping to fix a furnace, but it never gave him the languishing feeling of sickness he had suffered in that room. Why was Yeats afraid of a cooler air? He had, Sean knew, a tendency to chest or lung complaints. But the heat in that room would be bad for one even in the throes of bronchitis. It will do the man harm. Now why hadn't he had the courage to tell Yeats that? Sean, when his second play was in rehearsal, had walked, with a temperature from bronchitis, and a sense of suffocation, from North Circular Road to Nelson's Pillar, in falling snow; had there taken a tram to St. Vincent's Hospital, and had never felt the worse for it.

It wasn't a sensible thing to do, of course; but less dangerous than to live and sleep in such a torrid heat endured by
the poet Yeats. It will do the man harm. And the piercing
chatter of those yellow-clad birds—how can Yeats, the
delicate-minded poet, stand that chirruping turmoil? He
had no ear; he was tone-deaf—that was the reason.
Now Sean realised that there were different kinds of
bliss: what was heaven to one man might be hell to
another.

Another Dostoievsky! An Irish one, this time! And
Yeats only after reading the man's book for the first time
the night before. If it hadn't been for his battle with the
blast and the birds, Sean would have had a battle with
laughter. Yeats was trying to impress Sean with his knowledge of Dostoievsky. That was a weakness in the poet.
But why hadn't Sean the courage to tell Yeats that he
knew damn all about the Russian writer. That was a weakness in Sean. It was a cowardly omission. He should have
told Yeats he knew Lady Gregory had given him two of
Dostoievsky's books only a night or so ago. And, instead
he had put a smile of appreciation on his heat-strained face
when Yeats had said it. Christ Almighty, what a world of
deceits! Sean's father would have said how he felt and
what he thought without a hesitation. He had let his
father's memory down. He'd try to be braver the next
time. Some had said he was another Chekhov, others, a
Dickens, and another Ben Jonson. He knew himself that
he was like Sean O'Casey, and he was determined to be
like no-one else; for better or worse, for richer or poorer,
so help him God!

There was something lacking, even in the gods. None of them was destitute of human vanity and conceit. Sean remembered his very first evening (his last, but one) in A.E.'s house, how, when the company was leaving, after a long and abuseless spate of blather, James Stephens, the poet (who never, like the great little man he was, pretended to be what he wasn't; indeed, Stephens's weakness was, Sean thought, that he never fully realised the grace and grandeur of the delightful and dignified gifts he possessed), suddenly and hurriedly asking A.E. author of the *Homeward Songs*, for a Blood and Thunder novel, and A.E. had fished one out from his books without a search; he had plunged a hand in among the books, and out came the Blood and Thunder novel. No; these poets and dreamers hadn't fully embedded themselves in the Nirvana of literature and art.

And Lady Gregory, too. Returning with her once from Coole to Dublin, they had come from Gort to Athenry, and got out there to wait an hour and a half for the train from Galway to bring them on to Dublin. The two of them had eaten a lunch of ham and hard-boiled eggs, sitting on a bench in the dreary station. After they had eaten, Lady Gregory said she'd have a liddle rest, while he went to have a look at the town, returning in good time to be ready for the incoming train from Galway.

Athenry—Ford of the King. No king here now. Ne'er a sign of one even—bar the king of loneliness. Sean passed under a famous archway of which it was said that whomsoever it fell on, and buried beneath its ruins, would become the saviour of Ireland. Loneliness the king, and the wind his attendant. It blew cold and sharp through every narrow street. Like a scythe eager to cut down any sign of life that came to tease the loneliness around; or to disturb the town's drowsy restfulness. It came sweeping in from the levels of Clare-Galway bog and plain. The houses stood still, careless of stare of pity or of scorn. They looked old, oh, so old. And they looked neither sad nor sorry about it; they simply seemed set to wait for the end to come. They were lost in quietness. He heard a bell toll in the distance. The wind lessened it into the ghost of a chime. Somewhere in the town, maybe, someone had passed into a better quietness. The bell tolled, but the town did not stir. No sign of life anywhere as if the bell tolled for the dead town. Resignation showed a passive power everywhere. It even looked as if eternity was dying down here.

Away over the bridge, above, the seepy silence seemed startled by a passing train; passing by swift, as if possessed by fear; passing by noisily, as if to give itself courage; straining to get away, as if in fear of being caught in the fearsome plight of life here, standing still to watch its own decay, and to wait for its own departure.

Sean heard a sound like a leaf's rustling. He turned, and saw a young girl coming out of the doorway of a sunken house. She had to mount four or five steps to bring herself to the level of the side-walk. Sean stood perfectly still to look at her. She was a winsome lass. A mass of brown hair gave a golden hue to a pale and trimly-chiselled face, with delicate ears, a straight and slender nose, dignifying a saucy-looking red mouth; while a pair of blue, softly luminous eyes met Sean's admiring stare. She was dressed in a brown coat, open, showing a thin white blouse against which her young breasts pushed, forming a pattern that told Sean they were finely turned and tempting. When she came to the top step, Sean saw that her legs flowed finely into the delightful curving of her body. They had a charm that would entice a dead-tired man to take a long journey after them in the hope that favouring wind would lift skirt and petticoat higher, showing the legs off, and signalling Here is beauty. Her hand shot up to her head to recapture a lock of hair the wind had suddenly played with, and Sean saw that the hand was well made, though the skin looked rough, telling him that hard work was part of the girl's portion.

There the lass stood on the side-walk, facing him, framed in the muddy-yellow decay of the house behind her, like a lone cherry blossom thrusting itself shyly and impertinently forward through the ragged, withering foliage of an ageing tree. She was hesitating, maybe wishing him to speak, but he could say nothing. His mind had been too full of the loneliness and the ruin to be so suddenly called upon to reflect with words the wonder in his mind. He could say nothing. There she lingered, but his silence lasted too long. She lowered her eyes from his, turned, and went down the street, and disappeared round an alley-way a little lower down.

He looked at his watch: it was time to go back to Lady Gregory, back towards Dublin. He went slowly back to the grimy station, imagining what he would have said to the lass while she walked by his side, or stood where she

had been, to listen. He would have told her he knew all
the big men of Dublin, all the poets, and was a friend of
Lady Gregory's, and of the great poet, Yeats. He would
tell her that he himself was a dramatist, and even something of a poet. All the honours of acquaintanceship, all
his achievements he would place in front of her to win her
interest and secure her admiration. Neither for fame nor
for money would he do this; no, not one of them would
he summon to his aid for these things; but he would lay
them all down before her so that he might look at the
beautiful face, kiss a curving red mouth, and tune a lovely
form into the circle of his supplicating arms. Whenever his
mind wandered again to the lonely wretchedness of
Athenry, he would see this lovely figure, this bud of
womanhood, longing for life, standing, alone and radiant,
in the midst of the houses, quietly resolute in sinking to
their own decay.

He came into the station, and saw Lady Gregory sitting
on a bench, her head lovingly close to a book. Coming
over quietly, he bent over curiously to see what she was
reading. Catching in her dulling ear a sound of his movement, she snapped the book shut, but not before he had
seen that the book was called *Peg o' My Heart*.

—We won't have long to wait now, she said a little confusedly, adding as she noticed the look of bewilderment in
his eyes, Ah, dat book? I fordet who dave it to me. I just
wanted to see what tort it was.

Long afterwards, when Oliver Gogarty came on a visit
to him in London, what he had known before was confirmed again. Gogarty had entered in a whirlwind of rest-

lessness. He had flung down his suitcase, the impact had
burst it open, and a book flew out on to the floor. Sean's
wife and Oliver had made a dive together to get it, but
Gogarty was a second too late; and Sean saw the title of
one of Edgar Wallace's rich and rare inventions. Later on,
still, visiting W. B. Yeats in his Lancaster Gate lodgings
in London, he found the poet busy with his last anthology
of modern poetry.

The poet shoved the books on the table aside, and entered into a hearty chat about the Abbey Theatre, the new
Directorate, the sort of plays they should put on, and then
about some of the glories of the Elizabethan dramatists.
During the talk, Sean's eyes kept turning to glance at a
disordered pile of books strewing the marble mantelshelf.
Yeats noticed his glances at last, and cocked one of his own
eyes towards them—for the other was covered with a thick
green shade—and remarked that they were Wild Western
Tales and Detective Stories. Yeats made no bones about it.

—When the mind grows tired, he said, reading so much
excellent, and not so excellent, verse, I turn for shelter and
rest to Zane Grey and Dorothy Sayers. One can read
them while the mind sleeps.

—Dope, thought Sean. He uses them as dope to lull the
mind to sleep, just as the one-two, one-two mind of a
roman catholic keeps his mind awake by reading the tup-
penny booklets of the Catholic Truth Society. But Yeats
is quite open and honest about it anyway; though Sean
thought it odd entertainment for a poet. He himself had
read several detective stories, but they seemed to tire his
mind quicker than the deepest essay written by a John

Locke; though the antics of the Lord Wimseys and his mother, of the new-fashioned mind, coupled with the mighty mass of grey matter in the head of Poirot (like Chesterton's Father Brown beating his outward mind to solve a problem solved already by his inner one) were provocative of a quiet and comfortable laugh, now and again.

Ay, indeed; even the greater gods of Dublin had their frailties and their faults. They could sometimes build their little cocks of antic hay, and try to tumble about in them. The lordly ones weren't always quite so lordly with literature as they generally posed to be.

DUBLIN'S GLITTERING GUY

THEY tried to settle themselves comfortably on the hard-upholstered seat of the snug in the Blue Lion of Britain Street—Donal, Sean, and a young fellow, named Edwin Droop Grey, who had contributed two poems, *Sparrows on the Housetop* and *The Eagle in the Air*, to A.E.'s journal *The Irish Statesman*. Donal took a slug from his bottle of stout, Edwin moistened his lips with his small port, and Sean swallowed a mouthful of his warmed claret. The snug was a tiny cubicle, smelling of a thousand beery breaths, tightly holding its occupants with dirty panelled partitions, a little window in front from which the drinks were passed from the bar.

A.E.'s getting a little bent in the back, said Edwin D. Grey; and he looked old passing by us in O'Connell Street today. Curious guy.

—Dublin has her gods, her half-gods, and her guys, said Donal. A.E.'s our glittering guy. Dublin's logos, the word-final in painting, literature, poetry, philosophy, rural science, dreams, and religion. He's the fairest and brightest humbug Ireland has. There's a genuine humility in Yeats's arrogance, but there's a deeper arrogance in A.E.'s humility.

—And the other day, said Edwin, Dunsany, in an article, called A.E. the poet of the century. It's incomprehensible how Dunsany could overlook Yeats to hand the palm for poetry to A.E. What a mess of glittering monotony his poems are! All paralysed with a purple glow. Swing-exultation in them all. They make a mind dizzy. It's too much of a thing to be friends with the Ancient of Days; too big a thing to be the rocker of the infant suns; or to dip a forefinger into the fiery fountains of the stars; or to put on the mantelshelf of your room the Golden Urn into which all the glittering spray of planets fall. A.E. thinks he's God's own crooner. Listen:

When the breath of twilight blows to flame the misty skies,
With its vaporous sapphire, violet glow, and silver gleam,
With their magic flood me through the gateway of the eyes;
I am one with the twilight's dream.

   —It's too magnificent, said Donal. Portholes of the eyes, would have been better. Think of the poem where he conjures up a vast expanse of corruscating battlements, blazing with divine beings, surrounded by imperishable fires in which other gigantic beings, crested and plumed with fire, appear; and, after them, starry races, stretching out line on line into the infinite; while Birds of Diamond Glory flit about from perch to pinnacle, among crowds of demi-humans and semi-gods, wearing tremendous tiaras, branching beams of coloured flames spreading out from their spines, with a steady pointed light sticking up from their brows, out of the Well of Indra. A wonderful scene. The great white way! And when he wants to get rid of them so that he may sing of his loneliness, he just says Gone!
   —And they go, said Sean. These visions of flame-

feathered and plumed masters, of blazing stars, of inimitable light, are as full of tawdry, childish decorations as those seen by French kids at Lourdes, Portuguese kids in Fatima, Irish kids at Knock, and Latvian kids at Girkhala. And as superstitious, too; worse, even, for A.E.'s a grown man, who ought to know better.

—And he sees but one colour, with its various shades, in the world, said Edwin. Purple is his pride, and the one aspect in the mirror of the day is a purple twilight. There's hardly a poem of his left bare of the word Twilight, or of the colour usually associated with that time of the day— purple mountains, lilac trees, violet skies, heliotrope clouds, and amethyst ancestral selfs. And what an acrobat he is! A daring old man on a flying-trapeze! He swings from star to star, from planet to planet, as a kid swings from a rope tied to a lamp-post. And yet this great creator of greater things can write a thing like this—

> Your eyes, your other eyes of dream,
> Looked at me through the veil of blank.

—Monk Gibbon, the poet, says of him, said Sean, that he is such a high-blown mystic, his poetry should be read sacredly, one poem at a time. Otherwise, we won't be able to keep pace with the systems in their metaphysical universe. Each poem, Gibbon says, needs separate acceptance, separate meditation. As with his prose, A.E.'s poems should only be read at a time when our mood is already in some measure attuned to them. Trying to let Russell down easily said Sean, as he let some claret slip down into himself. As

if any poem, worth reading, doesn't need a separate acceptance, from *My Love Is Like a Red, Red Rose* to *Dies
Irae*; and a separate meditation, too, however different
the meditations may be in spirit and in thought.

—He no longer lives as a poet in the hearts of the young,
said Donal. They're laughing at the old humbug at last.

—I shouldn't go as far as that, said Edwin Grey, with a
tinge of remonstrance in his tone. Not a humbug; oh, no.
A.E. has his points; a quality of conviction, at least in what
he sings; and a first-class painter.

—There I'm altogether against you, said Sean vehemently. He never was an artist in colour or line or form.
Even though at one time, when he found himself short, as
he told me himself, he could dash out of the house with a
new-painted picture under his coat, and sell it for twenty-
five pounds before he'd gone through two streets. No one
who paints well could paint so many. His house is stacked
with them. He was heard counting a harvest of them, once
—forty-eight, forty-nine, fifty, fifty-one—there's one
picture missing! I looked at them one evening, along with
James Stephens. The pictures were stacked against a wall
in one room, facing inwards, and A.E. brought them out,
placing them, facing outwards, against another wall. Then
he'd step back to wait for you to say they were all lovelies.
It was pathetic and comical to see James Stephens going
down on his knees to get a better view of them; but it was
sad to hear him saying how grand they were; the misty
trees radiant with light in the middle distance, and the rest
of it. I could see little more than daubs in them, and remained silent, for I wasn't quite sure of myself as to how

best to show why one picture was good, and another one worthless.

—You talk like that because you don't know, said Edwin Grey. I've learned a lot from Paul Henry, and I can tell you that A.E.'s pictures stand steady against the best that's being done today. You just have another, and a longer look at them. The figures, saturated in sunshine, are deliciously ethereal, and you get from mountain, from flowing river, from the faery-like tint of evening skies, from the fugitive play of children and lovers, a Virgilian beauty that makes the transitory sister to the eternal.

—Jasus! said Donal, that's the kind of gush that gives the old bugger his reputation among the gulls who know no better. Him and his fairies! He even thinks that by putting in ae instead of ai into the word fairy he transfigures them into heavenly forms whose existence is undeniable. This grandee of incompetence is a danger to the young who desire to become artists.

—A.E., said Edwin Grey, you must remember, is a mystic, and lives embowered in the higher thoughts of the world's religions. A freelance saint, living an ascetic life, making it hard for us lesser mortals to fully enter into his vision of the invisible.

—A kind of ethereal faery himself! said Donal, with laughing scorn. Don't be talking rot, man! he went on, more hotly. Ask Orpen, and you'll know. Doesn't he tell us that A.E. paints two pictures every Sunday, one after a big breakfast of eggs and bacon, and the other one after a heavy midday meal. Ask Orpen. The fairies worried him; they were exactly like badly-drawn figures by Blake.

But the fairies vanished when Sir Hugh Lane brought the French pictures to Dublin. Then every Sunday produced two slimy canvasses by a would-be Millet. Each Sunday two came regularly, and aesthetic Dublin bowed its head, murmuring, How Wonderful! Then Millet got played out, and imitation Monticellis appeared on Dublin's house-walls, to be followed by Renoir, who was followed by Daumier, who was followed by Chavannes, till, Orpen says, I lost count. And all the time these Dublin aesthetes were bowing before A.E., they were shouting, Manet? Sure, he couldn't draw, much less paint!

—Maybe, now, murmured Edwin Grey, a smile of tolerant scorn dawning round his mouth, maybe, now, Orpen was jealous.

—Jealous? retorted Donal. Didn't Clive Bell call the ethereal ones, Dicky Doyle's Fairies? And didn't George Moore call A.E., The Donegal Dauber? I'm telling you I wouldn't put a picture of his on a wall of mine, if I was paid a weekly rent for hanging it there!

—Ay, said Sean, you're right, Donal. And to escape from any criticism that might be born of thought, didn't A.E. proclaim everywhere he could find a listener that he never wanted to be known as a great artist, for such was but vanity; and that he had turned away from this vanity so that he might search for truth, undisturbed by the cling-ing fingers of beauty. He hid his want of inspiration, his pitiable lack of craftsmanship in the statement that art was a self-indulgence, which, if yielded to, would stint his life, and hamper his homeward march to a lost divinity. The glorious art of painting, art of Titian, of Raphael, of An-

273

gelo, of Rubens, of Vermeer, of Constable, and Turner, a
practice that would stint a life! And Fra Angelico who put
the gold of heaven round his saints and angels! The fact
is that A.E. realised in his heart that he could never come
near to being a great artist; and so, in the foolish vanity
of man's nature, besought himself to believe that his nature
was too high, too noble, too precious to veil itself in art's
indulgence. He was never offered the gift by the Holy
Ghost, and therefore could never reject it. It is a gift given
to few, and when once given can never be rejected nor
despised without a soul's loss.

—Yes, said Donal, but did you ever hear tell of him
telling George Moore that the gods came to sit on the edge
of his bed so that he could sketch them? Didn't he say, if
he told people that, he could sell every picture he could
paint, and that they would think him a very wonderful
person. The gods, A.E. said, swished in to sit on the edge
of the bed while he sketched them. Cock your head a little
to the left, Mananaan Mac Lir; that's too much—woa,
that's just right. And you, Angus of the Golden Hair, of
the Ever-Sounding Harp, God of Love, I think you should
stand in the centre of the room, a languishing look on your
face, as if you were singing, *When First I Met Thee Warm
and Young*; and you Louisiana Loo of the Long Hand,
stand to attention, spear poised in the right hand, your left
hand on your hip hip hurrah, as if you listened to
the gathered Gaels singing *Go Where Glory Waits
Thee*.

—Oh, gentle and devout Fra Angelico, you could never
be so surely arrogant! said Sean. In deep humility, out of
the high imagination of your mind, you turned your men

274

and angels into gods in colour and grace and happy sim-
plicity of form. A.E.'s gods were as artificial as the light
he often painted by, for artificial light was nothing to him,
for most of what he painted never depended on the light
the sun gave. His palette was typical of himself, indistinct,
uncertain, to allow him to outspread a vision of thinly-
tinted dreams. He splashed on the dove-grey, the light
blue, and the pink, that coloured his empty heaven and his
emptier earth, symbols of his own vague mind, vapouring
everything in nature within lilac and pink and dove-grey
so as to fit them into the tinselled universe conceived in
the mirage of his own ancestral self.

—And no-one questioned him, said Donal; no-one ventured to deny his artistic greatness, and silence answered
every doubt, every contrary opinion put forward by some
braver fool. A.E. is a unique painter, they all murmured.
He certainly is, for there was none ever like him before,
and I hope to God there will never be again.

—Even Lady Gregory wouldn't say boo to the goose,
complained Sean. Once, when we came into the Abbey
Theatre Green Room together, she tightened her lips and
shut her eyes when I pointed out to her the dull effrontery of an oil-painting of herself, hanging over a settee, done
by A.E. Then noticing that I was annoyed, she caught my
arm, gave it a good-humoured squeeze, a gleam in her
bright eyes, a jovial twist round her expressive mouth, as
she said, "We won't look ad id; keep your eyes off id al-
todether. I know; bery bad. We leave id dere because we
don't want to turt poor A.E." So there it was left, swinging
away on the wall in all its dull presumption.

—Amn't I after telling you that, said Donal. And as

for the Art itself, is there e'er a one a body could call a painter left in the land, other than the boyos who put bright colours on the window-frames and doors of the haughtier houses? Donal answered his own question. Ne'er a one, he said, as he poured what remained of the bottle of stout into his glass.

—Oh, Gawd! ejaculated Edwin Grey in a tone of impatient resignation. Then he added languidly, I don't believe I heard the name of Jack Yeats once mentioned.

—He makes no appeal to me, said Donal.

—And so must be of no account as a painter, murmured Grey languidly.

—Oh, I'll say that in his early phase, said Donal defensively, each of his pictures gives a pleasant thought or two for a moment or two; but I've seen nothing to make you pause and wonder; nothing in colour and line that silently sings a lyrical song, like, say Giorgione's *The Tempest*, or his *The Sleeping Venus*; nothing with the grace and power to hedge one in to looking at it for a long time, or tempt one back again and again to do it reverence.

—And his latest work? queried Grey, touching supercilious scorn into the sound of his words.

—That, said Donal, is even less to me than what he used to do. He seems to be poking the paint on to the canvas; a dot and dash kind of art; a morse medley of colouring; an unruly ecstasy of patchwork painting.

Sean said nothing. He listened. One for, one against— which was right? He would take neither side till he felt he knew.

The narrow door of the snug was shoved open, bring-

ing in an evil air, hotter than the hot air of the snug.
Through the open door, Sean caught a glimpse of sparkling
mirrors in which appeared a multitude of dancing bottles,
red-labelled, blue-labelled, and black-labelled, forming a
tubular background to a number of excited faces, in which
eyes winked and mouths opened and shut, amidst a rowdy
murmur as of many raucous chattering daws. Then a
sturdy, plump woman wedged her way in among them,
and with a muttered, Excuse me, gentlemen, flopped down
on the little bench to the left of the snug's narrow window.
She carried a basket which she put down on the floor at her
feet, and Sean saw a few nosegays of violets left unsold
from the day's sale. She was followed by a man of middle
height, rather thin, but wiry, who held a brimming glass
of whiskey in each hand. Kicking the door shut behind
him, he handed a glass of whiskey to the woman, and
squeezed himself down on to the bench beside her.

The woman was nearing bulkiness in size, but Sean
noticed her shape was clear and firm, and in places, alluring. Her wide bottom covered two-thirds of the seat, but
it didn't softly spread about, but remained firm in its
rounded curves when she sat down. Sean saw, too, that the
big globular breasts, scarcely hidden by a light-blue blouse,
hadn't wobbled when she had flopped down on the bench,
though it was plain that she wore no corset to keep them
steady. Her head, bare of hat, was covered by a tossed
mass of light-brown hair, a little dingy with the street's
dust. It covered her head and the nape of her neck in
clustered bunches, as if the thick curls were shy, and had
crowded together in groups to hide themselves from star-

ing eyes. A curiously-pale face was wide and round, the full circle diverted by a rounder, and a buoyant chin, topped by a thick-lipped mouth. Her nose was gracious and slender, looking a little uneasy in the rather jubilant width of her face. Over her blouse, she wore a black shawl, bordered with lines of a deep yellow, and further set off with a fringe of the same colour. This she slipped from her shoulders, allowing it to fall into a cascade of yellow-bordered black cloth around her bottom and back of her thighs. A brown skirt was tucked up, and gathered in round her wide waist, and a stout, but invitingly-curved, leg thrust itself brazenly forth, for all to see, from beneath a short petticoat of dark red.

A woman for a man to play with after an hour of loud song, when the taste of wine was thick on the tongue, when laughing hope was high, and the passions reckless. There was comfort in her, too; comfort as well as illusion in that wide, white, violate bosom. Here was the earth-breath, the great mother whom A.E. had so often searched for, and never found. A stalwart man, doubting his courage, might find new life, warmth, and power within the shelter of her strong, deftly-turned arms.

The man beside her was about sixty years of age. He was of middle height, thin, and wiry looking. He had high cheek bones, and his eyes were black and small, but bright and beady as a squirrel's. His hair, apparently once brilliantly black, like his eyebrows, had turned to a dull brown, heavily sprinkled with dim grey tufts. A long, thin nose cut the face clean in two, its butt almost jutting over a close and surly-looking mouth; but when he talked, the

278

lips showed themselves to be red, and graciously well-formed. He was dressed in a thick coat of Melton blue, striped cotton shirt, and a white handkerchief was wound, cravat-like, round his neck. He wore heavy white corduroy trousers, so long that they showed but little of his thick-soled, heavily nailed boots. His head was covered by a rough, brown tweed cap, its peak shoved to one side so that the wearer could get a full view of the lady. Though his rather bony hands were big, Sean saw that they had carried the glasses of whiskey cleverly, and one of them now clasped a glass with sinewy and supple fingers. Hands, thought Sean, that could hold a woman down tight.

—Looka here, said the woman, as soon as she had settled herself, I'm tellin' you he shouldn't ha' done it. No matther what you say, you're wrong, so y'are. It was an eyeopener to me. Julia, says I, Julia, thrust no-one afther that; th' Man above, yes; but anyone here below, no. Afther sayin' he couldn't do it, an' he wouldn't do it, he done it, regardless of th' feelin' of others. How are we goin' to look decent people in th' face ever again? We haven't got a single thing to stand up for now. Oh, Julia's a friend of his no longer. He's no leadher of mine, now. I'm tellin' you, De Valera should never ha' taken th' oath.

—Maybe you're right, maybe you're right, Julia, the man murmured thoughtfully.

—Here's health! she said suddenly, gulping down half of what was in her glass.

—Good health, the man echoed, drinking all of his and depositing the empty glass on the ledge by his elbow.

—Sacred Heart, it's hot in here! and Julia undid some of the upper buttons of her blouse, showing Sean that her skin was white, and seemed as soft as velvet.

—The dhrink here isn't up to the mark, said the man. You dhrink up, Julia, an' we'll go to my place where there's prime stuff waitin' for a hand to pour it out; and his glittering beady eyes wavered between looking at her face and the white bosom peeping from the opened blouse. He pressed his sinewy fingers persuasively on to her thigh —Dhrink up, now, an' we'll go.

—I don't care what anyone says, muttered Julia, lowering the rest of her whiskey, he shouldn't ha' done it. He should ha' considered his followers' feelin's.

—Sure I know, I know, said the man. I know well how you feel about it. His hand went up slyly to her bosom, and fingered her blouse till another button was undone. It's aggravatin', right enough. He'll be sorry for it all one o' these days—you'll see.

—Eh, there, she suddenly said sharply, hitting his searching hand away from her blouse; don't start to open me up in public!

—Oh, Gawd! came from Edwin Grey in a whispered moan. Let's go—it's too revolting!

—It's time to move, said Donal, looking at his watch, if we're going to go to Stephens's tonight.

They led the way from the snug, Sean following slowly. He longed to stay where he was, watching common life unfolding on the bench opposite; smoky life, catching the breath with a cough at times, but lit with the red flare of reckless vigour. It was the last time he would go to these gatherings. He liked James Stephens, loved him, really, and many fine people assembled there; but they were never themselves; they were ever on their guard; cautious and prepared, posing even, for there were few things in Dublin more conventional than the boastful, free-and-easy manners of its bohemianism. He bid a silent farewell to the black shawl with its rich yellow border, the pale, serious face, made jaunty by the twist of the big, red mouth, the gleam in the grey eyes, and the bunchy recklessness of the curling hair.

Curious gatherings these of Dublin! Yeats's, and its very elect assembly; A.E.'s with its rather less select gathering of literature and timid politics; and Stephens's, with a few select, but many more of the lesser known, more homely, more honest-to-God, more happy than the other two conclaves. Sean strolled after the other two, thinking of how astonished he had been the first night he had gone to an A.E. *At Home*. When the room filled, desultory chat ended, and each settled himself for ordeal or treat. A.E. was climbing into his throne. This was a chair placed on a platform, and those present sat in a humble semicircle round this royal seat. A.E. climbed heavily, hoisting himself into it, the rotund belly and big backside eclipsing the throne for the rest of the evening. He ceremoniously lighted his pipe, while he waited for someone to start the talk rolling along like ole man river. It seemed plain to Sean that A.E. used the talk and the comments as a vocal rehearsal for what he would say in his Journal during the coming week. When he spoke, he did so as if his mind was the only one in harmony with the spheres. He became the policeman on point-duty directing the way through the avenues and lanes of this life, and those of the life to come. He had no music in him, for, like Yeats and Gogarty, he was tone-deaf. He poured out words in a steady, colourless torrent, full of sound, destitute of fury, signifying very little. It had struck Sean as strange how this man, so voluble in his own den, on his own throne, could be so silent when he was in Yeats's parlour. Sean had seen him there, sitting back in a fat settee, occasionally lighting his pipe with a casual air, as if to show an indifference Sean was sure he did not feel. There he sat, silent, as if this talk did not matter, for importance and immensity were with him only who sat upon the fat settee. That A.E. uneasily felt that Yeats was beyond and above his rivalry was a sure thought to Sean, as he listened to the one and watched the other.

The three of them climbed up the stairs to James Stephens's flat, away up, up at the top of a high house in Fitzwilliam Square. The old kentucky home of Dublin's literary crowd. All the faces he had begun to know were there, together with a few he didn't know yet. There was A.E. right enough, holding forth on the arts; and Sean slipped to a chair in the background, for he knew, if A.E. spotted him, he'd be over to deluge Sean with the economic solution of ills through his, and Horace Plunkett's, thousand years plan of agricultural organisation policy. Oh, will you listen to him!

—*There's no doubt that magic is rarer in art than in literature*, he was saying with tremendous assurance. *In literature, Keats, Coleridge, our own Yeats, make a magi-*

cal use of words. But in painting how rare it is. We can think of some, Turner and Monticelli. But it is Blake more than any other who suggests magic in his art. From him we get an excitement of spirit which far greater craftsmen are unable to communicate.

Ay, thought Sean, unable to communicate to A.E., for here his thought is rather of the magic of the medicine-man than of the artist. What an arrogant and conceited comment! Magic is rare in painting! We can think of some. It is Blake more than any other. Did this man know anything about painting? He couldn't know much. What kind of magic was he looking for? The pictured Christ that turned its eyes on the onlooker as he left the room would have made A.E. chant a *te deum*. He couldn't have meant the magic which beauty in colour and line and form raise in the minds of those who are able to see them; for in this world of strange and enduring magic there are hundreds of painters as good, or better than Turner or Monticelli, and very much better than Blake. And this man was accepted, not only as a critic, but as an oracle too. Oh, listen to him, now!

—*The painters Picasso, Braque, and Cézanne aren't good for beginners in the study of art,* rang out the arrogant voice. *Folk obviously inspired by Cézanne or Picasso should be sternly suppressed.* Evidently, to be inspired by the wretchedness of A.E's imitations was righteousness and peace; to be influenced by Picasso and Cézanne was wicked-ness and vice.

—Oh, holy God! mumbled Sean, he's on top of me now! A.E. had turned and had seen Sean; he made a bee-line for him, and had planked himself down on a chair beside him. Then he poured the abstract chronicles of his *The National Being* into Sean's dulled and puzzled ear. Some demon or another, for a lark, to torment poor people, had bestowed on A.E. a brain that could vividly remember every phrase, every word of whatsoever he had written, and another demon had inflicted A.E. with a burning desire to pour all of whatsoever he had remembered into an ear unpleasantly situated to receive it by the fact that the listener hadn't a chance to escape. So Sean listened and ached and murmured in his heart, This man is not for me; none of these here are for me; you must go, Sean, go from them, for their people are not your people, neither is their god your god.

Suddenly, those present clapped their hands when James Stephens called on A.E. to join the crowd by reciting one of his poems, and in a fine burst of enthusiasm, Sean clapped longer than the rest. A.E. murmured that it wasn't easy, after talking to O'Casside about things material for so long, to summon up the Divine Afflatus. The hands clapped again, a little more impatiently, either to give A. E. encouragement, or to show advanced appreciation of the beauty that was bound to come. A.E. was pleased, taking long breaths, puffing himself out, breathing solemnity and power into his psyche, amid a hush of awed silence. In the midst of the awed hush, Tom McGreevy's voice, like a thunder-clap, was heard saying, Give the poor man a chance—he has to pump himself up!

A titter, chokingly modified, rippled round the room,

silenced altogether by Stephens' warning murmur of disapproval, and by the sudden rage of A.E. He rose roughly from his seat, snarling out that He wouldn't stay to be insulted; broke through the circle of friends by shoving his chair violently backward, and rushed swiftly from the silent room. No-one spoke, till McGreevy added to the already given insult by saying, There goes the most conceited man in Ireland.

No-one was quite happy the rest of the evening, though James Stephens did his best to promote forgetfulness. So when Sean and his two companions left the house to walk home, their minds were fixed on the scene they had seen.

—McGreevy's right, said Donal. Under A.E.'s skin-deep humility is an insatiable vanity, a burning desire for acceptance. He filled his *The Irish Statesman* with his own articles under three or four different pen-names. He constantly talked to friends about the immensity of his booklet, *The National Being,* a booklet of tumbling words, weaving a useless and impossible pattern. He said that it had been translated into a number of languages; that it had appeared in India because Tagore wanted India to study it. He said his idea was used by Bulgaria, which, after the war, wasn't allowed to have an army; and that after the idea had been in operation for two years, a report on it was issued by the League of Nations. But these claims have died down, and were never confirmed. He told many that his *Thoughts for a Convention* created a great stir, for an editor had told him that the pamphlet had shaken the Unionist Faith in Ireland to its innermost tabernacle. Did anyone ever hear the like! The pamphlet hadn't rustled a hair of Irish Unionism's head.

—And look at what he said of Shakespeare, said Donal. Says he, *Shakespeare was the first supreme artist in literature who seemed to be absorbed in character for its own sake. And nothing is revealed in the Shakespearean drama except character. What did the genius of Shakespeare do for literature?* A.E. asks. And he answers, *More and more since his apparition have dramatist and novelist been artists of character for its own sake; and to be absorbed in character for its own sake is to be in a blind alley which leads nowhere.* And A.E. goes on, *Artists will revolt, and science which has been materialistic for a generation* (as if it was ever anything but materialistic!) *has become etherealised before the mystery of the atom; so the artist, always sensitive to spiritual atmosphere, may be inspired to draw literature out of the blind alley where Shakespeare has led it, to conceive of life as a part of a divine procession in which the personal dwindles, but the immortal may be exalted by a profound consciousness of cosmic purpose.*

—Terrible! said Sean. But then he couldn't stand Shakespeare's *Sonnets*, didn't like his plays, and no wonder, for Alexander Dumas, Zane Grey, and others like them, were the literary nectar his gods gave him.

—And this was the kind of blather, said Donal viciously, that has dulled the ears, dimmed the eyes, and twisted the tongues of the younger thinkers and artists of Ireland. A.E. has scatttered his divine processions, his ancestral selfs, his exalted immortalities, and his cosmic purposes as

286

no sower would dare scatter his seed. Has all the mystery
of the minds of all the great men and women of our race
dwindled down into the mystery of the atom? Not a mun-
dane mystery only, not a heavenly one only, but a cosmic
purpose was to jump out of the activity of the atom. Holy
and almighty atom, deliver us! Here was a man teaching
his disciples to play the flute by simply blowing down it,
ignoring the fact that they would have to use quick fingers
to make the stops speak out a tune. Imagine the statement
that in a divine procession, the personality must dwindle.
Imagine the personality of an artist dwindling when he
wrote, painted, or carved a greatness into a stone. The long
line of the greater painters, sculptors, architects, surgeons,
and scientists are a divine procession, and the things they
have done are their divine deeds, honouring God and
glorifying man. We are all caught in the adventure of life
through time and space, and to reap, plant, sow, mow, to
cook a dinner well, to bring up children, and keep a home
in order are divine deeds, calling for God's crowning and
the sensible approval of man. Surely A.E.'s gospel is
related to the mind of a man who secretly realises that in
art and in literature greatness is not for him. And it comes
ill from one whose talents were all derived, not from his
own quality, but in imitation and in the practice of the far
finer qualities of greater souls.

—The two of you are talking like a couple of barbarians,
said Edwin Grey, his thin body quavering with annoyance. Your minds haven't yet risen high enough to understand the man. He is accepted the world over as a saint,
a seer, the great philosopher of his day, a poet of the first

rank, a painter of exalted imagination and of fine skill, a first-class economist, and a pioneer in agricultural progressive organisation. What did Monk Gibbon, the poet, say of him? This: *I have known one great man, one man alone to rise head and shoulders above all his contemporaries.* Not this or that one, mind, but all of his contemporaries! And what does the poet, Katharine Tynan, say? This: *In Yeats, in Stephens, in Francis Thompson, I have not found the beauty of genius I found in A.E.* Good Gawd! are you two going to set your opinions against these two poets?

—Yes, why not? asked Sean.

—You would: in your pride, your vanity, your desire for notoriety, you would set yourselves up against finer ones than yourselves. A.E. was, as Con Curran, the writer and critic, in a sacred burst of enthusiasm, said, *the Tribunal before which the Ignoble dwindled. He thought nothing of what men thought important; he sought obscurity as a companion; and he was intensely indifferent to fame.*

—Ah, for God's sake, man! said Sean. A.E. hastened his death making himself known. In America, he had himself radioed from one end of the land to the other. He travelled from one end to the other, too, the sun blazing over his head one time, and frost under his feet at another. He rushed about everywhere, talking, talking, a Mr. Talkinghorn talking on things political, spiritual, artistic, philosophical, and rural, about which he knew as much as a new-born chicken; for what he thought he knew, he got from books stored in Plunkett House of Merrion Square.

He never once had a sickle, a scythe, a fork, or a hoe in his hand. He never plucked a grain of corn from an ear; he never led out a horse to give him a drink; he never soiled his boots in the mud of a byre; and he never touched with his stout, pudgy finger the udder of a cow.

Indifferent to fame! Yet he is full of the way he talked to five hundred business men in San Francisco; how mightily he impressed them, though apparently none of them would, since none of them did, put down money to keep *The Irish Statesman* going. These were like the roaring catholic business men, so intensely concerned about the faith of poor catholic children, but diligently neglect to give the money to maintain the schools in which to teach it to them. A.E. actually believed that he could hypnotise square-jawed business men who loved and praised the mingling of economics with the Aeolian poetry A.E. gave them. So they would, for there was nothing in either the poetry or the economics to alarm the business man. A.E. could safely say to them *Come with me, acushla, into the ancient hills,* for there was no danger that in the ancient hills their power would be questioned or their dividends cut. After telling us that Arizona reminded him of Zane Grey, he tells us that his *The Candle of Vision* is known everywhere. He lets out a cheer when he thinks that all scientists will soon become mystics, because Jeans, the astronomer, stated he believed in a divine mind; and he even plays with the idea that he may be elected an honorary member of the British Association, along with Yeats and other poets with an internal light! Internal light. Lady Gregory once said, in a merry mood, that A.E.

hides a mystical light in a turnip; but the fact is that he hides a turnip in a mystical light.

—Vanity was the well-spring of his life, said Donal, lighting his pipe with emphasis; and Notoriety and Love of Fame were the two gods who constantly sat on the edge of his bed to keep him company. But he let his helplessness be known once when he was terrified to learn that the American practice of being up and doing hadn't the result he expected. He tells us that overdoing production in agriculture and industry, and with fewer people producing more than the world could consume, the Americans were staring at each other in surprise, for they found that in producing so much, they had produced unemployment. More than they or the world could consume! This is the great economist for you! At that very moment, in the U.S.S.R., in India, in England, in A.E.'s own country, in America even, there were millions who weren't getting enough in either food or goods; and yet this know-all in economics told us that the Americans were producing more goods and more food than the peoples of the world could use or eat! This lover of truth wouldn't tell the truth; this destroyer of myths, this lover of humanity wouldn't say that the production was greater, not than the world could use, but greater than the world could buy; that profits, about which he is silent, ensured that half of the world could go hungry rather than that profits should grow less. But he lectured on the depression, and a Harvard professor tells us that they listened to A.E.'s solution for the depression in Agriculture and Industry, and immediately began to organise the farmers on old-world

lines, which terrified A.E. again—not because the method
was a silly one—but because the farmers wanted five
million dollars to set the scheme going.

—I still have the same reverence for A.E., said Edwin
Grey languidly, that I had before either of you began to
speak.

—Keep it bright and polished, said Donal a little bitterly; and do daily honour to him who hated fame and
courted obscurity; he got Hughes, Sheppard, and another
to make busts of his Olympian head. Indeed, during the
Easter Rising, when the Hibernian Academy went up in
fire, and the bust was lost, A.E. quickly sat for another,
one in marble this time. Sarah Purser and Countess Markievicz both painted him, and F. R. Higgins, the poet,
had a pastel done of him by a foreign artist; Yeats's father
did him too; and there's the Gilbert Bronze, and the dry-
point by Tittle, where he looks fat and gross, a thing that
displeased many; and Rothenstein did him twice. A portrait by Dermod O'Brien; lithograph by Mary Duncan; a
wax portrait medallion by T. Spicer; bust by Jerome Connor; portrait by Estella Solomons; and one by Hilda
Roberts. His bust by Sheppard blended in it the likeness
of Socrates, Ruskin, and all the sages of the world. A.E.
used to refer to it himself mockingly, as *Sheppard's
Olympian Zeus*, but when one heard him say it, one heard
a ring of prideful joy in the sweet mockery.

—Ay, and in America, went on Donal, savagely, he
hurried into a kinema to watch himself in a newsreel, as
anxious as any mortal in Skibereen to see himself as a
public show. Zeus watching himself on a screen! A god

veiling himself in the limelight. And how he rejoiced in telling that when Wilbur, one of Hoover's cabinet, held a meeting, the hall was half empty because everyone was flocking to another hall to hear himself.

—And what about his opinions of American cities and the people who live in them? asked Sean.

—I read it, said Donal. He said, *These cities are the last trap set for the spirit of man to draw him from nature and himself. The people who live in them are kind, but oh, so unhappy. They fly from one sensation to another and the way from body to soul is lost. If they close their eyes, they are in a darkness that frightens them. They cannot bear to be still or alone. They are thirsty for beauty, but cannot create it within themselves. When they meet a soul, truly living, natural and prodigal in itself, they are filled with wonder. They cannot help themselves, poor people. They were born into the mechanistic maze and do not know the way out. There was never anything in the world so pitiful as their souls.*

—The poor Yanks! added Donal sarcastically.

—Oh, it's maddening, said Sean. A.E. has always gone round preaching, that though we overcome material things, shortly after, material things overcome us. He was bitter in his cosy hatred of cities, so unlike Whitman, one of the great men he tried to resemble. There is as little (or as much) of what he calls spirituality in the country as there is in the city. He, himself, lived most of his life in a city. His home was in Dublin, and a very nice part of it too. All very fine to spend a few sunny weeks in the country, when everything was kind, and flowers bloomed in a haze of enchanting heat. But A.E. let well enough alone when the colder winds blew from the mountains and the bitter green sea foamed arrogantly over the beaches. In one of his books, he tells of a young artist fleeing from the fog, gloom, cold, and mechanism of a city, as if the country never knew these things; could never be cold, never gloomy, never have a fog in the valley, or over the hill, never vibrate to the whirr of the combine-harvester and drill. The young man was fleeing from the blighting, mechanistic life of the city which he hated but A.E., thoughtlessly enough, pictures him fleeing in a swell-upholstered, smoothly-running automobile. We see the young man, fleeing from mechanism, watching, through the window, the lemon light in the sky, the snowy fields, the cottages on the hillside; watching all from the centre of one of the finest mechanisms the mind of man has created. Away from the mechanistic city on the air-filled, rubber-tyred car, driven forward by the internal-combustion engine, conjuring up visions in the comfort of silent locomotion, soft cushions, and warm protection from the cold snarl of the snow. The young man, serene in the smooth-running car, comfortable against the cushions, wondered whether a time would ever come when all men would revolt as he had done, return to nature, and let that mother restore their lost likeness in soul and body to their ancestral beauty.

Could any reflection be sillier, more hysterical, or more hypocritical than this? Back to nature in a gorgeous car! Back to a lofty, roomy house, shaped like a Greek temple, with pillars holding up the façade, made of wood, and painted white! Oh, you mores, oh, tempores, how does your garden grow? Back to nature? How far now? To the skin-coat and the cave? To the tribe, or to the condition of feudal lord and feudal slave? Give up the tractor for the steel-bladed plough, or the steel-bladed plough for the deer's horn with which to scrape the ground? Give up the smoothly-running car, carrying the artist, for the sedan-chair, the horse, or shank's mare? Give up the electric glow in workshop and home for the candle or the rushlight? Give up A.E.'s own method in the co-operative creamery, with its fine machinery separating the cream from the milk, to make butter in the older, more natural ways of the bare hand and the wooden churn? Go back to the uncertain and hesitating probe, and abandon the Roentgen rays, making the surgeon's stab a sure thing, and so relieving pain and preserving life? Abandon the anaesthetic and germ-free theatre to go back to the old deal table, the meat-saw, and the tub of boiling pitch in which to plunge the stump and stay the bleeding? Smash all the delicate instruments denoting time, and go back to the days of the water-clock and the sundial?

Go back to nature! The yellow-bordered black shawl, the attractive face, pale as a new-born lily, with the luminous eyes, the big, red, defiant mouth, ascetic nose, crowned by the bunchy clusters of curling hair, the white bosom, pushing forward to be fondled, that had been flickering about on the screen of Sean's mind all through the talking, faded away now, for he was angry. It made him angry to think of these people murmuring from a chair, or shouting from a pulpit. Go Back to God; Go Back to Nature! Go back to nature. We had never left her. Go back to God, go back to nature, without telling us how to do it. This is not the cry of the shepherd, but that of an hireling, afraid to face what God has brought to pass in the changes of a changing world. These people know, or ought to know, that the things done now, however mighty they be, will soon be lesser things behind the greater ones still to come. But they are afraid, they shiver before every forward step taken by man, and try to frighten him, too, with their meandering, delusive cries of back to God and back to nature. These were they who wanted life to die with a whimper, and were embattled, in Press, pulpit, and poem, against those who were determined, if life should die at all, that life should die with a cheer. It was utterly useless, and a little dangerous, to go about singing the song of Go back, go back to nature and go back to God, for it could never be done in the way they wanted it. The ways behind man were closed; the way before him was open, and forward he must go. If a God existed, then man was going to meet Him; he was not going to go back from Him, or slide away into a corner out of His sight. If God there be, then He was with the aeroplane five miles high in the sky, sailing over the North Pole, as He had been with the first ploughman who fixed a steel edge to his wooden plough. If God there be, He is with the minds planning the bridge over the Severn as He was with the mind that flung a grass rope over a river to make a safer way to cross it; He is with the man of the combine-harvester sweeping over the prairie of waving, golden corn, gathering it and threshing it in big bundles, as He was with the lonelier one, heavily cutting his few stalks of grain with a sickle-curving flint-stone; He is with the scientist controlling or releasing the energy of the atom as He is with the anxious young mother kissing her baby to sleep. A wayward mother may bring misery and danger to her child, and wayward minds may bring misery and danger from the power of the atom; but, by and large, the mother will always be loving and true to her child, and the energy in the atom will be for man's redemption in the end.

—We leave you here, said Edwin Grey to Sean, when the three of them had halted on Binn's Bridge covering the canal, and within sound of the falling, gurgling waters on the lock. And remember even J. B. Priestley was constrained to admit that A.E. spent most of his time finding geniuses daily.

—And carrying them to the market in basketfuls, said Donal gaily—come on, if you're coming. Sean watched the two of them fading away down the Drumcondra Road, and turned to go his own way, thinking.

—It was said over and over, thought Sean, that adulation affronted A.E., yet no man of Ireland was ever more sicklied over with adulation than he; and he never seemed anxious to avoid it. He said he didn't like it, but followed it close, and was never far from where it was to be found. When the younger ones of Dublin discovered that A.E. had no real message for them; that he whom rumour said excelled in all things, excelled in nothing but the vast intention of his own importance, they left him. The yogi contemplative felt lonely. Finding the adulation gone from Dublin, he sought it out in London; and finding it

faint there, he sought it out in America. Desmond
McCarthy drawing a picture of A.E. in the last years of
his residence in Rathgar Avenue said, As years went on,
fewer young men and women came of an evening to drink
at A.E.'s fountain. When I inquired from friends visiting
England, I was told—A.E.? I haven't seen him. Nobody
goes there now.

Nobody goes there now. One would imagine that a
sage, such as he claimed to be, would have welcomed loneliness as his salvation. Nobody came, so he was lonely.
Socrates, Plotinus, Buddha, Plato, Confucius, were there,
but he didn't want them. The great books of the Vedas,
the Bhagavad-Gita and the Upanishads were there, but
they didn't go far enough for A.E. Alexander Dumas was
dead; Zane Grey didn't write stories often enough, and so
he was lonely. He had no place for the yellow-bordered
black shawl, the luring face, the snowy bosom; and so he
was lonely. Humour might have saved him, but there was
a sad lack of deep laughter in him. Neither had he song
in him, for his ear was dead and dull to all music; and so
he was lonely. All the glitter had faded. The glittering
guy, so gay-looking in artificial light looked drab and
tawdry in the light of day. There was nothing of the child
in him, so much of the kingdom of heaven laughed at and
eluded him. He was too often with his own gods. He was
never known to laugh at himself. He was never seen out
walking with his wife. He was never seen out walking
with a child. He would have thrown a yogi fit if a prepos-
sessing whore, parading Grafton Street, had stopped him to
ask If there was anything good in his mind. He was afraid

of Yeats. He wrote never-endingly, he talked incessantly, he painted persistently, he travelled immoderately, and, finally, he left behind him a handful of pebbles, sanctified with a little gilt, that he took to be jewels.

As Sean ambled home, the lingering vision of A.E. burying his face in the earth grass when it was sunny, never when it was harsh and sharp with frost; or chanting his highly-coloured Sankey, Moody movie emotion hymns; or watching, eye-shut, mouth agape, over the crest of a mountain, forms crested with many-coloured lights, gigantic forms that seemed shaped from some burnished and exquisite fire, went fading away to make room for Sean's own ungodly goddess, buxom and confidently aggressive in her womanly wisdom, her popular loveliness queenly cloaked in the richly yellow-bordered black shawl; and of the sinewy-handed, squirrel-eyed god beside her, dream-tipsy with the thoughts of the ecstasy and warmth hidden away from him in the swell of her white bosom beneath the blouse.

Gods of the earth, earthy, thought Sean; but none the worse for that.

THE GIRL HE LEFT BEHIND HIM

SEAN had passed away from two Jennies, one Bella, and this girl gave him the fullest experience of feminine good companionship he had had so far. She was a good-looking lass. Even now, glancing back after seeing many girls much more beautiful, his memory told him, with quiet insistence, that her big hazel eyes, her heavy mass of rich brown hair, softly-rounded chin, fine complexion, and full, white throat, made her a good-looking lass. Years before, he used to meet her on his way home from first quarter's work to breakfast, a sturdy slip of a girl, her long hair tidied into two long plaits, hurrying to a catholic elementary school where she was training to become a teacher. Then in his cement-embroidered dungarees, his hob-nailed boots clattering a morning tattoo on the pavement, she had attracted his attention; and he stared boldly into the soft hazel eyes, as he passed, seeking in them a soft, shy shelter in which to rest occasionally on the long, hard road that was stretching itself out before him. He had never spoken, and she had never tried to answer his soul's muffled appeal for the fanciful solace of a young girl's breast, and the red-lipped kiss of great encouragement. Yet a little while, and she passed by no more, for, a teacher now, she served another school far from where he walked.

Years after, they met again, during the beginning of an amateur drama club. She lived, not beside the Anner, nor on the Banks of Loch Lomond, nor even by the pleasant waters of the river Lee; but in a most respectable, self-dignified little house. It was odd the airs these little houses gave themselves. They were stuck down in little narrow turnings off a bigger street, and each narrow way was given the delicious name of avenue. They faced each other grandly on either side of the road, a few more select than the others, having an upper storey, reached by a stairway that was really a ladder grown a little stouter with the years. The front room, or parlour, was a little wider, but less long, than the floor of a furniture van. In one of these, he had listened to a piano being played, and the instrument had looked as if it were terrified of its own music, for the sound of the notes played, crowded back, and smothered the new ones the piano was trying to give. The bedrooms were so small that a dim glance from one eye enfolded all that might be there. If you stretched out of the bed from the far side, you could put your head out of the window. The houses were pressed close, side by side, back to back, and front to front, each with its patch of back-yard surrounded by a low wall, so that a glance from both eyes could see them all boxed together, and, when people stood in them, they looked like cattle in their several pens. Yet the neatness, the cleanliness, the comfort of these midget houses were as much out of reach of Sean and his mother as lodgings even on the cold, cold floor of Edinburgh Castle, Buckingham Palace, or the Pope's private apartments in the Vatican at Rome.

Backed up by the stern respectability of their little grey house in the west, Nora Creena's father and mother were immediately against her having anything to do with Sean. And, indeed, as Sean discovered afterwards, Nora was scantily equipped with the courage to defy, or resist, the bitter respectability of these superb people; for Nora enjoyed all the peasant's awe in the tinselled glory of religion's parade, in supernatural nursery-tale of hell, and folk-invention of cherubim and seraphim that merged with the devil's face grinning from the show's centre, amid the coloured candlelight of religious fear. It had nothing in common with the child's delightful acceptance of coloured stories, which, however colourful, however violent, are always decent. There is hilarity and a comic certainty in a child's belief, and behind the sound of bells in the sleigh advancing, with its crimson-coated driver, are the painted cart, the green and yellow engine, the pink-faced doll, the gleaming gun, the silver trumpet, and the tasselled drum; the cart the symbol of harvest; the engine that of the good sense bringing goods everywhere that all may have a share; the doll of motherhood; the gun of war; and the trumpet and drum symbols of glory and the laurelled head.

But she was good to look at, gentle in manner, wistfully patient in listening to his talk, so the seasons through which they passed, using the city street or the country lane, spread enchanted hours before them, in fretted splendour overhead and tapestry of frost beneath their feet; or sun-dappled meadows, flushed with plenty, giving peace to timid cattle calmly grazing; or autumn weaving her russet, red, and golden mantle, covering the hedges with a lovely turmoil of gay and dying leaves.

He often wondered to which foliage of the autumn he should give the palm of beauty. To the oak, the elm, the beech, the birch? Certainly not to the chestnut, for its brown hues grew too coarse, and its fading leaves looked shabby and mean, stretched, drunkenly curling, on pathway and road. The common bramble? Ay, the touchy, ill-tempered, hand-biting bramble. Their stems are rich with purple, saluting the leaves where the green still lingers. Often on the same boastful stem, there are the greenish-white of later buds, the pink smile of blossom, and the green, red, and black of the clustering berries. The leaves of the sycamore and maple are lovely, but never so gorgeous as the leaves of the bramble. This tough guy of the hedgerow dresses herself through the autumn as gay as a gay-hearted gypsy queen, thrusting her long, embattled arm through everything in her way so that bloom and berry may reign safe in the sun and the upper air. But autumn is all a revelry of decaying loveliness; the decorated garment of decline. Every field, meadow, and hedge a world of burning bush. Each dwindling tree, sensing the end of its summer hilarity, like a beauty preening herself with paint and powder before the final fading, slings around her cooling shoulders her gayest and most gorgeous shawl.

Sean deluged Nora's mind with the organ music of Milton's sentences so that they fancied themselves fighting side by side with Michael, and watched the resentful, squealing flight of the fallen ones; saw all of

Satan's impious war in heaven, and battell proud, with vain
attempt.

*Nine days he with his horrid crew lay vanquisht, rowling
in the fiery gulfe confounded though immortal, a place
where peace and rest can never dwell, hope never comes
that comes to all.*

They heard the gallant words of Satan rejecting servitude
in heaven for sovereignty in hell; shivered together with
the shaking of his mighty spear uplifted in the mighty
arm; and saw the black banner of evil streaming out from
hell to the very rampart of heaven's jasper walls.

Sean lingered with her over the sad, sensuous cynical
innocence of Omar Khayyám's rose-like meditations,
knocking with him at the tavern door of life, shouting for
its wider opening, so that they might

> *Make the most of what we yet may spend,*
> *Before we too into the dust descend;*
> *Dust into dust, and under dust to lie,*
> *Sans wine, sans song, sans singer, and—sans end!*

He read the lovely cadences of Keats to her, trying to see
things of beauty that would be a joy for the day; and often
the pair of them heard Shaw laughing as he peeped from
behind a tree, thrusting out a hand to guide a lover and
his lass to Socialism; they listened to his merry and shrewd
comments on children and their parents, on marriage, on
war and peace, and on the things that mattered most to
Rosscullen in the heart of Ireland. And well she seemed
to listen between kiss and kiss; listened, so that Sean, vain,
vain man, thought the flame of his fancy was but a reflection of her own. He imagined for awhile that in this glori-

ous din of argument and beauty, she would decry the silly voice of warning; that she would henceforth wander as the wind which bloweth where it listeth; move among the brave to dance and sing with them when the softness of evening came, and stars were at their best; or when the moon appeared in graceful arrogance to drive all watchers from the heavens, and walk the sky alone; to walk within the limits of the sun, and cease to grope about within the shadowy glimmer of a holy candle. To stride along by the side of life, laughing; to fall with life seventy times seven; to rise again, and go on, rather than woo a crooked back and bending head, from kneeling before the flimsy forms, in coloured clay, of men lost to Padua and Alcantara; to step aside from following fools, beset with fright that foxy-minded imps from hell, hid deep in every house and heart, sidling sly at every dark street corner, lurking even in every church, would, in an unguarded moment of a poor sinner's thought, snatch up their unwary souls, and carry them off in a carpet bag to deposit them, safe and sound, into the itching hand of Satan.

Sean, suddenly, in the midst of an unexpected meeting, would get a pathetic and agitated letter saying that she could see him no more. Her words were mean with woe and the tale of reproaches, admonition, and threats from her people if she persisted in her folly of going with him. And these were too much for her. They would lay her low if she tried any longer to prevail against them. So for months he would see no sight of her, or hear a word about her. He had then to hurry back to the constancy of his own companionship.

Then in the core of his heart, Sean knew that Nora Creena hadn't it in her to stand out safely against opposition. She wilted under the family resentment and the priest's advice. He knew, too, that she would never force a way, nor stroll delightfully, through the embattled, or flowered, way of literature and life. He guessed that there weren't ten books, the number of the commandments, in the house where she talked, ate, and slept her life away; nor the semblance of a picture worth the time of glancing at it twice. Such books as she read were borrowed from the local library, a sound and very discreet loom and lure of literature. No need to make the sign of the cross on entering or leaving the building. The place was faint with the conquering grey breath of the pale Galilean.

She listened—how well she listened to all he said, to all he quoted; but Sean felt there was no real heed behind it. She would never plant a foot on any peak of Darien, never stray to any point from which the cross could not be seen; to where the bald unjointed chatter heard around it could be heard no longer. Our fathers and hail Marys chained her fast to where she wished to stay; she would never wander even as far as where she'd feel them binding her. For her the hunter of the east would never catch a sultan's turret in a noose of light.

Places far out in the country were chosen so that they might win a chance of escape from prying eyes; and, starting off early, Sean would walk there in his decaying boots, fearful of any cloud in the sky that would send rain falling to soak his boots into a sodden mass and saturate his thread-thin trousers. He had rarely a penny in his pocket to halve the heavy journey by tram, though she, in her sweet kindness, had often offered him the money, had tried to persuade him to let her share this simple thing with her; but, in his sour pride, he had always refused, bitterly, whenever she persisted in her persuasion. He had to submit to many humiliations that ground rage and bitterness into his soul. Several times, walking down a street near the rural edge of the city, they had met her younger sister coming towards them on the arm of her young man; and Nora, squealing out a Sacred Heart! it's Annie! would frantically wheel about, to run off in an opposite direction, while Sean, red with anger and shame, would have to trot away after her. He who was tense with the velvet-tipped doubt of Omar Khayyám, full of Shake-speare's exultation, rich in the grandeur of Milton, and under the blessing of Shelley's ardour and the beauty of Keats, had to hide miserably for fear of shocking ignorant respectability; denied the right even to pass it by in a decent and orderly manner, while the girl he admired, breathless with fright, trembled at his side. He who would face with indifferent effrontery castle prince or castle flunkey—here he was hiding from the midget majesty of a bowler hat. He used to be sick with rage for many a long day after.

But he enjoyed a brighter spell of life throughout any short hour that brought her by his side. Then she became a red, red rose, a westlin' wind bearin' home the laden bees, or a calm moon changing a mean land into a queenly world for one night only. But he knew, though she did not, that the moment the hour would turn into a life, the charm would end; for he realised that all they had read together, all she had listened to, hadn't added jot or tittle to her courage; hadn't toughened a fibre of her will to write a new sentence in her life, or criticise an old one. The Catholic Church had moulded the expanding universe into a doll's house for her, and there she lived by thronging duties pressed, with sorrows surging round, death shadowing her and hers, her future all unknown, there she lived in peace, in perfect peace; for Jesus she knew, and He is on the throne.

But it wasn't so easy for him, Sean thought, as he slouched homewards along the hedge-lined roads from Santry, Nora's kisses still happy and warm on his lips. He could not understand the stops, the ventages, the lowest, or the highest, compass in the melodious and malicious organ-tune of man's existence. What is man, O Lord, that Thou art mindful of him? *Thou hast made him a little lower than the angels, and hast crowned him with glory and honour.* Not much help there. What is he, who, *Like a forward child, must be played and humoured a little to keep it quiet, till it falls asleep, and then the care is over?* Who and what is he who comes like water, and like wind he goes? A very superior being, thinks F. J. Sheed; for *Man is aware of his power to produce effects which have nothing whatsoever in common with matter.* What, nothing at all? But man being matter, and the effects coming from man, how can it be said that these effects can have nothing in common with matter? Because, says Sheed, *Man can think—thought is not reducible to anything that we can feel justified in calling material. It doesn't occupy space, it has neither shape, nor size, nor weight, and it is not perceptible to any of our senses; it cannot be made into something else.*

That's a queer saying, surely. May not a thought take the shape of a poem, a painting, a building. It may even turn itself into a war, national or civil. And hasn't catholic thought filled the sky with angels? How do we know that thought doesn't occupy space? How are thoughts sometimes carried over space from one mind to another? And we give them definite qualities; we call a thought a deep one, a shallow one; there are great thoughts, high ones, low ones; dark thoughts and light ones too; and many a one has felt the sting of a sharp, fierce thought. What are they but the reflections of the mind that gives them birth and the mind of man is made of first-class material—the brain. Does an electron, dodging about in an atom, have weight; what shape is it; can it be measured; and is it perceptible to our senses? But, then, it may have a mind, for all we know. *So this element, this utterly unmaterial thing,* says Sheed, *must be produced by some element in man distinctive from his body.* So this element, whatever it may be, with nothing behind it, or before it, is the soul. This is the everlasting I Am of each person. This thing, sans sight, sans smell, sans taste, sans everything lives on forever; the nothing is a thing immortal. An element in a body, forming the little I Am, all that's left behind from all we knew, that doesn't occupy space, has no shape, nor weight, nor size, isn't perceptible to itself or anyone else, is a queer thing to go on living forever. And this is the soul of man, not the soul of man under Socialism, but

the soul under the belief in the catholic faith. And this
spectral thing that Sheed shoves out in front of the Communist, saying, No, son, your system won't work, for it
doesn't take in, or account for, this strange and wondrous
element, standing, like a tank trap, in the way of a proletarian march ahead.

The possession of a spiritual soul is the one thing that
makes a fundamental difference between man and the
lower animals, says Mr. Sheed. Seems from this that there
is a corporeal soul as well as a spiritual one. However
that may be, according to Mr. Sheed, the lower animals
have been deprived of, or have never been given, the
imperceptible element. God did not think it well to give
them the power of thought, so in this way, he separated
them from man forever. Mr. Sheed seems very sure of
himself, and of man, here. How does he know that animals can't think? And is he sure that the bulk of mankind
make much use of this imperceptible element of thought?
They seem to be beginning to do a bit of it now, and Mr.
Sheed is getting a bit anxious about it all. Is he sure that
animals, other than men, do no thinking? Who was it said,
The more I think of men, the more I love my dog? G. B.
Shaw tells us somewhere that a sheepdog understands his
master better than most men can understand the story told
by an astronomer. We had better be humble here. Sean
remembered sitting in the kitchen of a friend when his
host whispered to him to watch the big black cat, calmly
sitting beside the fire between them, washing her face
with graceful movements of her paw. Occasionally she
paused to give a glance at the dresser where two herrings

lay on a plate, while the woman of the house trotted
round tidying things up serenely. To fetch something,
the woman left the kitchen, and, immediately the cat
ceased her washing, listened a moment, then calmly
walked over to the dresser, jumped on to a chair, and
from the chair, jumped on to the dresser, pausing a moment to listen before she bent to eat the herrings. A little
later, her quick ear heard someone coming, for she raised
her head, cocked her ears, then jumped from the dresser
to the chair, from the chair to the floor, trotted back to the
fireside, sat down quietly where she had been before, and
once more, in all innocence, the graceful paw was moving
rhythmically, washing the fur behind her ears. What a
comic rogue that cat was in thought and action!

One time, Sean's brother, Mick, had a lovely, sturdily-
built Irish terrier that became very friendly with Sean. He
was a handsome animal, with a fine carriage and a proud
mien; but Mick, when he was drunk, or trying to recover
from the effects of drink, used to try to force the animal
to crouch before him, after hard beating, so as to show
to all who wanted to see how superior man was in thought
and deed to the lower animals. Whenever he knew the dog
was being beaten, and happened to be near, Sean hurried
to the help of the animal; and many a row took place
between Mick and him when he ventured to take the dog's
part. One time Sean heard savage growling, mixed with
Mick's curses, while he talked to a friend at the door, and
hurrying upstairs he found his brother trying to land
blows from a stick on the back of the dodging, snarling
terrier, wild-eyed now, his back bristling, his lips curved

savagely back to show his sharp, shining teeth. Sean caught
Mick's arm, holding it easily, for the wild look of the dog
had put something of the fear of God into Mick's mind;
and the biting mood of the animal showed he was in no
humour to crouch before his lord. Never had he done this
before, and Sean loved the dog for his independence; for
there was some of the fine animal's quality in Sean himself.

Keeping angry eyes staring at Mick, the animal edged
towards the door which Sean opened for him. He followed
the animal, and found him waiting at the back door. He
looked up at Sean, plainly asking that a way might be
opened for him to leave the house. Murmuring sympathetic words to the animal, snarling softly now, Sean with
one hand stretched to open the door, while with the other
he softly stroked the animal's rough neck. Sean opened
the door slowly, hoping that the dog would give him a
friendly look, but he never raised his head, nor ceased his
quiet snarling; then, when the door was open, he trotted
out to the yard, jumped on the low, surrounding wall,
and began to walk along it determinedly. Sean whistled
him lovingly back, but the dog went on; he whistled again,
putting an imperative tone of authority into the shrill notes
but, determined and stately, the dog went on, and neither
Sean nor Mick ever saw the animal again. The dog had
thought about it all, and had decided to go and never
come back. It was no flight; it was too determined and
dignified for that: it was, to Sean, a cold and calculated
decision, to seek a newer, and, perchance, a better life.
Since Sean, the man imaging God, couldn't protect him
from violence, then this dog, this lower animal, decided

to rebuke Sean by leaving him. To this day, the picture
glows sadly before Sean's eyes; the pensive sky overhead,
grey as a fasting friar's face, unmoved by a sharp, erratic
wind that stirred the dust in all the yards into eddying
uneasiness; the sturdy, arrogant church spire thrusting
itself into the sober sky over the shabby, shaking houses
all around, like a wealthy parvenu, newly-nobled, rising
to give advice to a gathering of charity-children; and by
it all, walking steadily along the low wall, the dog passed
on to where he might find shelter and food without paying for them with abuse and blows; or a place, maybe,
where he could die without them, in silence, self-respect
honouring his own last breath.

We are told, canonically, that this insubstantial, everlasting element is the bosom of pain, for without it, the
body would lose its power of feeling. We feel pain because
we are conscious, and we are conscious because we have a
soul. All nice and comfortably arranged, if you don't ask
any questions. But the lower animals feel pain, so what of
them? All nicely settled too. Animals feel pain because
they too have souls, but their souls are not immortal. Sean
was taught that all souls were immortal; but here are
souls which die when the body dies. Dead souls. How, and
when, were these souls given to the lower animals? When
Adam named them in the Garden of Eden? How is it that
while animals aren't conscious that they have souls, we
know they have them? Who told us that now? Were they
awarded souls only so that they might feel pain? Not
much of a gift, that! Are these souls graded? Are the
souls of the lowest among the lower animals equal in

unsubstantiality and precision of feeling? Is the soul of the
mouse the same as that of a lion? And how far down in
the scale of the lowest animals do souls go? Do they van-
ish at a certain point in the lowest of the low among the
lower animals of life? This element of thought, separating
man from the animals, according to the theology of Mr.
Sheed, having no shape, nor size nor weight, is the outward sign of the soul; so the soul should be as light and
airy as the thought it manifests. But the church says, The
soul is a substantial part of the body, and if this be so,
then one is prompted to imagine that a soul is something
more than smoke. Watch my smoke! Seeing, then, that
the soul, though not, maybe, consubstantial with the body,
is according to Mr. Sheed's own church, a substantial part
of it, that body which craves food, shelter, gaiety, health,
security, then the element which—Mr. Sheed says—pre-
vents a man from accepting Communism, is the very element that will run about to seek it, and finding it, will
embrace it as its own. How this good roman catholic
writer trots along the road of life without an effort, truth
and certainty gamboling along at his feet like docile
spaniels! He lives in a world where no bell is cracked;
no breeze is bitter; no sun to make him sweat, and no
frost to nip finger or ear; where birds chant the Athana-
sian Creed; where the brooks are Aristotelian waters dis-
tilled by Aquinas, giving sweet drink to all who saunter
by their banks; drink good for the body, saving the soul.

Easier to him than it was to a fine, brave, catholic theologian, Dr. McDonald, asking many questions that had
been settled forever by minor minds, with their glib

cathetical call of Supernatural Qualities. But what is a
Quality? asks this anxious theologian, and how does it
contribute to action? Don't ask me, mate, thought Sean;
I'm one of the higher animals, but I can't answer you.
"Then in what sense is the soul a substantial form of the
body? Or in what sense is the matter of which the body is
composed—chemical ingredients, such as are found in the
inorganic world—in need or capable of a substantial form?
Is it that the soul acts as a source of energy? But is there
any smallest fragment of the energy of the human body—
nerves or muscles—that does not come into it from the
ether, as to any other machine? Conscious sensation, you
will say; but is there any sensation that does not reside
in the nervous system, consisting entirely of material mo-
tions, which, no less surely than the movements of a black-
smith's arm, arise chemically? They tell us, now, from
Rome, that this difficulty has been cleared up by the writings of John Peter Oliver; which, however it may have
decided the question in dispute between Cardinal Zigli-
ara and Father Palmieri, S. J., has left the real difficulty
precisely where it was. In what sense, capable of being
brought into harmony with modern biological science, is
the human soul substantial form of the body wherewith
it is united?" Ask us an easier one, O theologian!

So Sean pondered deep in his heart on what he was and
what he might be; whether annihilation's waste would be
his when the end came; or whether what he was would
flame with life eternally, as he wandered in winter by the
tangled pauperism of the hedgerows, forlorn, save for an
odd robin perched well within them, looking like the soul

of a young saint, determined to be happy in the midst of desolation; or, in summer, when Nora had left him to journey home alone, when the hedges were jaunty with the trumpets of the bindweed, sounding their tiny tucket to the sun; the dainty wild rose, not too delicate to be arm in arm with the less tidy and rowdier blackberry blossom; the scarlet pimpernel's tiny red star gleaming among the eager, careless growth, like the fiery thoughts of a brave man in a pushing crowd; and the speedwell's blossom so blue that it must have been dyed by God's own steeping.

Yes, in politics, he was a Communist; and in religion, a Rationalist. From a casual friend, he had once persuaded a loan of Lecky's *Rise of Rationalism in Europe*, but had read only the first chapter when its return was demanded, and he had had to give it back. A precious book, he was told; expensive, and one to be guarded against staying away too long from its proper home. Afraid the book might hurt his soul, Sean thought, for all Ireland dreaded the danger of a book. He had watched for a copy on the second-hand bookstalls, but none ventured there. A rare book. In the Public Library? Not there, not there, my child. Not in his locality, anyhow. He heard of a library in Capel Street, that held a finer and fuller collection. He hurried to the President of his O'Toole Club, Johnny Kirwan, Manager of Murray's Belfast Tobacco Branch in Dublin. Certainly, Johnny would sign the guarantor's form for him. Next day Sean found Johnny had changed his mind—he refused to sign the form. Why? Can't you trust me to care for the books? asked the puzzled Sean.

Oh, dear, yes, Johnny could; it wasn't that; and after humming and hawing, Sean squeezed out of him that he was afraid Sean would read a book which might be bound to imperil his immortal soul. He'd buy Sean a book as a present; but Sean bowed, and told Johnny he could put the book where the monkey put the nut; and went his way, resolved that public libraries would know him no more, and that any book he might have in the future would be his own.

You see now, Sean, he argued with himself, the road you travel would never do for Nora. The rationalist would be pulling the religious forward; and the rigid religious would be dragging the rationalist back. She walked with him through the golden land; but would she trudge through the one of doubt and sorrow? Through that of sorrow—yes; through that of doubting—no. Revelation, coupled with tradition, gave insufficient answers to many questions he was asking. Ay, and as yet to many questions, there wasn't any answers at all; except those which refused to fit the answers, proved correct, confounding them. Was is right for such a mind as his to try to find an answer, rather than to abide with the answers found by others? Was it just vanity? Did it matter whether he moved forward, or stood still, when moving forward meant the shoving aside of some he loved? Mattering little or much, it was his way to go. He could no other. His nature had now led him to where he was; and the growth of past and present would inevitably shape his coming thoughts as growth brought forth blossom and fruit onto the blackberry and the acorn onto the oak.

Nora wasn't for him: she would forever shelter in the lee of credulous respectability. He remembered well, once, when she was telling him she'd have to cease from seeing him, how savagely she had declared that if he failed to make a name for himself in what he was trying to do within six months, their sweet alliance must end forever. He remembered how resentfully his soul laughed at the threat, for his development was with life, and not with calendar or clock. The Holy Ghost was not a panting creature of time, yet here was a good catholic girl trying to goad him into a hurry. The Holy Ghost in a hurry! She was measuring the gay-coloured wings of the Holy Ghost, hiding eternity with their spread, with the pale wings, stable as dust, of the frail, flying moth of time. There were other months in the year as well as May in which to go gathering nuts.

Let her cling to the little house, with its tiny windows and door; its four small rooms, with their neat little beds; the windows graced with curtains. They were her due, and she did well to claim them for her own. They were genuine things, to be sought after by the sensible and satisfied. The lions had long departed from the Christians. Sean didn't despise them, either; he wished he could dwell in one of them, in peace, secure as this world goes; with freedom to go, if ever one of these tiny, gentle things tried to enwrap his soul with lies. But he would be safer, if need be, walking the roads, or crouching, like blind Rafferty, under a dripping bush, while the rain fell and the wind blew keen. Not for Nora the charm of embroidered cloths under her feet, but the firmness of well-glazed

317

oilcloth, or the softness of a carpet, well woven, covering a floor. Not the red rose, with its agitating thorn, for her swan-white breast, but a black cross, nestling chill and steady there.

Never once had he mentioned the Bolshevik Revolution to her, though it was ever in his mind; never once had he tried by a word to attune her ear to an echo even of the march of the Red Guards, though he himself had followed, with quaking heart, the advance of Kolchak from the east, and the advance of Denikin from the south, till from where they were, Denikin said, they could see, on a clear night, through the windows of Moscow, the tight-lipped people getting ready to quit the city. The Press was full of the death and defeat of the Red madmen; then, suddenly, they fell silent; and Sean knew that the Red Flag was high in Moscow and Petrograd. O, Silver trumpets ye be lifted up, and call to the great race that is to come! Yeats, Yeats, they are sounding now, though your ears are cocked in another direction. Sounding loud and brave, not for all ears yet; but for the many to hear; and Sean's were the first of the Irish ones to hear them. Christ the king was becoming a Communist!

He knew in his heart that Nora and he would never fix themselves together in the world. Freethought to her would be but blasphemy and ruin eternal. A big part of her life would become a mumble of prayer that he might recognise the truth, accept the faith, be converted, and live. Jesus! that would be death in life to him! After the first while, or so, her creed would again form her life, and then his crowded loneliness would end forever. Let her gentle, quiet nature live a quiet, gentle life; let his doubting, strenuous one live out its activity and struggle, however bitter and painful, any, or all, of it might be.

He stood still to watch the tired and shallow flow of the slow waters of the Dodder, near Rathfarnham; hard set at times to push a way through the thick and sturdy herbage, growing querulously far out from its banks, shoving a passage often to the centre of the river; so like the flow of Ireland's life. Above him, the evening had pulled a curtain over the sky of quiet rose and daring green, now patterned with the shapes of hundreds of deep-black rooks, like darkened souls flying off, half afraid of heaven; while in the east, a pale moon, shy and pearly, stole into sight like a shy lass stealing out to meet a wild lover alone for the first time in her life. And around in the sheltering herbage he saw dim forms of life commingling, each a lover and his lass embedded in all the loveliness surrounding them.

> You say there is no substance here,
> One great reality above;
> Back from that void I shrink in fear,
> And, child-like, hide myself in love;
> Show me what angels feel. Till then,
> I cling, a mere weak man, to men.

He felt that he could never be alone, however lonely he might be.

SILENCE

It was everywhere round the place; round Maynooth College; as if heavy snow had fallen, covering every sound deep, so that there was no echo of any footstep, nor of a voice; no, nor the song of any bird: as if heavy snow had fallen, and no wind blew: silence.

One cold, windy day in Webb's second-hand book-store, that stretched drunkenly along a lot of Aston's Quay, Sean's hand flicked over shelves, holding selected volumes, looking for something new. One caught his eye, labelled *Reminiscences of a Maynooth Professor,* for it reminded him of his visits to the College. He passed the book by, as having no interest for him, and went away with a volume of plays by Brieux, fortified with a preface by Bernard Shaw. A week later, he was in Webb's again, and there was the Professor's book still staring him in the face. He took it down, and looked within to see the price. It was marked eighteen shillings, and Sean hastily put back the book on the shelf again.

Maynooth, a town in the County of Kildare, having a population of under two thousand, containing the Roman Catholic College of St. Patrick. One could as readily say, Ireland, an island with a population of four millions, containing the College of Maynooth; for this College is the brain, the body, the nerve and the tissue of the land, controlling two-thirds of the country, influencing it all. There stood the wide, heavy gateway, iron-hard as the discipline within; flanked on one side by the tower of the old Castle of the Geraldines, Lords of Kildare in the old time, and once nearly Lords of Ireland without division; and on the other by the Barracks of the Royal Irish Constabulary.

Ye Geraldines, ye Geraldines!—How royally ye reigned
O'er Desmond broad and rich Kildare, and English arts
*   disdained;*
Your sword made knights, your banner waved, free was your
*   bugle call*
By Glyn's green slopes, and Dingle's tide, from Barrow's
*   banks to Youghal.*

Behind the ruined tower, shrouded in ivy, rose the College, enshrining the voice of Ireland's ecclesiastical oracle, outside heard as the barking of Cerberus, inside as silent as the grave. And here, in this College, lived Dr. Walter McDonald, Professor of Theology for forty years; for forty long and lustrous years of thought and striving in the quiet room where he wrote, and in the quieter room where he slept at night.

Sean had visited the College three times, once in gay kilt, coloured shawl, and feathered cap. He had sat in the church while a young student had played sacred music (what is sacred music?) on the electrically-blown organ; he had watched the Mother Superior of the nuns sitting, frightened and breathless, on the altar steps, convinced she had a heart attack, while she murmured complainingly that she should never have ventured to walk so far, or stepped out so quick. He had tried to convince her that no heart could be hurt by such a short walk on such a level road; that if she had had a real heart attack, she could never have risen from the altar steps to walk back again, that the breathlessness had been brought on by her nervousness or need of exercise; and that she should try not to let her heart be troubled, for as long as she could stand on her feet, and trip about her business. He had caught a glimpse of half a cow hanging from a hook in a hall, savoury meat for the sustenance of those soon to become Levites, dispensers of holy grace and truth to fallen man. Sean had looked, and had commented politely, at the long row of oil-paintings of past presidents hanging on the cloister walls —poor paintings of poorer men, one of them only prominent, as far as Sean could remember, for the part he had played in hounding to poverty and death the proud and gallant Dr. O'Hickey. Sean had played hand-ball in the ball alleys, and had taken tea afterwards in a big room of the College. He had watched groups of lusty young men on their way to the fields, some to play hurley, others to play football, a few of them, later on, to be canons, a smaller number, lordly bishops, one of them, maybe, a cardinal, but none of them a pope—no Irish need apply there; the Irish, notwithstanding their devotion to the Faith; their world-wide contribution to the priesthood of the world; their readiness to accept, open-mouthed, every word spoken by Italian cardinal or pope; the Irish were still reckoned as heathens, and their land was a mission field, and is still subject to the Congregation of the Propa-

ganda. The land that did so much to re-Christianise the
civilised world when it was peopled with warlike pagans
after the break-up of the Roman Empire. The land of
Columkille, of Columbanus, of Aidan, of Bridget, of Dun
Scotus, and of a host of halo'd followers, is still subject to
a group of red-hatted Italians who are as much interested
in their Church in Ireland, and all that she has done for
them, as is Dan Muldoon the Solid Man, and care a lot
less for her than he does.

There were the students, hurrying to the playgrounds,
loudly restless, talkative, as if wishful to be forgetful of
the life they would, sooner or later, have to pretend to
live. Occasionally, a nun would flit up or down a path,
hurrying head down, noticing no boys, and boys passing on
their way, as if she had been invisible. Over all was a
strange silence, not a dead one, but a living silence, pale,
venomous, striking out the humanities from a man's heart.

A week or so later, the book was still on the shelf, and
Sean took it down, paid for it with a sign, and went home
with it under an arm. What he read there, jolted Sean
into silence too. He said nothing, but pondered the things
he read deeply in his heart. He had seen and heard many
strange things during his long association with catholic
comrades at work, in the Gaelic League, and in the Irish
Republican Brotherhood. He had heard of a book called
Priests and People in Ireland, written by a Michael Mc-
Carthy; had heard Gaelic Leaguers laughing at it, and he
had laughed with them. Everyone who could afford to buy
or borrow it, read it; but ridicule was all the praise it got.
A great controversy raged in the papers about what it had

said, and the pictures of towering churches dominating miserable village hovels; but the battle died down, and, Sean heard after, that McCarthy had left the country. Later on a book by Sir Horace Plunkett, on the same kind of theme, caused another sensation; and opposition, generated by the clergy, became so strong that it threatened to undo the work of the Irish Agricultural Society, so that many had to plead excuses for the Knight's unworthy opinions about the bad influence of the priests in all Irish activities. The catholics again rose out, and filled the streets of the towns and the lanes of the country with their outcries. West-Briton and Irish-Irelander joined together to threaten the writer and mock the book; and Sean, though he hadn't read a line of it, mocked the book with them.

But here was a book that couldn't be mocked, neither could the writer be threatened, for he was in his grave, having arranged that the book should be published only after he had died. Here were the cold, sober thoughts of no "renegade catholic"; nor the criticisms of a protestant and impatient Unionist: no; here were the spear-like criticisms of a flower of the flock; of one writing from the very core of the catholic fortress, Maynooth; of a rebel confined to the bed of obedience. By God, here was a showdown of the mitred oracle of Maynooth!

Dr. Walter McDonald, the writer of *Reminiscences of a Maynooth Professor*, was born in the tiny village of Emil, in the Parish of Mooncoin, famous for its hurlers, in the County of Kilkenny. He was the son of a small tenant-farmer, rather a hard-drinking, sit-at-ease fellow, who left his patient wife to do most of the work, surrendering her life so that she might sew, clean, wash, iron, and cook, while, in her spare time, she milked the cows, made the butter, cleaned the dairy vessels, and helped to prepare the food for the pigs and cattle. A refined woman, this hard-working countrywoman, eager to wrap part of her life in literature, but forced to be satisfied with the coloured scarf of *The Arabian Nights* which she got in the house of the protestant Rector with whom she was friendly. She so loved the book that she hurried over ditch and fence, taking short cuts through the fields, the book under her petticoat (for the reading of such a book wouldn't be thought decent by her neighbours), so that she might for a few moments lie under a fence, to take an imaginative journey with Sinbad, or sit in the magic rays of Aladdin's wonderful lamp, before the others came up to lift her from loveliness into the dull ardour of field-work.

Dr. McDonald started school before he was five, a bitterly cold school for such a sensitive little fellow in body and soul. When he became a young man of eight, he went to another as a weekly boarder, a school seven miles from his home, and anyone leaning over the half-door of his cottage on a Monday morning early, would have seen the youngster trudging the lonely road, carrying a big basket of butter, eggs, oatmeal, and cake to serve him for the week's provisions. The long journeys on the hard indifferent road nurtured in the childish mind of the boy that resignation and patience which he was to carry with him— like the basket—all the days of his life. Happily he had a finer collection of literature than had had his mother, for the cultured condition of the island of scholars threw in his way *The Lives of the Saints, Robinson Crusoe,* some copies of *The Dublin Penny Journal,* a book descriptive of Irish scenery, and *The Five Champions of Christendom,* so that the boy caught a cloudy glimpse of what letters was like.

In his young boy-student days in the College of St. Kieran, learning was loved in Ireland, for, we are told, Latin and Greek were literally hammered into him, so that, oddly enough, he hated these languages for years. Wilful, obstinate boy, showing what an evil thing is original sin. This was the only way to education. "If you won't let it in at one end, I'll hammer it in at the other!" shouted an indignant father, laying on the lash to his squealing boy, as we were once told by *The Leader.* I'll learn you, with the holy help of St. John of Bossco! Seize that boy! Bring me my burnished cane and shining rod. Cane him, cane him, till pain forces him to honour God and coaxes him into a love for learning! They are tainted with original sin. That was the churchman's way of teaching then; it is the churchman's way of teaching now. Educate the young into slavery so that with many stripes from rod and cane we may hymn our way to heaven howling. Oh, sacerdotal sadists, your way has at last been checked by disbelief, and disbelief will go on checking it till kindly human reason will not suffer cruelty to live.

When McDonald left the mediocre men behind him at St. Kieran's, he found more of them waiting for him at Maynooth, such as Dr. Gargan whose lectures on Ecclesiastical History were so poor that McDonald didn't like to speak about them; Mr. Hackett who sat easy in his

326

Chair, for he didn't seem to have any interest in Philosophy; and a Dr. O'Hanlon, whose *Notes on Canon Law*
were "elementary—such as one might find in any text-
book". Oh, God! Oh, great Maynooth!

The only enemies the College recognised then, were the
protestants, and little thought was given to the new Ration-
alistic spirit sweeping England, and which has since become such a mighty force in most protestant and catholic
countries today. Though there was no danger of anyone in
Maynooth becoming a protestant, some of them were
agitated and disturbed when they could no longer avoid
the arguments put forward so forcibly by the Rationalists.
"Indeed," says McDonald, "so imperfect was the system
formulated even on the old traditional lines, that it was
turned inside out not many years afterwards by Dr. Salmon
of Trinity College, whose work on *Infallibility* still remains
without a sufficient answer." And, adds Dr. Coulton of
Cambridge, remains so still. Don't worry, now; don't fuss
—all's well, as long as the coloured symbol of the Sacred
Heart hangs on the back of every door. These for the simple; the higher educated are saved by Archbishop Mc-
Quaid's declaration of excommunication on any catholic
student who ventures to put his nose within the gates of
Trinity College. But a wider and a deeper force is sweeping catholic and protestant countries today. The laity are
busy building a church of their own outside of the animos-
ity of worldly cardinal and worldly priest; a "country
where the State is the Church and the Church the people;
a commonwealth in which work is play and play is life; a
temple in which the priest is the worshipper and the wor-

shipper the worshipped; a godhead in which all life is human and all humanity divine".

And another bright light of Maynooth was Dr. Murray, "more of an ultramontane than the pope, and a bigot, if ever there was one. Whatever view extended most to the exaltation and honour of the Holy See, the Church, or of God, the Blessed Virgin, or the saints, became, for that reason alone, to him more probable." But they weren't all composed of Maynoothian fudge and froth. Wise and wary as she was, even Maynooth couldn't altogether keep personality from striding through her cloisters. Father Gowan came, by God's providence, at the beginning of Dr. McDonald's second year's divinity course to show the students the way of teaching and preaching the Christian Doctrine. He came in well-worn old coat and hat, strong shoes, between which and his short trousers, the stockings showed; and though he never really appealed to those who judged a man by his clothes and his way of talking, he brought close to him the hearts of those who had respect for a good man. By God, a man in Maynooth at last.

Dr. McDonald was a happy and confident young man then, for he hadn't yet collided with any of the ecclesiastics. "He knew no fear whether of professor or dean; and, if called upon, would have spoken truth, however unpleasant, to the College of Cardinals, for he had no notion that an honest, well-meaning man could be injured by anyone, and especially by any ecclesiastic." He was very innocent then. His troubles began while he was teaching at St. Kieran's on *Certitude, and its Criteria*, a treatise as big as a strong man could uncomfortably carry, beloved and trusted by

328

the professors of the divine way to life and eternal understanding. But it gave such a confused exposition of Certitude to Dr. McDonald that he flung it from him in anger,
and never peeped into it again. Some time after, to renew
his courage and faith, Dr. McDonald read Murray's tome
on *The Church,* reading on and on till he came to the two
hundredth objection to Infallibility, each of them lying in
the book as neat and as precise as the pectoral cross on the
breast of a bishop, and all so ineffective that Dr. McDonald,
in a burst of anger, flung the great book out of the window.

Silence, Dr. McDonald, silence. Say nothing; keep all
this to yourself.

"Oh, it's all very well to say," said Dr. McDonald,
"that this or that is the traditional catholic view, and hence
must be satisfactory, until its unsatisfactoriness has been
burned into you. I say now, very solemnly, that the con-
servatism in which I was trained very nearly drove me out
of the church on many occasions, and these good easy men
who for the honour of God and in the interests of religion,
insist on these traditional views—making dogmas of
what are but school traditions—are tormenting souls and
driving them out of the church."

School traditions adorned with the sacredness of dogma,
with cardinal and bishop moulding new ones out of little
wit and lesser knowledge, till every one of them, backed
by monsignor, canon, and parish priest, comes to imagine
that whatever any of them may say, on whatsoever subject,
must be accepted without quavering, must be believed,
acted upon at once, without misgiving; perpetuating their
theology within the dribbling stage, so that the attention

given to them by sensible men, in the light of what we now know, can be but the smiling attention given by the same sensible man to a child's nursery rhyme. It has its uses, for it is this sort of thing that sanctifies the orderly, money-making orgy of Lourdes, strange tinselled waste, and woeful issue of a sick child's slick dream; tipping rose-leaves out on running sores and eating cancers; setting its comic, codified cure, by dipping the sick into a well, thick with the scum of a thousand tumours, against the calmly measured scientific healing of millions, without the singing of a single psalm. God's gift of penicillin is worth ten thousand Lourdes.

Driving into a happier nonsense, Dr. McDonald tells us of how the bishops and the clergy were disturbed (like Dr. Johnson) by the swelling bosoms venturing forth from the low-cut bodices of the ladies. Before a Garrison Dance, to be given in Kilkenny Castle, to which many catholic ladies had been invited, the ponderous question faced the clergy as to whether these lasses could dance such a thing as a waltz, and wear evening-dress while dancing them. So they warned all whom it might concern, that, at the first Synod of Maynooth, all such dances had been condemned by the pastors of the church; and the bishops called on all to whom God had entrusted the care of immortal souls to banish from their midst what was so often, if not always, an occasion of sin. So the Synod warned the ladies that it was a mortal sin to dance a waltz or a polka, in evening-dress especially; but the impudent lasses insisted that they, who had often done this before without thought of sin, knew better than the bishops. So the bishops sat round in a circle again, and thought and thought deeply on this vexed and sexed question, finally deciding that the ladies might go to the Ball, provided the dress they wore was cut merely into a V-shape at the throat; and that they might dance waltzes, provided the gentlemen held both hands of his partner in front.

Eyes front, gentlemen! Keep your hands steady! What if a gentleman embracing a lady, allowed a wandering hand to slip down, and rest on her bottom! And what if the lady happened to like the feeling? Where would we be then! And what of the knowledge of sweet things seen within the movement of a low-cut bodice? What eager eyes would see, the eager heart would grieve for, and the gentleman's soul with the lady's soul would go dancing down into amour mortal sin. And what about when the Ball was over, after the break of day? What villainies of immortal sin might be committed on the slow way home. Illegitimate children swarming the streets of the town in their bare feet. But with deplorable recklessness, the ladies, ignoring the bishops' and the gypsy's warning, went to the Ball, and had a fine time of it.

What an odd bunch some of the professors were whom McDonald met in Maynooth! Murray who denounced Parnell and the Land League as if it had been aimed at the Papacy; Dr. Farrelly who added to the denunciation as ignorantly, for he was the slave of the cant of respectability; if he couldn't find a lord to fawn on, he fawned on any of the gentry he met—even in print; and Dr. Mc-Cauley who disdained to listen to anything said by an uneducated plebeian like Michael Davitt, who had the temerity to set himself up against Mr. Gladstone, and all the education, wealth, and respectability of the British Isles; and Dr. Healy, after setting these gentlemen on, applauding all they said in denunciation.

Soldiers of Christ, arise,
And put your armour on;
Strong in the strength a lord supplies,
Or even a lord's first son.

Worship respectable things,
Keep thoughts well comb'd and trim;
The one who this sage counsel heeds,
Will always be in the swim.

Pray to saints, kindly and grim,
But keep your bishop calm;
Make all his pleasure, every whim,
Your pray'r, your hymn, your psalm.

Oh, for a Bishop to be;
Or else a Monsignor gay;
Promotion sensible men will agree
'S the life, the truth, the way.

False pretence, deceit, and intrigue in Maynooth too. No! Oh, but yes; and since inferior officers in Maynooth are guilty of indiscretions, surely there must be rank blasphemy shown at times by the superior officers in Rome. Dr. Carr, one of Maynooth's professors was out hunting for the Bishopric of Galway, and Dr. Walsh the President of the College (afterwards Archbishop of Dublin), wanted Carr to get the job. At the same time, the notorious Papal Encyclical, *Quidquod de Parnellio*, condemning Parnell-ism flew over to Ireland, to be read from every altar; an Encyclical engineered by the bishops and other enemies of Parnell and his people. The followers of Parnell raged, like the heathen, against it, even Tim Healy being constrained to call it "an idiotic circular". It hadn't any effect, and subscriptions to the Plan of Campaign, instead of growing less, demonstrably increased. And among those who sent subscriptions were five professors of Maynooth—McDonald, Hackett, O'Dea, Boylan, and O'Donnell. They sent the subscription in jointly, and through the public way of the Press. At the identical moment, the name of Carr had been sent foremost to the Vatican for selection to the Bishopric of Galway. Now what would Rome think of the name of Carr of Maynooth, when five of his brother professors had sent in, jointly, a subscription to a movement that the Vatican had lustily condemned? Well, what about it? What about it! Don't you see, man, that poor Carr's chance of the Galway job was lessened—endangered even—by this unseemly action on the part of five men on the College Staff? Strutting to their rooms, Dr. Carr, highly indignant, threatened them, one after the other, that they would hear more about it. And they did, too.

Immediately the Trustees of the College went into a huddle, and passed a resolution that Members of the Staff must not take sides on public questions about which the bishops were divided, adding, cutely enough, that the resolution was not to be recorded on the minutes. Keep it quiet; must be known only to ourselves. Ourselves Alone! All the bishops were united on the question of creating, whenever possible, an opposition that would trample into dust the heart of the Irish Leader. To make sure that the resolution couldn't escape into the Press, the Trustees decided that it was to be read privately to each of the five members of the Staff, and that a copy was to be given to none of them. Fair is fair. But fair is sometimes foul in Maynooth College. So armed with a scrap of paper, Dr. Walsh (afterwards Archbishop of Dublin) came secretly by night, like a creeping Nicodemus, and read the resolution privately, by the dim light of a candle, to each professor in turn; all listening in silence, except Hackett, who asked for a copy, and when told he wouldn't get one, refused to listen to a resolution that wasn't given to him in writing. "There was grit in the man," murmured McDonald, astonished that there should be such a thing as grit nesting in the nature of a Maynooth Professor. "This was the first occasion," says Dr. McDonald, "on which I knew—or felt—that an act so solemn as that of the Episcopal Body could be drawn up on false pretences. None of us could believe that we were reprimanded in this way merely for taking a side in a matter of public interest on which the bishops were divided. It was passed, we were sure, because Dr. Walsh and Dr. Carr—the Bishop presumptive of Galway—feared that Dr. Carr's appointment to the See of Galway would be endangered by so many of the College Staff subscribing publicly to a testimonial which the Vatican had discountenanced. The Papal circular was falsely coloured, striking at the testimonial without daring to strike openly, just as the Episcopal resolution struck at us, not for the reason assigned, but for one which had to be kept concealed."

And these are the customers who lead the van in the curious, comic fight for "the sacred rights of the individual." The Gasquets, the Chestertons, the Logues, the Walshes, and the Hinsleys. These are they who allow and encourage their anxious dupes to festoon themselves with miraculous medals, Hinsley crosses—found as often on the mangled and the unreturning dead as on the living—and Winnipeg angels, guaranteed to bring young air-fighters back home safe and sound; or, at the worst, to furnish them with immediate entrance into heaven (on payment of forty-nine dollars first). These are they, too, who shudder into violent opposition the moment the faintest ripple of new thought appears on the catholic mind, on any matter, literature, art, education, or the social necessity for a wholesome change in the way the greatest part of the people live. Like the Pope's government of the Papal States, after Napoleon's defeat, abolishing street lighting as being too democratic and revolutionary. As the Vatican was in the days of Napoleon, so the Vatican was in the day of McDonald, and as it was then, so is the Vatican today. That's why the Dublin laddo in purple imposes excommunication on any catholic young man who ventures within the gate of Trinity College, forgetting that the student kept safe outside, will meet, later on, opinions more dreadful than those of Trinity College in the wider university of the world.

Rome, Maynooth; one sack, one sample. Intrigue, false pretences, expediency, concealment, silence. And, unfortunately, the Protestant Church in Ireland, and, indeed, many in the Anglican Church, too, are rallying to become hardy non-commissioned officers in La Grande Armée des Vatican; as Newman himself was, while life left him with them, Cardinal Deacon and all, as they made him—a non-commissioned officer only. So it will be till honest and courageous men in the churches stand out for a proper conduct in God's service; or for no service at all.

Dr. McDonald soon fell in love with theology, as Joan of Arc had first fallen in love with religion, and then in love with war. He began to try to dress her more in the manner of the day, and, immediately, he began to feel the fierce wind of opposition blowing against him, battling to throw him down; but he stood up to the wind and the rain like the man he was, and fought the bad fight, ensuring himself a deep and honoured place in the dead silence of Maynooth College and the Catholic Church in Ireland. Theology in modern dress wasn't to the liking of the other theologians, the most of whom fought her battle in the armour and dwindled plumes of the five champions of Christendom. Dr. McDonald began to point out that times had changed, and, changing, had brought new discoveries. He asserted that even the most conservative would hardly deny that considerable light has been thrown recently on passages of Scripture (Genesis, for instance), as to which the theologians of a hundred years ago were, surely, in ignorance; that even conservative schoolmen could not complain of the statement that a hundred years ago there was no little error in the schools of theology, even as to the content of the deposit of faith; and, of course, that what was true in one century might well be true in another. Dear me, will this man never learn to keep his mouth shut! He went on to assert that it was only the definite teaching of the church that might not be in error; and that there was comparatively little defined, even as to the content of the deposit of faith, and there was, therefore, a wide field for inquiry and speculation. Oh, Dr. McDonald! not in Maynooth, Dr. McDonald! The faith me mother taught me is the faith for the men of Maynooth.

He saw that a good part of catholic traditional theology depended for its truth on natural science. He saw that the school of natural science from which it was derived was in many parts quite different from, and opposed to, what are now the received conclusions of modern physical science; he saw that theologians had got to choose between some of the received conclusions of modern physical science and an equal number of those of speculative theology. It was a long, hard road for Dr. McDonald, trying to harmonise the knowledge of modern science with a newer conception of themes of theology based on the revolutionary outlook of the modern mind. He fought his way out from the thicket of threadbare tradition to where he thought he could still see the light of heaven. He lets us know that he managed to get over the difficulties that arose, partly by satisfying himself that the conclusions of modern physical science, in so far as they were opposed by definite church teaching, are not such as commend themselves to a prudent man; and, in other part, on the ground that, when such conclusions cannot be rejected in prudence, even though they seem opposed to traditional or even official church teaching, the teaching in question may be regarded as non-definite, and may, in such circumstances, be rejected without disloyalty to the church.

But Dr. McDonald's new light on the faith dazzled the dim eyes of Maynooth and the Vatican, and the daring Professor was told to be silent, for they couldn't bear to look on this new thing that he had unveiled. *Cover her face: mine eyes dazzle: she died young.* He was watched; he was guarded from his own thoughts. He was soon to make the moan made by Cardinal Newman: *However honest my thoughts, and earnest my endeavours to keep rigidly within the lines of catholic doctrine, every word I publish will be malevolently scrutinised, and every expression that can possibly be perverted sent straight to Rome.*

Sent crookedly to Rome, he should have said, for these ecclesiastics, who are so deeply immersed in the love of God and charity for their neighbours, never hesitate to do a bad turn for a man of whom they are suspicious, for the man's own good. Just as what was done under false pretences to the five professors who stood by Parnell's policy to the extent of subscribing to the funds. And was later done to Dr. O'Hickey. So when Maynooth can turn to false pretences to furnish a crony with a job, what will the Vatican not do to preserve and develop its pride, its power, and its vast private property? So McDonald's book, *Motion,* was held up by the bishops. This McDonald wouldn't be content to let bad enough alone. A disturber of the peace. A raucous voice in the quiet city of God. So in a very smiling, friendly way, they told him his book must be submitted to the Holy See, instanter. No, no; no discussion. These No, No, Nunettes said No out loud and in whispers. The echo of No was heard everywhere, in refectory, in the lecture rooms, the dormitories, and it went stealing through the cloisters. No discussion. Pass the buck to the Holy See. The Bishops guessed that the No of Rome would even be more distinct than their own No, and that peace would be born again. And Dr. McDonald complains: *They shut us up in Ireland, and make us abide by the report of a couple of third-rate Roman theologians. The old, open church system has disappeared long since; now we are ruled by way of secret inquiries, conducted, no doubt, by good men, animated by the best intentions. We have got so much into the habit of these secret investigations that we look at public discussion as an evil; for no other reason, apparently, than because it is not secret; or, perhaps, because it gives too much information to the public and enables others besides ourselves to judge.*

Ah, there you have it, Dr. McDonald! Secrecy is the foundation on which their power is placed, from the modest presbytery of the village parish priest to the red-hatted consistories, congregations, and conclaves of the pompous, wealthy Vatican. Public discussion gives too much information to the public! This from a roman catholic priest and an eminent theologian, Professor of Theology in Maynooth College for forty years! Rest, rest, perturbed spirit. It will be hard for the brightest Bellocian logic or the loudest echo of Chesterton's vacant laughter, at the modern way of thought, to veil these opinions and this accusation against Maynooth and Rome away from the more seeing eyes of men.

One would imagine that a book on such a subject, by

such an earnest theologian, on such a subject as the pheno-
mena and effects of energy and motion in the natural world,
compared with, or allied to, the action and effect of grace
in the spiritual world, would have absorbed the thoughts,
for a month of Sundays, of the theologians basking about
in the sunny Courts of the Sacred Congregations; that,
faced with so many instances of these analogies made by
Aquinas from the physics of his day, they would have
hastened to welcome the attempts of one of their very own,
anxious to harmonise theological speculation with the
newer knowledge of their own day. But no; for it was a
dangerous thing to do—or so they said. The concept of
Motion attached to things theological and religious might
lead to the rejection of things familiar from babyhood,
with which they were at home. New thoughts would commit them to uncertainty and discomfort. But surely these
sun-bathed theologians of the Sacred Congregations should
have paused when they came across Cardinal Mercier's
opinion that *Vital activity is not an absolute commence-
ment or creation, but a transformation;* and again, that
*Vital movement is subject to the general laws of determin-
ism;* and again, that *Vital movement is not spontaneous in
the strictest sense of the word.* Perhaps, even in the case of
St. Paul, there were some determining influences at work
within him, before the thunderbolt of exciting grace struck
him down on the way to Damascus. Such a man as he was
could hardly have felt easy in his mind when he remembered his consent to the death of Stephen. Grace was there
before it came.

The Consultors of the Sacred Congregation condemned

Dr. McDonald's *Theses,* and this is what Dr. McDonald thought of their report: *I noted that the document I received was drawn up by some Secretary, who had before him the report of the Two Consultors, from which he copied in the main. When I examined the animadversions, I had little respect for either his or their philosophy or theological attainments. Cardinal Mercier went further than I had gone, so that the admonition which I received should, with far better right, have been sent to Louvain. I felt, however, that the Holy See would think twice before sending them to that quarter.* Dr. McDonald had little respect for these theologians, though it is laid down that the knowledge required for degrees in theology must be *Not common or ordinary, but ampler; profound, exquisite, and varied.* There's richness for you!

Anyway, Dr. McDonald persisted in questioning the theologians of the Sacred Congregation, through letters sent to Cardinal Ledochowski, defending the parts of his *Theses* which had been condemned. The Cardinal, tired no doubt of the insistence of the Irish theologian, and not being very well able to answer himself, sent a sharp letter to McDonald, and referred the remarks of McDonald back to the Irish Bishops. First the bishops passed the theological buck to Rome, and then Rome passed the buck back to the bishops. The way, the best way, of course, of finding the truth that is to make men free. This manœuvre forced Dr. McDonald to believe that neither the Roman authorities nor the Irish bishops could reply to his questions without throwing over the Consultors of the Sacred Congregation of Propaganda. As his book had been condemned, though the very things singled out for special condemnation had been set down by other eminent catholic theologians without a word of censure, something had to be done to save the face of Roman authority; and so the Irish bishops forced forward the condemnation, but in a very vague way, so as not to mingle in the condemnation a number of others, whom it wouldn't do to condemn, for they were far more powerful than Dr. McDonald. So the bishops wouldn't tell Dr. McDonald definitely what he was to teach and what he wasn't to teach. The fact was that the Irish bishops and the Roman luminaries knew as much about God as anyone else, and a lot less than Dr. McDonald. Their God had become the God of Belloc and the God of Chesterton. So here they were, busy suppressing and silencing a man, who, in the profound warmth of his honest soul, was trying to get closer to the God these others pretended to honour. They just looked upon Walter McDonald as a nuisance to Maynooth and Rome, with his anxiety to tell how the grace of God transmitted power and exciting activity to the human heart; trying to probe into the secrets of divinity, and seeking to find an analogy between the energy of matter and the energy of God's grace working in the human soul.

To definitely condemn McDonald, it seems, the Vatican and Maynooth would have had to condemn Cardinal Mercier, Satolli, Pecchi, Father Baudier, and Father de Regnon, S.J. When Maynooth at last got a professor who was a theologian, they didn't know what to do with him! So they concentrated on thinking what they could do to him. If he was let go on, he'd be stirring up trouble always.

342

The fewer questions that had to be answered the better.
Silence; oh, silence, for God's sake! Yes, but listen,
Eminent Cardinals, Most Reverend Bishops, and Right
Reverend Monsignors; listen: McDonald says that he
ventures only to admonish the theologians who were arguing on principles of physics that had been altogether, long
ago, discarded and thrown away by present-day scientists.
Silence, we're telling you! Maynooth's the Pater Silentio
of the Irish Church, for it is the spice of our spiritual life.
We can't afford to let this fellow keep us wriggling in our
episcopal chairs. In silence, remember, God brings all to
pass. Only hell is noisy, and that is why Maynooth sits
mum. And so must McDonald. It is far better to know
more about the things that are Caesar's than to know about
the things that are God's; for this brings danger; that
brings security. So to silence the blower was the best, the
just, the only thing to do; and silence him they did—for
a day or so.

As it was in matters called religious, so it was in matters
called political. The strife over the love of Parnell for a
woman had begun in Holy Ireland, even the Theological
Faculty of Maynooth couldn't keep out of it, for they as
Irishmen would be vitally affected by the battle and its
eventual outcome. The Liberals had declared that they
could no longer co-operate with the Irish Party unless
Parnell left it. Like the good catholic he was, Dr. Mc-
Donald then hated Liberalism, and thought Parnell
should resign. But like the man he was, Parnell refused to
do so; and at a meeting of the Irish Party in Dublin, he
was supported in his determination by its members, Tim

343

Healy shouting out that no-one should be let interfere
with the man at the wheel. The bishops, it was said,
weren't consulted; they were silent, but they were biding
their time. Then, suddenly they and the Liberal Party
protested simultaneously, and many in Ireland thought
that negotiations had taken place between the Irish Hierarchy and the English Liberals (the many who thought so
were probably right); and that the bishops resolved to
protest only when they were certain of support. Said Dr.
McDonald: "This was very galling to me, to find
not only our nation, but even our Church, dominated by
the English Liberals, and I made little secret of the dis-
gust I felt. I couldn't restrain a suspicion that though the
bishops claimed to speak merely in the interests of mor-
ality, this was not their only, not even their strongest motive.
It was convenient for them to say so, as their pronounce-
ment was thereby raised above hostile criticism. And some
of them—their leaders—as I suspected, knew this well,
and calculated on it; putting it forward as a very efficacious
shield to cover the real, or, at least, more prevalent motive,
which was political. Not, of course, that even these leading
bishops did not think public morals in some danger; but
that *their concern was much more to weaken or even destroy Parnell.*" Christ Almighty, to destroy Parnell!
There are the Irish bishops for you, men and women of
Eireann! What a gang they were! In his heart, Sean had
known it all along, and he had always hated their hypocrisy, made more splendidly odious by the Tyrian dye of
their purple magna cappas. He had heard of it all about
Parnell; he had seen their trickery in the Gaelic League

344

and in the Irish Republican Brotherhood; he had been in the fight against them when they had hunted down poor Dr. O'Hickey; he had seen and heard their hypocrisy throughout the great fight Jim Larkin made to ensure a fair crack of the whip for the Irish workers; and now all that had been confirmed by one of their very own thoughtful theologians, the best they had ever had (since they kept him in his Chair for forty years, they too must have thought so), the best, probably, they will ever have again.

And this is one of the reasons why so many Roman Catholic countries are in revolt today—clerical domination in lay activities has gone too far to be put up with any longer. The prelate and the priest want to say, without the slightest contradiction, and under the dark cloak of their care for faith and morals, what the people's politics are to be. And so thought Dr. McDonald. "The greatest danger to religion is likely to accrue from any serious attempt on the part of the clergy to deprive the laity of their political rights, under pretence that such rights counted as nothing when weighed against danger to faith and morals." Wherever roman catholic power is potent, the minute anything new is put forward, something with which the prelates aren't fully familiar, in politics, in social amendment, or even in art and literature, these prelates begin to bark about faith and morals.

During the war, at a distribution of prizes in Maynooth College, Cardinal McRory (who had been a professor in Maynooth with Dr. McDonald) said, "He couldn't help thinking of the charges so often made against the Church of Rome of ignorance and opposition to knowledge." Yet this very man experienced this ignorance, this opposition to knowledge when he was a comrade-professor with Dr. McDonald in Maynooth; and was one of the editors of a *Theological Quarterly* when Dr. McDonald, another editor, was harried out of writing for it by the bishops. Then touching on H. G. Wells, the Cardinal said, "Lately in the papers appeared charges of this kind made by a writer of considerable notoriety in England, whose name I abstain from mentioning." There we go—not open enough, or else afraid, to guide any of his flock to the name of Wells, lest their precious souls be lost. The Cardinal went on: "I wish that writer could have come to see our distribution of prizes, to see the wide range of subjects and the vast field of knowledge covered by the Maynooth course, the great bulk of which had to be read by every student of the College." There's a cardinal's idea of knowledge— reading over a great bulk of books! *Finnegan's Wake,* one of them, maybe! Maynooth disposes of knowledge by bulk. Wholesale dealers in learning. Said the Cardinal: "The Catholic Church is never opposed to knowledge, that is real knowledge, and that is not in some way injurious."

There, thought Sean, we have the old, old bladher again that McDonald had heard so often. Real knowledge, mind you, which their greatest theologians had declared, again and again, to be old fashioned, leaving the students, when they left the seminary, a laughing-stock to any able man who happened to discuss things with them. When this Cardinal McRory died, he was hailed by the secular Press and the Catholic Press as an "eminent and distinguished theologian", though McDonald expressly says of him that while he knew something of the Scriptures, he couldn't be called a profound theologian; meaning that he knew very little about it. That is the way a lot of these cardinals and bishops get their reputation and authority.

Later on, Dr. McDonald wrote a review of a book in the *Freeman's Journal* (a Dublin daily paper of the day), called *Government of the Church in the Fourth Century*, written by another theologian, but one not on the staff of Maynooth. This review called down upon McDonald the wrath of the bishops, angering them into declaring with all the vehemence of a resolution that "They deprecated Professors carrying on a discussion in ordinary newspapers of difficult questions of theology, which may easily be misunderstood, and lead to the disedification of the laity". The laity! How the bishops love the laity! So they mustn't allow them to know too much. Imagine two professors saying, in public too, that the office of bishop wasn't once the exalted job the bishops reckon it to be now. Two bishops, highly annoyed, came to Dr. McDonald, one gripping his right arm, the other his left, and asked Why did he do this thing on them? It wasn't fair, it wasn't proper, nor was it at all expedient to say these things. It was wrong, decidedly wrong, to say that the presbyterians had some right on their side; for even though they might have, it was a grave mistake to admit it, and so give them an opportunity of crowing over the accepted beliefs of the catholic church. "That", thought Dr. McDonald, "may be good politics, but it isn't the scientific spirit, which does not hesitate to admit any error that has been proved. No small part of the weakness of Catholic Theology is due to this, that we

347

persist in maintaining positions, which have been long since shown to be indefensible, with the result that the adversaries of the Church, carefully avoiding us where we are strong, defeat us easily where we are weak, and are thereby able to crow over us, with justice and to our real disgrace, I might have discussed Dr. Moran's book *ad nauseam*, if only I had made out that the episcopal office was from the beginning what it is today. That would be false; but, then, falsehood of that kind would not lead to the 'disedification of the laity'." Falsification of facts is a common thing with those who stand as champions for the Vatican. Dr. Geoffrey Coulton has commented, time and again, on these seemingly irremovable characteristics of all Vatican apologists. He has even declared that if they will not hear the prophets of an outside creed, they should listen to their own, Newman and Acton; and now this courageous and honest man, Dr. McDonald, can be added to the number. Why even in their own special matter of catholic theology, it is plain from what Dr. McDonald writes, that their professors are a poor lot, in spite of "the vast field of knowledge" even the students cover, and the "bulk of books" every student of Maynooth has to read. Swallow them down, lads.

A curious and impudent boast, thought Sean, when one remembers the millions of books on the Index; and that, backed by the bishops, the Censors in Ireland ban every book that has within it a single thought that might question the power their own invented tradition has given them; any idea that might bring discomfort into their own easy-going thoughts; anything that "might be injurious." Might be, not would be. Anything that they think shows the slightest sign of an arresting thought, and under it goes, banned for good. For fear souls might be lost, they say; but some have a hearty opinion that this fear is bred out of the fear of losing the monarchical power a bishop holds over his see. No wonder part of the Catholic Press, in reply to an inquiry, said that it was part of Canon Law that anyone molesting a bishop was automatically excommunicated. Stepinac, stop!

The cardinals' and the bishops' divine love of learning, as proclaimed by the cardinal, who was afraid to mention the name of H. G. Wells, is indeed vindicated by the Trustees' choice of a church spire rather than that of a library during the day of Dr. McDonald. When he spoke for a library rather than for a church tower and spire, he was told they "could get fifteen thousand pounds for a tower and spire, but couldn't get a fifth of that amount for a library." But, he adds, the bishops by dint of propaganda pressed the money out of the people, and Dr. McDonald was certain that, had they used the same energy and eloquence for a library, they would have got the sum required.

How can we give a sizeable opinion about the result of all this wonderful love of learning on the part of the catholic students, most of whom later become priests, and mix and influence the thought and the culture of the laity? Surely, one way will be to judge them by what is called the catholic Press so fulsomely blessed by the Holy Father. Well, what of the catholic journalist? Is there anything so timid, so commonplace, so ready to say anything calculated to bring a pat on the back from a monsignor; so ready to dodge away from fact or from truth as the roman catholic journalism of the roman catholic popular Press? But when this cowardice, this false witness even, is to be found among the higher, more dignified professors, among the godlier sections of the catholic Press, need one wonder when it flashes forth in the commoner and more popular section of the Press? And why? Well, let Dr. McDonald—whose love for the Faith he held could hardly be questioned, and never was, by those who knew him—answer for us: "A Journal kept in leading-strings will do little good to its members or readers, and very little to the Church, State, or College for which it works—in fetters." Is he by any chance confusing the U.S.S.R. here with something else? In fetters! Do catholics really have to write in fetters? Dr. McDonald says so. Since you can't keep silence, Dr. McDonald, go on—we'll get you yet! "If the Catholic Church has in her service hardly one (hardly one, mind you!) strong, well-conducted newspaper or periodical, that is the price she pays for keeping all (all, mind you!) journalists in bondage; no really strong man will continue to serve under the restrictions that prevail." Still in the land of Egypt, still in the house of bondage.

Dr. McDonald, full of unwise zeal for the fair fame of his church, and for her holiness, advocated the publication of a yearly balance-sheet to show how the money, so generously given by the faithful, was used; smiling broadly at the sanctimonious dictum of "that while kings and their servants need to be watched, lest they convert the public funds to their own private uses, such a thing is, if not inconceivable, at least so rare as to be negligible in the case of churchmen."

350

Publish a balance-sheet! What a startling and a shocking suggestion! To set the eternal church down beside a common, money-making business firm, the church that pulls a revenue from the living and from the dead! Bishops are far above the thoughts of money. And yet, if we read Coulton's *Five Centuries of Religion,* we'll be astonished at the effect money had on the monasteries as set down in the old Latin Records, where we find that even the good St. Charles Borromeo was loaded with benefices in his early youth, and Cardinal Mazarin received the incomes of twenty-seven abbacies, not counting the pickings of a number of bishoprics. Cardinal and bishop and abbot seemed to have an itching palm for the gold pieces. In sorrow, rather than in anger, Dr. McDonald says, "I verily believe that the Roman palaces of Popes and Cardinals have cost the Church something more infinitely precious than money; the history of the Papacy justifies the faithful in being on their guard against the maladministration of the Roman Curia. For if the Curia lost the hold on Europe it had in the Middle Ages, it is mainly because of misappropriation of church funds. Even Leo the Tenth held twenty-seven benefices, topped by the Archbishopric of Amalfi (the Duke of Malfi!). There would have been no Reformation, and no French Revolution, if Church and State had had the good habit of publishing their accounts." Isn't this childish! Didn't Mr. Chesterton and Mr. Belloc set it down, with a thump, that, in England at least, the Reformation was due to the hankering of a king after the trim ankle, the seductive bust, slim legs, and bright eyes of a lovely lass? Is there anything more to be said? Can nothing silence this man?

Nothing. He even ventured to declare that the parents of children should have a say in the matter of managerial control, opposing a priest, who, giving a lecture, claimed a divine right and a canonical declaration for the dictated control of the schools by the priest. Didn't Cardinal Griffin imply recently, when dealing with the question of catholic teachers for catholic schools (and catholic teachers for protestant ones, and secular ones, too, if he had his way), that everything taught had a catholic importance, even arithmetic: catholic grammar, catholic geography, catholic orthography, etymology, syntax, and prosody.

These men, and the women who follow them, in the garb of the religious, or in secular clothing, want to dominate life from the cradle to the grave, greeting the present rise of the people against this madness with the wail of "the repressive and oppressive movements of the people are interfering with, and strangling, the sacred rights and freedom of mind of the individual." If the summer was icumen in, you'd hear the cuckoo calling. Back to the muddle ages, says Chesterton, rushing out of a pub after a quick one. Oh, a lovely time the common people had in the Middle Ages, bossed by pope, cardinal, prelate, prior, monk, and priest; and if the Roman Catholic Church only had now the power she had then, we'd all be revelling in the lovely sensation of ecclesiastical serfdom and slavery. This enlightened condition of things clung to life even up to the dawn of a more liberal day, for there were three hundred and fifty thousand ecclesiastical slaves bound to the monasteries of France alone at the time of the French Revolution.

At a public meeting Dr. McDonald advocated the entry into Trinity College of the catholics in an organised body, which, he felt sure, would preserve them from losing, or even weakening, a faith at once catholic and national. A whispered chat was carried on about this daring suggestion, and in the beginning of the twentieth century, under an English Liberal Government, a Commission was set up "to inquire into the present state of Trinity College, and of the University of Dublin, upon the place they hold as organs of higher education in Ireland, and the steps proper to be taken to increase their usefulness to the country." Everyone that had a thought left in the head got busy to try to bring harmony out of bitterness—but the bishops sang dumb. An effort to make Trinity College more like a Continental University was made by a College Committee, and a scheme "for widening the Constitution of the College was drawn up and sent to the sitting Commission, first being signed by twelve Junior Fellows, one Senior Fellow, and eight Professors of Trinity." A Catholic Laymen's Committee corresponded with the Trinity men, and, in the main, agreed with the proposals put forward for a settlement that would shove the College of the Holy Trinity right into the centre of Irish life and thought. Four hundred and sixty-seven catholic laymen set down proposals, which, according to Dr. McDonald, "were, practically, what had been agreed to by the Trinity Junior Fellows and Professors, with the sympathy of the Provost and by far the greater part of the College Staff, so that practical agreement had been reached, as regards a basis of settlement between Trinity College and the Catholic Laity." Then the

day after that on which the junior fellows and professors
had been presented to the Commission, the roman catholic
bishops, timing the thing nicely, woke and spoke, saying
simply, calmly, and with cool finality, "The Bishops in-
form the Commission that under no circumstances will the
Catholics of Ireland accept a system of mixed education in
Trinity College as a solution of their claims."

A roll of drums, boys! The divine voices had spoken,
and the Commission, jerked out of its happy assurance,
declared plaintively that "As the Standing Committee of
the Roman Catholic Bishops have assured us that the
Catholics of Ireland would on no account accept any scheme
of mixed education in Trinity College, we cannot hope to
render the College acceptable to the Roman Catholic
Episcopate by reasonable changes in its Constitution." The
gallant Four Hundred and Sixty-seven Catholic Laymen
were swept away as so much chaff; gone with the wind
raised by the bishops' blast. And yet these bishops are the
boyos who are continually roaring out for the preservation
of "the sacred rights and freedom of thought of the individual."

And, mind you, these Four Hundred and Sixty-seven
Laymen were of those who had themselves received what
was deemed to be a "good education"; men who would be
likely to give their sons a University education. They
weren't "The boys of Ormond Quay" whom Wolfe Tone
longed to have at his side when he headed rebellion in
Ireland; nor were they of the dockers, carters, and coal-
heavers, who afterwards, under Jim Larkin, became the
spear-point in the battle for the "sacred rights of the indi-

vidual." No; they were those who had been toned down to respectability; professional men of good education and secure standing in both Church and State; and yet they were just pushed aside without comment by the bishops, as a Dublin policeman might push aside a Dublin whore who ventured to explain a point of duty to him.

As it was then, so it is now: there is no more chance of harmony now than there was then. For a catholic it is spiritual death to enter the College without the archbishop's permission. If he should, he suffers automatic excommunication. Ecclesiastical electrocution! A hothouse faith to have! And so damned silly, for however the catholic young man may jib away from Trinity College, sooner or later, he has to plunge into the widespread world, a pressing, challenging world, and McQuaid's writ of excommunication doesn't run there, me man. There the north winds do blow, and there's free-thinking snow; and what will this robin do then, poor thing? The big mistake in Bunyan's book is the escape of Christian. There is no escape. Willy-nilly, like it or not, Christian must dwell forever in Vanity Fair. Even St. Bernard found that out, for Vanity Fair followed him into the monastery; and there was eating, drinking, dancing, and all kinds of merriment. And St. Benedict fared as badly, for austerity brought a quick decline in discipline, and seclusion brought no safety to the aspiring soul. The lure of the world without was within as well. Even Monte Cassino, now in ruins, came in for more than one swift, sharp condemnation, even from Dante, who thought that "the walls that were wont to be a house of prayer have become dens." Vanity Fair knocked at the monastery door, and the monks opened the door softly, and the revellers entered to make their abode with the holy men. There is neither shelter nor seclusion that can save us from the world. We live there and we die in it.

Sean sent his memory back to see Maynooth College again. Maybe this very Dr. McDonald looked from a window at him and his companions playing hand-ball; or listened to the skirling pipes when the band marched round the College grounds. Later on, when Dr. McDonald was gone, and Sean was in Maynooth again, he had looked over the many windows of the building, wondering which showed the room where the theologian had lived, had worked, perhaps had died. No word is given of how he died, or where he lies quiet and silent now. Possibly in the cemetery of the College he tried so hard to serve so well. Sean at his last visit had asked a passing student where McDonald was laid, but the busy student had hurried on, after saying he didn't know, and had never heard of him. He had disappeared from the College as if he had never been there. Even Chesterton's famous Father Brown wouldn't find him now. Wouldn't want to try either.

Ireland was safe now in the big hands of the bishops. The land was rocking in the sea with the dint of penance and prayer; rosary beads will festoon the land without division from one end to the other; holy pictures will be as thick as autumnal leaves that strew the brooks in Vallambrosa; scapulars will overlap every breast, like chainmail of the Middle Ages, ready to quench the fiery darts of the evil one; the younger writers and poets will be all on edge to win a passing nod of approval from the prelate. The gael will be pickled in penance.

> *Through the open door the hum of rosaries*
> *Came out and blended with the homing bees.*
> > > *The trees*
> *Heard nothing stranger than the rain and the wind*
> *Or the birds—*
> *But deep in their roots they knew a seed had sinned.*

Even the trees feel the malice of original sin. Even the trees; even so.

An article, written by Dr. Coghlan, attacking Dr. McDonald's book on *Motion*; an article cunningly written, with the words *To Be Continued* at the end of it, implying, of course, that there was more to follow, and persuading Dr. McDonald to wait for the additional attack. It never came, for Coghlan had shoved all he could into the first one, had taken advantage of the editor's absence to slip it into the Journal. The *To Be Continued* bluff was evidently meant to check Dr. McDonald's reply, so that the editor would be back to prevent its publication. The editor of *The Ecclesiastical Record,* Dr. Hogan, refused to print Dr. McDonald's reply to Coghlan, to whom he wrote, saying, "Having allowed Coghlan's article to slip through, you may take it from me that the series will not be continued. I must add, however, that I certainly will not consent to have my Journal made the medium of further controversy on the subject." Short and sweet, like a Christian ass's gallop! Hogan added, "This, I daresay, will be less an inconvenience to you, as you can get it into the *Theological Quarterly.*"

It was a cynical reply, or so thought Dr. McDonald, for Dr. Hogan knew only too well that Dr. McDonald's reply would not be let into the *Theological Quarterly.*

Later on, Dr. McDonald published a pamphlet containing the correspondence with Hogan, and added an onslaught on Coghlan's views on *Motion*, which, it was said, left the wily Professor speechless. And sorrow mend him, for, says Dr. McDonald, "He made an attack which he felt sure I could not repel, for he knew well that neither he nor I would be allowed to continue the discussion in the *Irish Ecclesiastical Record* or in any other publication subject to ecclesiastical control. There was nothing the bishops wanted so much as to stifle discussion on the *Motion* question, in regard to which they were uneasily conscious that neither they nor the Roman authorities had covered themselves with glory."

The bishops' "prime aim was to stifle discussion!" That is their prime aim everywhere, and about everything. Only what they themselves say is to be the sterling currency of thought. And yet these gay lads on altar steps, on platforms, in pulpits, at cocktail parties, proclaim, chant, assert, and demand full recognition for "freedom of expression, and the sacred rights of the individual". Well, we can hazard a guess as to what would have happened to H. G. Wells, if the Vatican had had supreme control of things as they once had—he would have gone up in smoke!

And they ask, preach, even command tolerance in others than themselves. Catholics are canonically forbidden to have a peep at a protestant wedding, or a protestant christening, however friendly they may be with the parties concerned; a dead protestant isr't allowed to lie side by side with his catholic wife in a consecrated catholic cemetery (according to the catholic press); the humblest roman catholic clergyman isn't allowed to join directly or indirectly in any national celebration or ceremony at which anglicans and non-conformists participate, even though it be but to say the Lord's Prayer, sing a te deum or de profundis, and say a creed common to all. Why? Because catholics "expose themselves to the danger of losing their Faith by taking part in the services or prayers of a false religion". It would seem that if one of another faith wagged a finger at a catholic he would immediately shed his faith, quicker than a snake would shed a skin.

So neither Dr. O'Hickey nor Dr. McDonald was allowed to put forward a fair case in their own defence, but were subdued into silence by the vanity of the bishops and the dodgery of a pope; Archbishop McQuaid imposes immediate excommunication on a student entering Trinity College; the parish priests walk about in mortal dread of their bishops; Dr. Coulton, of Cambridge University, could say in his book, *A Premium on Falsehood*, dealing with the deliberate misstatements made by Cardinal Gasquet on historical facts, "Meanwhile the Gasquet policy is successfully continued by Belloc, Father Thurston, and other less-known writers. It is almost demanded of them that they should twist the truth, and they do that job to perfection." Dr. Coulton, in the same publication, gives a list of Roman Catholic Journals, *The Month, The Tablet, The Universe*, and others, which refused to publish letters from men replying to letters criticising them, which had appeared in the Journals; some of them refusing, not only letters from non-catholics, but even from catholics anxious to get at the facts, just as their own theologian, Dr. McDonald, tried to do.

Indeed, Sean himself had more than one experience with this kind of people. One was a professional catholic lecturer. He once wrote to Sean asking for a subscription to a catholic charity to meet the needs of abandoned children. The subscription was sent, and back came a letter glowing with thanks and praise of Sean as an angel, the thanks flowing on into high praise for Sean's work, which the writer loved. A few months later, when the Abbey Theatre was having a Play Festival, lectures on the dramatists were given, and at the one on Sean, this boyo attacked the "angel", calling him an atheist, an anti-catholic and an anti-Christian, adding a postscript as to the vulgar, low, and uncatholic nature of Sean's work. Insincerity and dishonesty are nothing to most of these professional catholic apologists—lay or clerical—they take them in their stride. And these are the persons who go about yelping for tolerance and fair play!

Dr. McDonald frightened and angered the Maynooth authorities by arguing that Latin ought to be abandoned as a serious study for the students. What Chesterton cheered (or was it Belloc?) as a bond, uniting in love, understanding, and thought, the whole catholic world, Dr. McDonald calls a millstone round the necks of the students of catholic seminaries. The bishops, in Ireland and elsewhere, share Chesterton's enthusiasm, dreading the more critical line of thought that the use of the vernacular would bring into the minds of the faithful. "The fact is," Dr. McDonald points out, "that Latin is used only with

360

reluctance in all the offices and tribunals of the Holy See; where, if you want to get business done quick and satisfactorily, you must speak or write in Italian—the natural language of the place. None of the Irish Bishops are at home with Italian, and so are frightfully handicapped when they go to Rome on business."

—Good God! ejaculated the Bishop of Belloe, would you criticise propaganda itself! Ah, now, you wouldn't do that, would you, Dr. McDonald?

—Yes, and criticise greater than Propaganda! History proves that laws have been better made and better observed since subjects became free to criticise them; and there would be ever so much less to record, with shame and tears, if there had been more criticism, reverent and fearless, of those who occupied high places in the Church, even in the past.

—Dr. McDonald! Silence, sir; silence, Dr. McDonald!

—What are we to do? Are we to go on, silently, though convinced that things are rotting before our eyes?

—Silence!

A Doctor of Divinity wrote an excellent work on Ecclesiastical History, which won a Doctorate from the Faculty of Theology; and, later on he made an application for a vacant Chair of Theology, but was quietly shoved aside by the Visitors, for the book he had written stirred up fear within them, and they thought it wise to cool his ardour by leaving him out in the cold like the king at Canossa; their cowardly rejection of a fine mind in favour of a mediocre one forcing from Dr. McDonald the bitter comment of "If you wish to succeed, oh, my students, you should take care not to write at all, or to write good commonplace; above all, not to write anything original, however excellent it may be." So signs on it, the stigma of the commonplace is plain on almost everything written and said by the present-day leaders of the Roman Catholic Church. One has but to listen to the speeches or read the pastorals of the bishops, or skippily scan the simpering, pompous columns of the Roman Catholic Press, to realise to what a low imaginative and intellectual plane the present-day catholic mind has fallen, when dealing with things, spiritual and temporal, as related to their faith. From the leading articles in their Press to the book, *The Road to Victory*, by Cardinal Spellman, all that is said, all that is thought, sinks down, as foretold by Dr. McDonald, to the level of the commonplace.

A sad thing happened soon—Dr. McDonald was told by his doctors that he had but a short time to live; but facing it bravely, as he had faced everything else, he set about writing the last will and testament of his thoughts. When the world was deep in the dark of the war, he wrote a little book called *Ethical Questions of Peace and War*, causing the bishops once again to roar out Silence, in their own quiet, sacramental way. Here, he showed them up when they were bursting with love for Ireland; he showed them up as fools and cowards, just when they were posing as patriots. The word that wasn't with God went round that the book was to be left severely alone. It was not to be written about, not even to be mentioned, except in private, with doors closed and windows shut, and all light extinguished. The catholic *Month* said, in a short notice, that "Dr. McDonald's book challenges all, Bishops, Politicians, Professors and Editors; challenges beliefs which are almost axiomatic among his brethren; challenges them mostly by name, and no doubt the lists will soon be thronged by eager combatants". Well, wait till we see.

Dr. McDonald sent a copy of his book to the *Irish Ecclesiastical Record,* but the Journal never answered; he sent a copy to the *Irish Theological Quarterly,* but it took no notice; he sent one to *Studies,* but it sat silent. Dr. McDonald was told that the editor of this Journal was very angry with him for the attack he had made on Father Lehmkuhl, S.J., and through him, on the moralists of the Jesuit Society for teaching folk how to defraud governments; and the editor threatened some terrible things in the next or another number. The clock went on striking till it struck twelve, but no attack came from the editor, or from any in the Society of Jesus.

Why did they spare him? Dr. McDonald asks, "was it some remnant of a grace of courtesy, or of an ancient friendship, that bade them now suffer eclipse themselves rather than see my reputation injured? It would be nice to think so, but I do not think it true. Since then there was no answer to my challenge, it can have been only that it was felt there was none to give; that the Professors, Politicians, Editors, and Bishops had put themselves in a hopeless position, making use of rotten arguments, bogus history, and indefensible ethics. To get at me they must hit at Rome; and no one who knows the higher ecclesiastics of Ireland would ever deem them capable of such folly as that. So all they could do was to belittle me, and keep silent about the book."

During the course of the World War, Cardinal Logue

broke out into a cold sweat one day, a warm one the next, when he heard that a Professor of Theology had been teaching that it was lawful at times to revolt from what had up to then been legitimate sovereignty, and that in this way the great French Revolution could be justified, and also that of the American colonies under Washington. The Cardinal had learned all this from McDonald's book on *Peace and War*. The Cardinal threatened to make visitation of the College, and punish severely all who had taught doctrine so much opposed to Catholic Tradition. But changed things in Ireland made the cautious, cunning, ignorant Cardinal stay where he was in Arrah na Pogue Coeli, silent, sad, and anxious, for he didn't know the hell what might happen next. And as it would not, and could not, be denied that this principle was a development and new, Dr. McDonald said, "I take some little pride in being the first Catholic Theologian, as far as I know, to proclaim the principle that political sovereignty, which was quite legitimate and morally unassailable, up to a certain stage of its duration may at that stage become illegitimate, making it lawful for the subjects to throw off the yoke then, if they can, without doing greater mischief thereby."

And this is the condition Dr. McDonald finds his country in at the time when he is getting ready to depart forever: "History has already judged some of these cases of conflict, that, for instance, over the case of Parnell. Many good judges now admit that it was a mistake not to have come to terms with Trinity College; and more still are becoming convinced that all isn't right with the Managerial question; the *Irish Theological Quarterly* hasn't set the Liffey on fire since it was taken under the protection of the bishops; and the new Code of Ecclesiastical Law has left us with the old abuses of patronage, finance, and even of punishment without real trial. Parish priests may now be deprived of their benefices almost at the episcopal will, while bishops are being appointed with increasing disregard for public opinion; and should the regulations for the United States be adopted here, as is to be expected, the bishops can appoint their own successors practically, and the government of the church will pass more and more into the hands of a ring. For having stood up against all that, reverently and modestly, to the best of the weak power allowed to one in my position, I do not apprehend any severe judgment when I pass into the beyond."

A pathetic, a brave, and an honourable farewell. All these cool, studied accusations are made, not by a secularist, but by one of their own theologians; one who was Professor of Theology in the core of Irish catholicity for forty years. And yet Miss Maisie Ward neglects this great, brave man, this great Questioner, to write down the life of the chirruping Chesterton. Oh, folly, folly to crown the jester and shove the seer aside; to colour with flags the shallow ship sailing shallow waters, and tug the great ship, asking a deeper sea, to a hidden harbour, there to rust alone.

The questions the Questioner asked are with us still, unanswered; and, now, even unasked. There they are in the lonely room, where he pondered deeply in his heart about them; or in the place where he slept, thinking, thinking, before sleep stole him away from his thoughts. "There is danger in them, but comfortable Bishops, Cardinals, and Consultors—who became what they are because they never had a difficulty—will not see the danger coming, as their predecessors could not see the Reformation, and as the counsellors and parasites of the Bourbons could not imagine a Revolution. Congregations and Commissions would have us depend almost altogether on tradition, and shut our eyes to difficulties that strike us in the face." A prophet come to judgement, by God; and the judgement given hidden in the grave!

Was St. Paul right in his outlook on pagan Greece and Rome? Were these poor idolators as inexcusable as he represents them to have been? Was Samuel ethically right in pressing Saul with Jehovah's supreme displeasure for not having put to death even the women and babes he had taken from Amalec? Are we bound to the arguments for the existence of God set forth in the *Book of Wisdom*, or by St. Paul in the *Acts of the Apostles*? Did the human writer of Genesis mean to teach that the world was made in six days of twenty-four hours each, that the Deluge was absolutely universal, and destructive of the life of land animals everywhere; that any species that survived, did so by being brought into the Ark; that all men of the time were present at the building of Babel, and it was there that diversity of tongues arose?

"We know that there have been answers which satisfied our fathers: as that God could have placed fossils in the earth to try our faith. He could, of course, but did He? Can one now rely on such a possibility for an explanation of the difficulty? These are but a few of the questions that

366

torment, and will continue to torment, honest students of the Bible."

"So too in the early history of the church, and especially of the papacy and of episcopacy: when there were no monarchical bishops anywhere, can we believe that there was one in Rome? Did Cyprian and Fulgentius, who recognised no 'bishop of bishops', believe in the primacy of the successors of St. Peter, as that doctrine is now set forth in the Vatican decrees? Did St. Augustine, with his belief in the necessity of divine charity, recognise the sufficiency of attrition to remit mortal sin? Or, if charity was necessary, did he think mortal sin first remitted by the sacraments? Were, in fact, sacraments of the dead instituted and administered for the remission of guilt, or only for that of punishment, and for the giving of graces to lead a purer life in future?"

"And, then, grace and virtues; supernatural qualities? But what is a quality, and how does it contribute to action? How does grace operate, and when is it given: before, or after, justification? Can human souls be supernaturalised in part—in the intellect, while the will remains in its natural state? Where does the supernatural begin in the roots of faith? Can faith be lost without formal mortal sin? And what is the testimony of modern life in this respect? What is mortal sin, indeed? How does it stand with regard to charity—in its commission and its remission?"

"When trouble arises, as it will, over certain Church definitions with anathema attached, the standard and great test may well be," says Dr. McDonald, "that decree of the

Council of Vienna as to the human soul being substantial
form of the body. That the Council taught it to be in some
sense I take as evident from the words of the decree; as
also that the definition is one of supreme authority, claiming infallibility. Is it infallible? Is it even true?"

On these questions and many more such, Dr. McDonald
tells us he found peace on lines no little divergent from
the tradition. "I have done my best," he says, "and the
results will be found, in great part, in the unpublished
books I leave behind me. I should dearly love to see these
volumes published, but I must pass away without hope of
that. They might do a little to withstand the Revolution
which the official guardians of our religion will not see
coming, or will endeavour to keep out with broomsticks.
Good men, animated by the best of motives, but so short-
sighted, and so cruel, too, in their religious blindness to
such as cannot shut their eyes." The Revolution has come,
and the broomsticks wave; but though they have the shape
and order of croziers, they are broomsticks still.

In spite of creeds and things of faith defined, every
thoughtful Christian, like Dr. McDonald, must catch his
own peculiar glimpse of God; even that Christian who sees
nothing where he seeks to find Him, and then, as an honest
man, becomes what the creed-coveting crowd call an
Atheist.

Few of the younger catholics have heard of the man,
McDonald, and the older ones never mention his name in
the presence of others. His name is never mentioned either
in the religious or the secular Press. No one seems to know
why his books have never been published, or even where

the MS. of his work is to be found. There is a sombre and a secret and a sinister silence about this man who so modestly and so reverently questioned God. In Dr. Hyde's *Mise agus an Connradh*, the name of every Irishman, known and unknown, is mentioned, even that of Dr. O'Hickey, the life-long friend of McDonald, yet the name of Dr. McDonald is absent. Since the Irish Vatican prelates allow this, encourage it, even enforce it by their own supreme silence, then it must be thought that they consider this man was a dishonour to their core of catholicity, Maynooth College. Yet they held him there, with odd persistence, for forty years. They let him die silently, they lowered him into the grave silently, and left him there to disappear from Irish thought forever. If an eye looks in that direction, if a thought strays there, they raise the shout of Great Is Chesterton of the Roman Catholics! And silence falls again.

Here are the heavy iron gates of the College, St. Patrick's Roman Catholic College of Maynooth. Silence. It is everywhere around the place; around Maynooth College; as if heavy snow had fallen, covering every sound in sleep, so that there is no echo of any footstep, or of a voice; no, nor the song of a single bird; as if heavy snow had fallen, and no wind blew. Nothing but silence. Even the echo is silent. Outside the gates Honesty and Courage stand. Honesty in her white robe, Courage in her red one. Do you hear the shout of them rending the silence!

McDonald!

INISHFALLEN, FARE THEE WELL

It was time for Sean to go. He had had enough of it. He would be no more of an exile in another land than he was in his own. He was a voluntary and settled exile from every creed, from every party, and from every literary clique, fanning themselves into silence with unmitigated praise of each other in the most select corners of the city's highways and byebye-ways. He would stay no longer to view life through a stained-glass window, a Sinn Fein spy-glass, from a prie-dieu, or through the thigh bone of a hare. He would go beyond these, and view life through his own eyes. From where he would go, he'd look back now and again to see how the figures looked with a more distant sun shining on them. Oh, steer my barque from Eire's isle! He would be sorry to leave behind the few friends he had there. Each of these had binding cords to hold them there, while he had none.

It had often been recorded in the Press, by those who could guess shrewdly, that Sean was a slum dramatist, a gutter-snipe who could jingle a few words together out of what he had seen and heard. The terms were suitable and accurate for he was both, and, all his life, he would hold the wisdom and courage that these conditions had given him. Wheresoever he would go, whomsoever he might meet, be the places never so grandiloquent and rich, the persons never so noble in rank and origin, he,

370

O'Casside, would ever preserve, ever wear—though he would never flaunt it—the tattered badge of his tribe. Not that he thought of praise or blame for it, but simply because he had to bring his life around with him. But he would sew on to that badge, soiled with the diseased sweat of the tenements, a coloured ribbon or two of his own making, and, maybe, fix in its centre (like the jewel in the toad's head) a ruby or an emerald, giving the poor badge a gleam as good as that of any ancient order of chivalry, or that which goes with the posing piety of the Papal Court.

One thing that was good—he would never be in contact with any controversial literary Dublin clique. One of these cliques, not long ago, had tried to entangle him into an effort to undermine the literary influence and authority of Yeats; and he had been shocked to watch this mean and reprehensible envy of the poet's literary standing bubbling up in the minds of educated and cultured, but lesser men, who had been so safely and so comfortably nurtured in cradle and in school.

Yeats didn't praise them enough; he saw through them, but said nothing. Some of them were the fame-fleas that A.E. wanted Yeats to recognise with a little, or, maybe, substantial praise; pointing out that the poet had praised what others had sung or said, forcing from the lordly Yeats the little verse,

> *You say, as I have often given tongue*
> *In praise of what another said or sung,*
> *'Twere politic to do the like by these;*
> *But was there ever dog who praised his fleas?*

Masked pompously he was, in style and manner, but under all was the poet immortal who will be remembered forever. Friendship with Yeats was something Sean couldn't reach yet, for the poet was almost always hidden from view by this group of Gaeligorian guards who, now and again, wrote an article for *The Irish Statesman*, or sent an occasional poem to the Journal to fill a vacant corner. Wherever the poet stood, there they stood too, and followed meekly where he led, though secretly hating the man's true greatness. All that one could see from the fringe of this guard was the noble head of the poet, wearing now the mask of Sophocles, then the pompous one of Plato; again, the mask of contemplative Robartes, and, anon, the wild, warlike one of Red O'Hanrahan; and, to Sean, the deep, medieval voice, seeking impressiveness, however it might sound in laughter, or whatever it might say, always seemed to be murmuring, *Regina, Regina, Pigmeorum, Veni.* Though Gaumalfry followed him everywhere, Sean felt sure that Yeats, without his guards, could be simple and childlike, ready to gambol seriously, and would be inclined to gossip about, and laugh at, the follies and fripperies of men. So Sean kept away from the poet and his guards, for he was captivated by his own work, had been made a prisoner by himself, and his captivity had set him free.

Sean had always felt a rude desire to laugh whenever he found himself among this group of guards; he felt that most of them realised this; sensed a sound of silent laughter somewhere. He remembered once when he went to the house of Yeats, in Merrion Square, to see *The Hawk's*

Well played in the drawing-room. The room was full of them, dressed in their evening best, the men immaculate in shiny sober black, the women gay and glittering in silk sonorous, and brilliant brocade, all talking animatedly and affectionately together, like teachers and children waiting for trams to come to bring them away on a Sunday-school excursion. Sean tried to attach himself to the conversation by listening, but there was nothing to hear. No one spoke to him, and, right or wrong, he felt that they were uncomfortable with a tenement dweller in their midst. Yeats suddenly caught sight of him, came quick to him, and guided Sean to the front, where he wheeled over a deep and downy armchair as a seat for Sean.

—You'll be able to see well here, he said.

Yeats had read in a big book all about the Noh Plays, had spoken about them to others, and had seized on the idea that he could do in an hour what had taken a thousand years to create. And so with the folding and unfolding of a cloth, music from a zither and flute, and taps from a drum, Yeats' idea of a Noh Play blossomed for a brief moment, then the artificial petals faded and dropped lonely to the floor, because a Japanese spirit had failed to climb into the soul of a Kelt.

Passively funny was the sight of Mr. Robinson doing a musician, and Mick Dolan, the Abbey actor, acting Cuchullain, so serious, so solemn, his right hand, extended, holding a spear, saying so surlily-amiable, I am named Cuchullain; I am Sualtam's sin. No; charming and amiable as it all was, it wasn't a Noh Play. Poet and all as he was, Yeats wasn't able to grasp a convention, grown through a thousand years, and give it an Irish birth in an hour. Zither and flute and drum, with Dulac's masks, too full of detail for such an eyeless play, couldn't pour the imagination into the minds of those who listened and saw. The unfolding and folding of the fanciful cloth couldn't carry the stage to the drawing-room. No, the people's theatre can never be successfully turned into a poetical conventicle. A play poetical to be worthy of the theatre must be able to withstand the terror of Ta Ra Ra Boom Dee Ay, as a blue sky, or an apple tree in bloom, withstand any ugliness around or beneath them.

There was a buzz of Beautiful when the cloth had been folded, and the musicians had taken their slow way from the room; and Sean wisting not what to say himself, added Very. There was grace and a slender charm in what had been done, now that he had had a long time to look back at it; but it wasn't even the ghost of the theatre. Sean tried to murmur a few remarks, but no head turned to listen, and the chatter went on as if he had been a wraith invisible. Only one spoke to him—a Miss Estelle Solomons, a tall and stately young lady, shielding herself in a shining purplish blue silken gown, moving a gold-covered shoe in and out under its hem, as she talked to Sean. Though Sean never saw her again, he remembered her as a clever and charming young woman.

But in this crowd, outside of Yeats, there was no friend for him. He could foresee that much. Most of them had gathered here, not to see the play, but because Yeats was Yeats. As Sean stood, watching, trying to listen to what they said, he wondered how they would feel, what would happen, if Fluther, furiously drunk, came tumbling into the room, looking for someone to fight him.

—Any two o' yous, any three o' yous; your own selection; anywhere yous like—here or in th' sthreet!

An ignorant, ignoble savage, shouting that He wouldn't let that poet fella make little of Fluther's religion; lost to, and separate from, these elegant ones here in Yeats's drawing-room. And yet, Fluther was of the same family; bone of their bone, flesh of their flesh; a Christian, too, never missing Mass on Sundays. What headlines his visit would make in the morrow's newspapers! Fluther runs wild in Yeats's drawing-room; Shocking scene; The poet tries to reason with him; A number of dress-suits ruined; Six constables remove Fluther Good!

Yet there was life in this Fluther that these elegant persons lacked; and life in them that Fluther hadn't got. What a pity, what a shame, they couldn't share their gifts between them. Fluther had his rights and he had his qualities. Fluther, on Sundays, sober; his old suit brushed, a faded bowler hat set rakishly on his head, a newly-washed shirt showing over the top of his waistcoat, coming up the poor street, would be surrounded by children, some preceding, some following him, and all crying out, Sing us a song, Fluther; give us *Th' Weddin' o' Glencree*! And, shy and self-conscious, Fluther would set his back to the wall of a house, remove his hat, and sing the song for them. When it was done, Fluther to regain his confidence, would say, I've a wing (penny) left; come on all of yous. He would lead the way to a sweetshop, buy the sweets, and share them equally. Once, Sean saw him go back to the shop, and say, I want to give the chiselurs three each, an' I'm three short; and, for peace sake, the shopman would hand them over. But the children would never pester him; never beseech him to sing a song, till they saw him wearing the clean shirt and the bowler hat, and saw that he was sober.

And, bar Yeats and a few others, Sean was as far away from these elegant people as the doughty Fluther. Far farther, for he was nearer to Fluther than he was to them. There was something of the wildness of Fluther in Yeats himself; and Sean could clearly see Lady Gregory listening attentively to Fluther shyly singing his *The Weddin' o' Glencree,* if he happened to come to Coole; for this was Fluther's one shy way of giving a bow to the glory of literature and song.

No, this trifling group of the drawing-room would never deliver Ireland from what was coming—they thought of themselves too much. Knowing so little, and still lacking confidence, Sean was silent. There was no chance of a growing carnival of thought here. There was nothing in the fervency of their talk; no honour to Yeats in it; he was simply circumscribed with hesitant murmurs of Beautiful: it was as if a tired and unbelieving priest was murmuring the last words of *Missa est.*

Sean thought he could sense two systems of censorship sprouting out in Ireland. One was the group gathered here in Yeats's room, among the richly-heavy blue curtains, the seductive settee and cushions, the gleaming glass, and shiny silver; a censorship of brittle badinage and dainty disdain for anything written different from what they wanted, or were used to, because they had tried it themselves. The other was a prelatian-led crowd of ding dong dedero devotees, roaring out opposition to everything outside of what Father Tom, Dick, or Harry thought proper to put in poem or book. Holy water would soon be raining down for forty days and forty nights, and the sooner Sean got into the ark of England the better, if he was to escape the deluge. It was time to go.

Almost as long as Sean could remember, the life of Ireland was lived in a hall whose walls were roof-high stained-glass windows, nationally designed; but these were giving place now to glass that gave back the colours of pietistic twist and glossied tantrum. The window where Wolfe Tone had shone in his sky-blue coat and bright epaulettes of a Brigadier, now showed the wan figure of Bernadette raptly listening to the Bells of St. Mary's; in the one which had Robert Emmett in his gay green coat, carrying a plumed hat in his hand, stood now the black-clad, smiling-faced Father Malone in his new Sunday hat. Here was Father Dempsey ordering Mat Haffican to behave himself; and over there, the huge one of sickly-yellow and muddy-black glass, showing Matt Talbot, the tenement labourer, on his knees at full steam in prayer; the rusty steel chains he wore round his middle eating into the flesh of belly and back, changing into a bonny ring o' roses O. Opposite this was a big one of Chesterton and Belloc, entitled Comrades since we were Boys, supported by the impediment of nicely-trimmed alto-relievo figures of the Middle Ages. Chesterton's

Father Brown was there too, taking a rabbit and a blue cross from his clerical hat; beating his noble brow to get some sublime intuition about a head severed from a body by a sabre stroke, into coherent thought. And over, under, and around them all, were panes and panes of figures of friars in grey, in black, and in white; a robal army encompassing all things Irish that journeyed from the cradle to the grave.

The bishops began to climb into the saddle after the death of Parnell. Then came a vicious disunity, and the bishops got their chance to dominate both parties. The clergy didn't mind when William O'Brien called Tim Healy "a disgrace to human nature"; and they never turned a hair when Healy replied, accusing Dillon and his followers of "selling O'Neill's county, Tyrone, to an English party for £200 per annum per seat". But when Lamb of Newry and Dr. Kenny ventured to say, "they would not take a Catholic University, if the present Hierarchy had anything to do with it," they were soon squelched by the episcopal statement from Maynooth of "We cannot tolerate the use of such language. We trust this admonition will be enough, and that we will not be forced to an exercise of our spiritual authority for the prevention of this very great evil." Aha, excommunication for them who spake against the bishops! Silence! Discretion is the bitter part of valour.

The Orders will be let loose over the country to tighten up the faith of the people; the Civil Service will become the Third Order of St. Formulus; the Knights of Columbanus would become the soldiers of the Legion of the

Prayer Guard; the Pope's Brass Band would be developed
into a symphony orchestra, Armagh conducting, with
Dublin as the first fiddle; the gay rustle of a girl's skirt
will be hushed by the discreet rustle of the priest's cassock
and the friar's gown; and, like the cleric in Sierra's *Two
Shepherds*, the priests will drag the people of Ireland into
heaven by the scruff of their necks.

It was time for Sean to go.

All outward trace of the distant grandeur Sean's youth
had known, from afar off, had gone into the mothering
dust. Yesterday was as if it had never been. Gone were
the ladie ardilauns, alone and unhappy often, in their
swelling mansions, having as many rooms as cells in a
beehive. Gone forever was her daintily-made thought of
charity of bringing tenement women to her gorgeous gar-
dens to sip tea, trembling; to be presented with a geranium
in a pot as they got up to return to their home sweet homes.
The return from Fingal! Gone the majesty, and even the
interest, of the scarlet, blue, and gilded covering of the
plaster-made lion and unicorn, hanging haughtily over the
shop-front of butcher, baker, and candle-stick maker who
enjoyed the privilege of being a spasmodic provider of
goods to the king's Lord Lieutenant. Gone were the
Arabian nights of dance and delicate Erosion devotions in
Dublin Castle, where rows of debutantes, half hidden in
clouds of brocade and tulle, waited for entrance with military or naval escorts in scarlet and blue and gold, topped
by helmet or busby, over-topped with spike or plume; and
after the bow and the greeting, when the streets flowered
for a moment again with silks and tulle and muslin med-

ley, they waited wearily in queues, wearily waited to have
their photographs taken in Lafayette's or Chancellor's,
striving to make a moment immortal through a picture of
fading shadows. Gone the home and colonial governors,
carrying away their gnomish glitter with them—the Aber-
corns, the Wimbornes, and the Cadogans; their absence
blotting away the yearly dotting of Ireland's name with
the honour of baronet or knight. Gone indeed, were the
cometic visits of king, queen, or prince, prancing through
a pompous fairy thoroughfare of steady light and fluttering flags. The Balfours had said goodbye to Ireland, and
the Clancy name had come to take their place. All had
faded out of the land of prayer and dreams, and most of
them had crept out of the world itself. All the display,
the pertinent confidence, the complacency of show and
tangled tinsellry, the everlasting words writ on parchment
and sealed with coloured wax, had all been subdued into
dust, blowing about, restless, no-one knew whither or
where. Even the memory of them was growing cold in
the clasp of the mothering earth. The braid, the bugles,
and the blast of their blessing had all gone.

These pantomimic figures—the harlequin-viceroy with
his sceptre-shaped lath, the columbinian grand lady, the
clownish office-seeker, the pantaloonian judge with his
policeman hanger-on, had run from the stage of Irish life,
frightened off by the rage of rifle-shot and machine-gun
fire; the chorussed clang of violent opposition that had
developed out of the first shot fired at Bunker's Hill.
Earlier, even, than that: the Leveller's fight for what is
on the way now; earlier still: the sign of things to come in

the curse given by the peasant serf outside of his lord's castle; and his brother's bony hand in rage buffeting the thick stone of my lord abbot's monastery wall, which he prayed would fall on the abbot, killing him stone dead as a reprisal for robbing him of his labourer's fee, and of assisting the lordly ones in keeping the peasant a slave; though the angry peasant fell quick to his knees when the abbot came out on his caparisoned palfrey, out through the wide gateway, with his cavalcade of nineteen horsemen, his hawk on his wrist, his dozen of dogs, and his string of servants, on his way to the Manor House; the peasant getting to his feet when the abbot's out of earshot to fling a complaint, in the rage of his poverty, after the glitter of God's man: *What doeth gold in your bridles? It may not put cold or hunger away from your bridle. It is ours that ye so spend in pomp and vanity.*

So the abbots and the lords took, and so they spent, though tongues cursed them and hands hammered the stone walls. But the hands have grown stronger since, and will grow stronger still.

As of the first, so of the second phase of Sean's life—it had almost all gone. The singing lark in the clear air had left the sky, and the cawing crow was there now. The minstrel boy went to the war no more, and the harp that had once roused Tara's halls had corded strings that gave no music. The Gaelic League had dried into a skeleton, and was carried round to be exposed at every feast with the green flag wrapped round it. The boys in power mouthed an odd tribute to the Gaelic, then hurried home to dress themselves in the bits and pieces scattered here and there by the English Garrison when they had lived in the country. Even in religion, there was little to distinguish the Irish catholic from the English one. Bernadette, St. Vincent de Paul, and The Little Flower were the popular triad in Ireland to-day, with St. Anthony of Padua runner-up. Not a church from one end of the land to the other seemed to show a sign that the church was an Irish one. They were all lick-spittle imitations of churches in other lands. Was there a sign in any of them of an Irish touch in the painting and sculpture that called the faithful to remember things past? Was there a sign of art, even, in any of them? In all the badges, the symbols, the aids to piety that had been delivered out of heaven to this saint and to that, God seems to have forgotten that Ireland existed.

All of the Irish significance had gone to the grave with the older saints, and Bridget, now, couldn't hold a candle to Bernadette; though there was something silly, sensational, and tawdry in Bernadette; while about the name of Bridget clung the essence of charm, of poetry, and a realistic love of life. But now Kildare's holy shrine was dark and empty, while Lourdes was a blaze of candles carried by crowds. Oh, the trains, the yellow, the blue, the white, the brown, that race, tirra lirra, along to Lourdes! Racing along, carrying their rotting crops of humanity, to where a hymn and a prayer are to prosper them back to health. The woe and the waste of it all! Lourdes, where hope is swallowed down by misery to be vomited up again, more miserable, and lost. Where Lazarus is offered a crumb, but can never crawl near enough to get it. Where miserere jingles little bells of expectation, and never hears them sounding. Where belief plays her last joke on the dying. The church's great sweep of misery and woe. You may be the lucky one. Take your chance and keep the bells a-tolling. If at first you don't succeed, try, try again. Keep smiling—someone has got to be cured. The Coney Island of misery, agony, and woe. And when the festivity of death ends, and all gather to go home, wending slow through voluptuous chants of *Ave Maria*, the untouched ear can hear the sickly growl, sombre and low, with a hiss in it of *She never cured me, She didn't cure me.*

When all the lights from a hundred altars had been darkened; when the priests had divested themselves of their sacerdotal grandeur; when the swelling hearts of the ailing had been emptied of desire from very weariness; and the treasures given for the Virgin's glory were being counted; go the sad souls back to the vigil of the lonely couch, the biting sigh, the broken prayers, born of the broken hope of going forth broken and coming back whole. What could not this ill-spent energy do, this waste of transport, this garnered wealth do, if all were devoted to those efforts, those saintly efforts, to conquer the direr ills of man, sending more young to the grave than Lourdes can cure in an eternity of time. Disease can never be conquered, can never be quelled by emotion's wailful screaming or faith's cymballic prayer. It can only be conquered by the energy of humanity and the cunning in the mind of man. In the patience of a Curie, in the enlightenment of a Faraday, a Rutherford, a Pasteur, a Nightingale, and all other apostles of light and cleanliness, rather than of a woebegone godliness, we shall find final deliverance from plague, pestilence, and famine.

And all the other centres of sacerdotal healing are envious of Lourdes: Fatima, in Portugal, Kirkhala in Latvia, and poor little innocent little Knock in Ireland's sweet Mayo; for only Lourdes has succeeded in forcing a way into the limelight from heaven. A stream of water flowing out of it, a stream of gold flowing into it. A gigantic bazaar of tapers, holy images, holy water, in a storm of prayer, with frightened souls embedded in bodies braided with tumours, phthisis, scrofula, and cancer, hoping against hope for an impossible pardon, bringing solace, joy, and good fortune to the holy fathers of the Assumption. The battle-ground where Father Sempé fought with the Abbé Peyramale; fought like tigers for the possession of Bernadette, one tugging her to the old town, the other tugging her where he saw a new town rise up, till Peyramale was dead, and the old town with him; so that spires and towers and great churches rose up in the new town, under the guardianship of the Fathers of the Assumption, guided, day by day, by the care and strict cunning of Father Sempé all heavily embossed with godly pomp, pious pride, and wealth no single bank could hold. Oh, St. Patrick, St. Patrick, dear saint of our isle, what were you thinking of when you let little innocent little Knock be ousted by the impudence of Lourdes!

There had to be a song about it, and so there was: *The Song of Bernadette*. Poor Werfcl, panic-stricken, flying from the brown onslaught of Nazi gun and tank; flying breathless, with the screaming crowd, promised Bernadette that if he came safe, he'd visit Lourdes, and sing a song to her. He didn't wait to think why God should single him out from the thousands of fleeing Christians, hundreds of them good catholics, letting them die, while He was busy finding a way to deliver Werfel. It was a tall request, a terribly selfish one, too, and highly impudent; but it was a success, and Werfel was piloted, safe and sound and high and dry, to the promised land to sing his promised song to Bernadette. This Adeste Fideles to Bernadette has been sung and chorussed by millions of catholics, in seminary, in college, in the cloister, on the street, in the market-place. But somehow there is something wrong with it; something mean, paltry; and something crawling that nibbles at a noble, resistant resignation. There is something like the moaning of a sick slave in it; and through the sounds of its sickly chords there is a bitter tuning that some say is the sigh of the thousands who died unaided; who suffered so monstrously in the concentration camps; who were executed in heaps; who prayed, too, but got no answer; who promised, but weren't let live to keep them.

It would seem to be something elusive, or delusive in God to suggest that He would sacrifice so many to save one for such a song. If it had been for a Shakespeare, now. Ah, a Shakespeare! Or a Tolstoy. Ah, a Tolstoy! Or for a Strindberg, an Ibsen, a Yeats, or a Joyce! But for this thing of a song! Was it, indeed, God who gave this song to the world? Did God, or the Blessed Virgin, bring this man safe from the flood of fire—leaving all the rest to die as best they could—in order that this song might be made, and that it might be extended into the slimy gory of an orgiastic film? Its poor pietistic preaching brings new wealth and fresh power, maybe, to the good Fathers of the Assumption, and through the Fathers, to the Vatican Congregation of Propaganda; but it adds not one tittle to the glory of God in the deeper thoughts of any Christian's heart. It plasters rouge on the Virgin's face.

So let the blue trains run, and the red and the white ones, and more if they be needful, this year, next year, and all the years that follow; bringing the selected delegates, representing the diseases of their countries, to the Lourdean parliament of death, where speeches are pitiful prayers; resolutions, pain; and amendments, a moaning hope, held too long, turning now into a brooding vacancy of rejection.

There they go—the red trains and the brown trains, tcheh-tcheh-tcheh-tcheh-tcheh-tcheh, straight down through France, passing through fair valleys, by fruitful vineyards, going quick, but not quick enough, tcheh-tcheh-tcheh-tcheh, diving under tunnels, rushing through town and village, straight on to Lourdes, white train and yellow train, their carriages carrying the incurables; Muldoon the Solid Man's son and Mick McGilligan's daughter among them, on to the Maid of the Grotto, tcheh-tcheh-tcheh-tcheh,

O Maid of the Grotto, Heal us,
From thee all skill and science flow, all pity, care and love;
All calm and courage, faith and hope—oh, pour them from above;
Tcheh-tcheh to Lourdes, to Lourdes, to Lourdes.

Sean felt that if he stayed in Dublin, life would become embarrassing to meet. Dublin was too close to everyone. All its streets led into the one square where everyone met, where hands were shaken, shoulders clapped, and drinks taken to every other person's health. Sound and happy association, with one reservation—that when one was on the way to a good creation, he might be waylaid, left by the wayside, to die there, unfortified by the rites of the church. He remembered what he had gone through with his last play: Mr. Robinson agitated during rehearsals; silent sullenness stiffening the dialogue spoken by the actors; Lady Gregory anxious, and talking to Yeats about what might happen; and gigantic whispers wandering from one room to another in the Abbey Theatre, making the sullen more sullen still. "I refuse to say the word Snotty," said F. J. McCormick, while someone, in the background, murmured For righteous men must make our land a nation once again; "and I," said Miss Eileen Crowe —having first asked her priest about it—"refuse to say the words, 'Ne'er a one o' Jennie Gogan's kids was born outside of th' bordhers of the Ten Commandments'." a chorus in the background chanting,

Oh, sure you're right, allanna, for decent people know
That every girl in Ireland, as things at present go,
Is the soul of truth and of melting ruth,
With a smile like a summer at dawn;
Like the colleens that trip up and the colleens that trip down
The sweet valley of Slieve na Man, amen.

O Yes, O Yes, and there was Mr. O'Brien, the Abbey Director, running round moaning, "The Song, The Song!

387

That'll have to come out; Yeats, you've got to be careful."
And the lights in the pubs went higher and higher, and
everything in them were agog and aglow. And Mr.
Michael Dolan, the Theatre's Manager, writing to Lady
Gregory beseeching her, with tears in his eyes, beseeching
her, of her charity, now that the theatre was booming, to
have nothing to do with this play; for the language, oh,
the language in it goes beyond the beyonds; and the song
at the end of the second act, oh, the song at the end of the
second act, sung by the girl of the streets, is, is unpardon-
able; and we don't want to give any enemy of the theatre
Anything To Grasp At. And Mr. Michael Dolan, eaten
up with his zeal for the good name of the theatre, went on
assuring Lady Gregory that there would be real difficulty
in getting the Company to play in it, so he begged her
ladyship to have a care. He had had a hot argument with
O'Casey over the recent performance of *Man and Superman*, when O'Casey called the production a very bad one,
and then added a letter to prove he was right; but this, of
course, had nothing whatever to do with Dolan's dislike
of, and fear of, this new play of O'Casey's, which, in his
opinion, would do harm to the dear little, sweet little
theatre of Ireland.

And all this time Mr. O'Brien, the one and only catholic Director on the Theatre's Board, was going here and
going there, asking all whom he met, "Would the Song
be cut out? You know, the song at the end of the second
act, the one which tells about the woman's objectionable
preference for a sailor—will it go; will it tarry; will Yeats
do the right thing, and have it removed?" And the whis-

pers of the pubs quivered like things infirm when they
touched on the beyond the beyond language of the play;
and some said this, and others said that if the play was
allowed to go on the public stage as it was, it would have
been just as well if St. Patrick hadn't come to Ireland at
all. The song in it was bound to slip over the seas, and
destroy the reputation of the Irish Race. Now, just imagine
it! After five hundred years of work here and intercession
in heaven, just imagine St. Patrick (I won't mention the
name of Bridget in the circumstances) hearing that song
for the first time in London or in New York; and then,
when St. Patrick rebuked the English or the American
saints for allowing this song of bawdry, to hear that it
was first sung in holy Dublin, See of St. Laurence O'Toole;
and that a catholic actor had sung it out loud, and shame-
lessly! So even a blind man could see clearly that something must be done.

All the time, in the foyer, a Mr. Holloway, who had
superintended the architectural change in the theatre,
under Miss Horniman, spluttering spit over anyone stopping to listen to him, kept saying, "This play was an
abominable one, for there never was a street-walker in
Ireland since reliable history began to be written; and, if
the truth had to be told, he'd say every girl in Ireland was
an angel's whisper. Look at poor O'Brien, there, going
by, his honest heart sore troubled with the echoing in his
mind of that song at the end of the second act in O'Casey's
play! The implicity of that song is appalling, and it'll go
down the ages against us, if it's allowed to be sung."

Sean looked around the room at all the furniture he

389

had. All of them would fit into a small container—settee, desk, chair, filing-cabinets, and books; and he could get them over to England a day or two after his own arrival. He would leave all the rest—the linoleum, curtains, bed, saucepans, crockery, and oddments—to the lady below him. Then his customary footfall would never again be heard in a Dublin street. And the lamp—he'd leave that too; for he felt that, in England, there'd be electric light wherever he chose to live. A tip of a switch, and the room would flood with light. That in itself would be a great step forward. Lead kindly light, amid the encircling gloom—electricity now one of his gods. More light, murmured Goethe with his dying breath. Let there be light! said Faraday; and there was light. How much richer, how much more like a god, than the bishop in his gaudy dalmatic, does Faraday look in his dalmatic of light.

Sean realised now that the theatre, called the Abbey, as a whole, was against him, and that it would be a good thing to put a greater distance between them and him (though it was very ironical to look back to see that some of these very actors, who had so strongly protested against the play, afterwards—when the tumult had died down—carried it all over the United States to their own advantage, bringing back many dollars which happily made their future a little less uncertain for them than it had been). At present there wasn't even the width of the Liffey between the theatre and him; soon the expanse of the Irish Sea would separate them. To go a fair distance away was the best way to check a developing difference. An' seas betune us braid hae roared, sin auld lang syne.

He packed his few last personal things into his one suitcase; the suitcase that had gone with him to Coole, and was now to shepherd the things that would allow him to strut respectably through the streets of London. There was nothing to keep him here: he had no part in Cosgrave's party, or in De Valera's policy; nor had he any in the Labour Movement bossed by William O'Brien; no, nor any part in the Protestant Church of Ireland, or that of the Roman Catholic Mission here; though each and all of them had had a part in making his life as it was now, and in streaking it with many colours. He would soon be crossing the border of his own life. To London! To art galleries and picture shows. He would learn a lot more about painting. He would see something of what Van Gogh, Cézanne, Renoir, and Manet had done, for, as yet, they were but glittering names to him. London! He wouldn't have to listen to A.E. any longer, who couldn't comment on a painting unless it had a label. And Augustus John's *Galway*—he had seen it pictured in a magazine; but now he'd see it as John had done it—life-sized and magnificent. This magnificent man as well as magnificent painter had come into the Abbey Green Room once, fleeing from Count McCormick who was beseeching John to paint him; and Sean had asked the artist why he didn't do it, to be answered, brusquely, Because there is nothing to paint!

Yes, London would mould him into a more fully-developed mind and man. The booming of Big Ben would deafen his new-listening ears to any echo from the bells of Shandon. Though he felt curious, and a little anxious, about meeting things he did not know, he felt relief at leaving behind the things he knew too well. The Easter Rising had pulled down a dark curtain of eternal separation between him and his best friends; and the few that had remained alive and delightful, now lay deep, with their convivial virtues, under the smoking rubblement of the Civil War. It was getting very dark in Ireland, so his flight to London would be a leap in the light.

He strapped the suitcase tight. Any minute now the jaunting-car would come to take him to the station where he was to take the train for the boat. He went to the window, and looked out—a cold, windy, harsh March morning. Early on a wild March morning. An old song strayed into his mind:

And as I stood upon the quay, a tear fell from my eye,
For divil a blessed soul was there to say, old friend, goodbye;
They were glad to see me sail, far away from Inisfail,
Early on that wild March morning!

The weather meant a rough passage, but he'd stick it calmly, however roguishly rough it might be. His day in Ireland had been a long one, but the long day was over at last; a long day over; long day over; over at last.

He would leave Yeats on his Island of Inisfree, standing pensively at the door of his small cabin of clay and wattles made; or moving, slow and moody, between his nine bean rows, thinking of peace where there was no peace; for Ireland's red-rose-bordered hem was muddy now, **and** ragged. There was no making love to Kathleen, daughter of Houlihan now, untidy termagant, brawling out **her** prayers. He would leave Lady Gregory in her Seven Woods of Coole; and the lesser writers, too, conceiving little things of verse chipped from the touch of little things timidly seen and carefully handled; and his brother, Mick, with his dream of an endless queue of pints waiting to be swallowed.

Here comes the car. Sean swung his suitcase up on it, and climbed into a side-seat; and away they went on the first trotting steps to England. England? Well, Sean was going into a land enslaved to ill-doing and left alone by God, according to Father O'Reilly, who, at a meeting of Maynooth Union, whose members were priests, is reported to have said but fifteen years ago: "The character of the English mind ought to be understood in Ireland. It is a fleshy spirit, bent towards earth; a mind unmannerly, vulgar, insolent, bigoted; a mind whose belly is its god, yet which cannot endure the word belly; a mind to which pride and lust and mammon are the matter-of-course aims of life; a mind where every absurd device, from grossest Darwinism to most preposterous spiritualism is resorted to, and hoped in, to choke the voice of eternity in the conscience; a mind to which the idea of a churchman possessing real, efficient, and spiritual authority over his flock would be unspeakably ludicrous."

A bad place to be going to, certainly. But while this reverend cleric was speaking, down south a farmer had become certain that his handsome young wife was possessed of a witch, and got the local reverend cleric to say

393

Mass in the house to deliver her. But the intention failed, and the farmer, with the help of neighbours, set about it himself, burning her with a red-hot poker, forcing her to drink things made from herbs gathered over the mountains; and when these sensible and holy acts didn't do, carried her down in her shift, and held her over the fire till she was roasted alive; and then buried her away in a lonely place of gorse and thorny briars. A week later she was dug up, displaying purple marks round her throat, and with the muscles of her spine burned away. And, after the inquest, neither lay nor clerical would give a hand to bury her; so the police had to do it by the light of lanterns, and in the dead of the sympathetic night.

The outside-car swung along down Dorset Street, where Sean had first seen the peep of day; past George's church, in the pocket of which had lived the Dalton family with whom he had trod, as a youngster, the stage of the old Mechanics Theatre, now known the world over as The Abbey; down Cavendish Row where the Dispensary had been from which the gentle Dr. Oulton had come to cure Sean of a fever; down Sackville-O'Connell Street, catching a good glimpse of the Post Office, where Padraic Pearse had sounded the horn that roused Ireland out of her sleeping. In this very street, on the top of a horse-drawn tram, when a little boy safe beside his mother, he had swept into the galaxy of illuminations, lit to honour an English queen; and, years after, had been almost suffocated in this very street by the surging crowd escaping from the batons of the police. In this very street.

The car turned down Abbey Street, and swung into Beresford Place, trotting past Liberty Hall, once the sweltering, weltering University of the Dublin workers, now a dead tomb held by an enemy, with Ichabod written all over it, for Larkin had gone, and its glory had departed; down Tara Street, surely the drabbest and dirtiest street in Dublin, looking as desolate as Tara itself; wheeling into Brunswick Street, passing the Queen's Theatre where Sean had seen his first play, *The Shaughraun*; past the Ancient Concert Rooms, where the National Theatre performed some of its early plays, before it had a habitation or even a name. It was this street that had been Sean's via dolorosa, through which he had passed, three times a week, year after year, for fifteen or more of them, with his mother first, then on his own, to the Ophthalmic Hospital to seek ease for aching eyeballs. Ah, here was Westland Row Station—the last spot of Dublin that would feel his footfall. It was from this sad site that the coffin holding Parnell came slowly out, borne by strenuous, tearful men, hesitating to part even with the dead body of their persecuted Chieftain. Oh, God Almighty, the life he was living now had almost all been spun from what he had felt, had seen, had touched in these few Dublin streets!

He was on the deck of the mail-boat, feeling her sway and shyly throb beneath his feet; watching the landing-stage drift afar away, getting his last glimpse of Eireann— separated for the first time from her, and never likely to stand settled on her soil again. It was bitterly cold, with a fierce, keen wind blowing, and soon it was sending sharp sleety hail and salty spray into his face, stinging it deeply

—Ireland, spitting a last, venomous, contemptuous fare-well to him.

Well, everything of any value he was carrying away with him: the moral courage and critical faculties of his father, and his love of good books; the gay humour and dogged resolution of his mother, and her love for, and understanding of, the bright colours among dead, drab things; the remembrance of the warm clasp from the Reverend Mr. Griffin's firm, white, delicately-shaped hands; the love of his comrade workers, catholic and protestant, with whom he had fought and starved and fought again; all the fair things he had learned during his sojourn with the Gaelic League; the affection and goodwill of Lady Gregory; the reluctant godspeed from Dr. Cummins; a fond recollection of brother Tom; pity for his sister Bella, and a little less of it for Mick; and, above all, a strict and determined confidence in himself. Jewels he could never sell; jewels that no thief, however cute, could take out of his hands.

> *Sail on, sail on, thou fearless bark,*
> *Wherever blows the welcome wind,*
> *It cannot lead to scenes more dark,*
> *More sad, than those we leave behind.*

The ship turned giddily to right, to left, plunged with upturned bows, dipping them again as quick, for there was more than a half-gale blowing. Sean had been anxious about sea-sickness, but he felt no discomfort. He was a good sailor. He faced resolutely towards where the ship was going. Sweet Inishfallen, fare thee well! Forever!

396